5/21

SAINT-SAËNS

SYMPHONY No. 3

in C minor—Opus 78

FOR ORCHESTRA WITH ORGAN

SCORE

No. 2122

INTERNATIONAL MUSIC COMPANY

511 FIFTH AVENUE   NEW YORK CITY

PRINTED IN U. S. A.

Mon cœur s'ouvre à ta voix Comme s'ouvrent les fleurs

C. Saint-Saëns

SYMPHONY No. 3

I.

CAMILLE SAINT-SAËNS, Op. 78
(1835-1921)

Published by International Music Company, New York City

Cor Ang.
p
pp
Bons
1º
p
pp
Timb.
pp
Allº moderato 72=
p
Velles et C.B.
pizz.
p poco marcato
arco
Cl.
1º
p
Bons
1º
p
1er et 2e Cors
pp
Timb.

2122

1re Fl.
2e Fl.
3e Fl.
Hb. 1o
p cresc.
Cor Ang.
p cresc.
Cl.
p cresc.
Cl. B.
Bons
C. Bon
Cors
3o
cresc.
Tromp.
Tromb.
Timb.
Col C.B.
f
mf

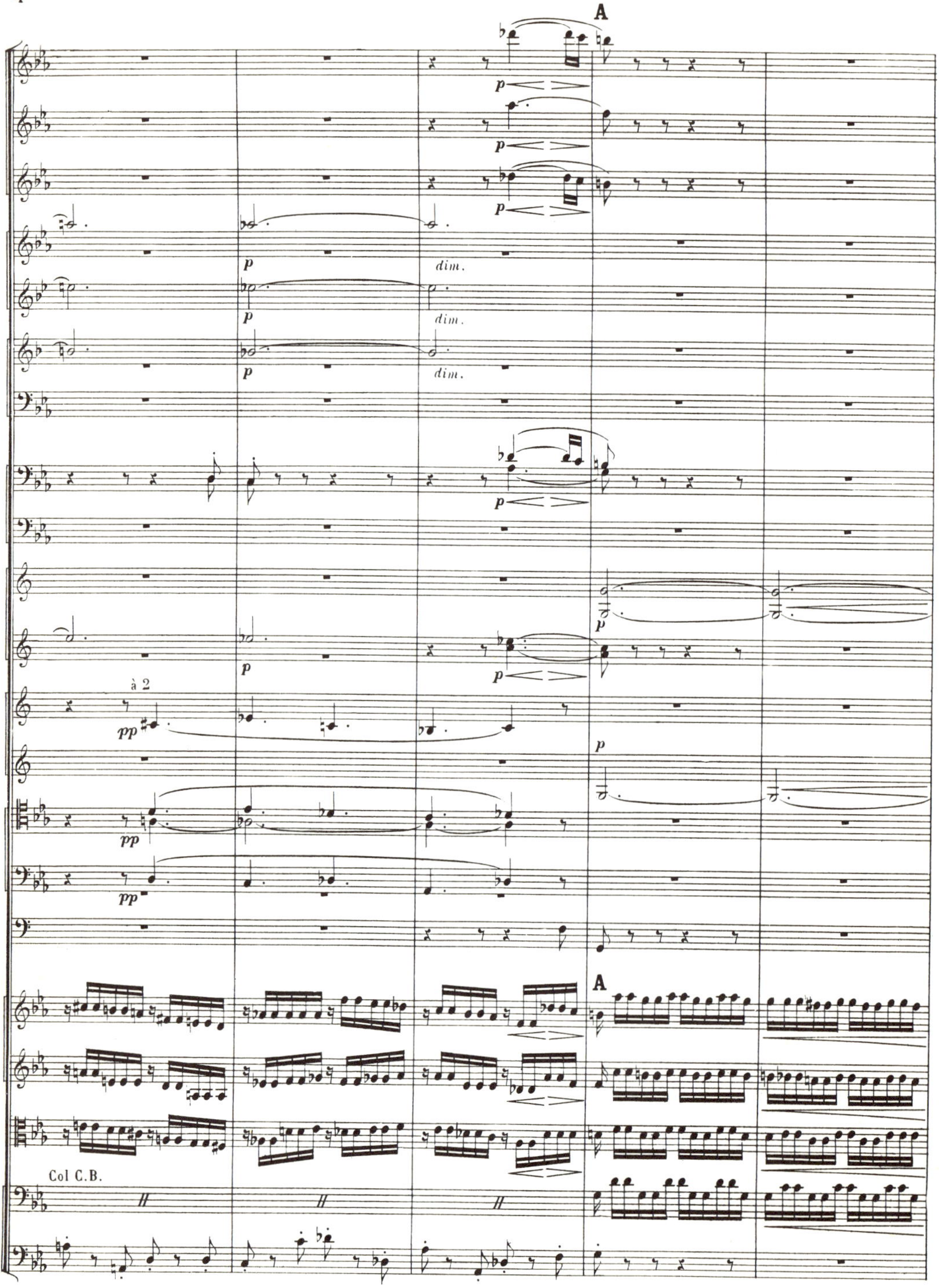
A
p
dim.
à 2
pp
Col C.B.
A

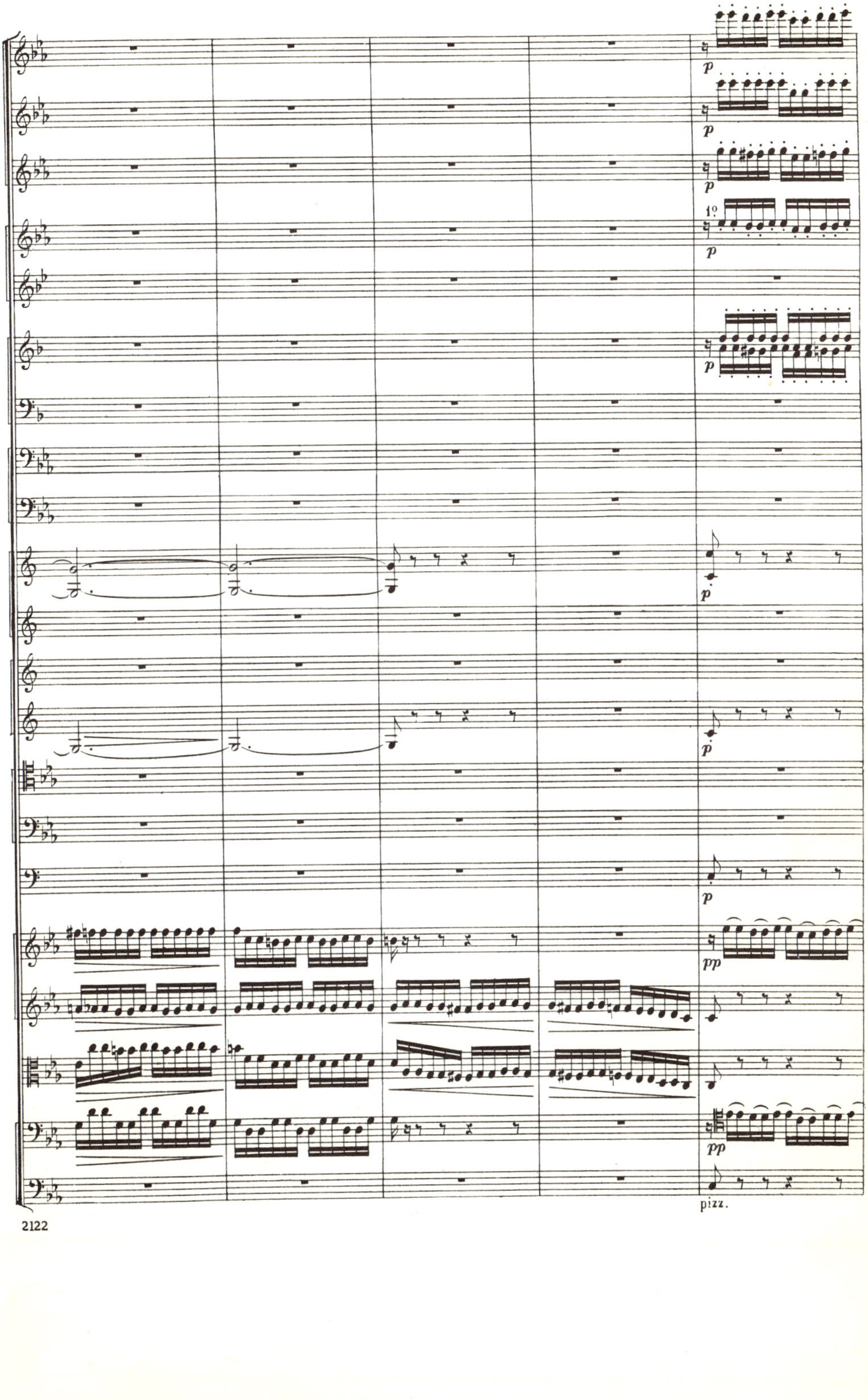

1º
p
pp
pizz.

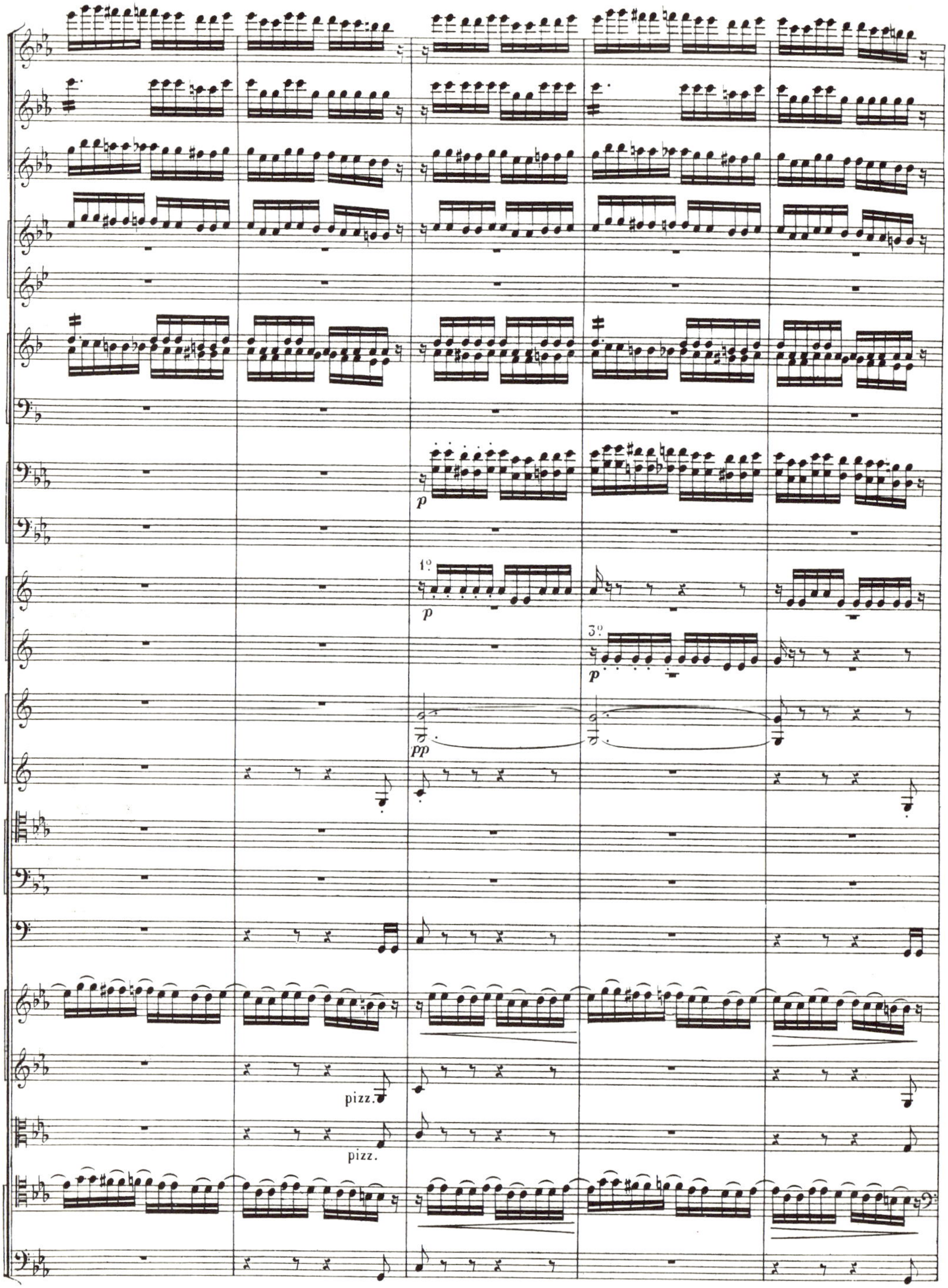
1º
p
3º
p
pp
p
pizz.
pizz.

B
cresc.
cresc.
p cresc.
f
f
cresc.
à 2
f
cresc.
f
cresc.
à 2
f
cresc.
à 2
f
cresc.
f
à 2
cresc.
f
à 2
f
B
cresc.
f
arco
cresc.
f
Div. f
cresc.
pizz.
cresc.
f
cresc.
f
f

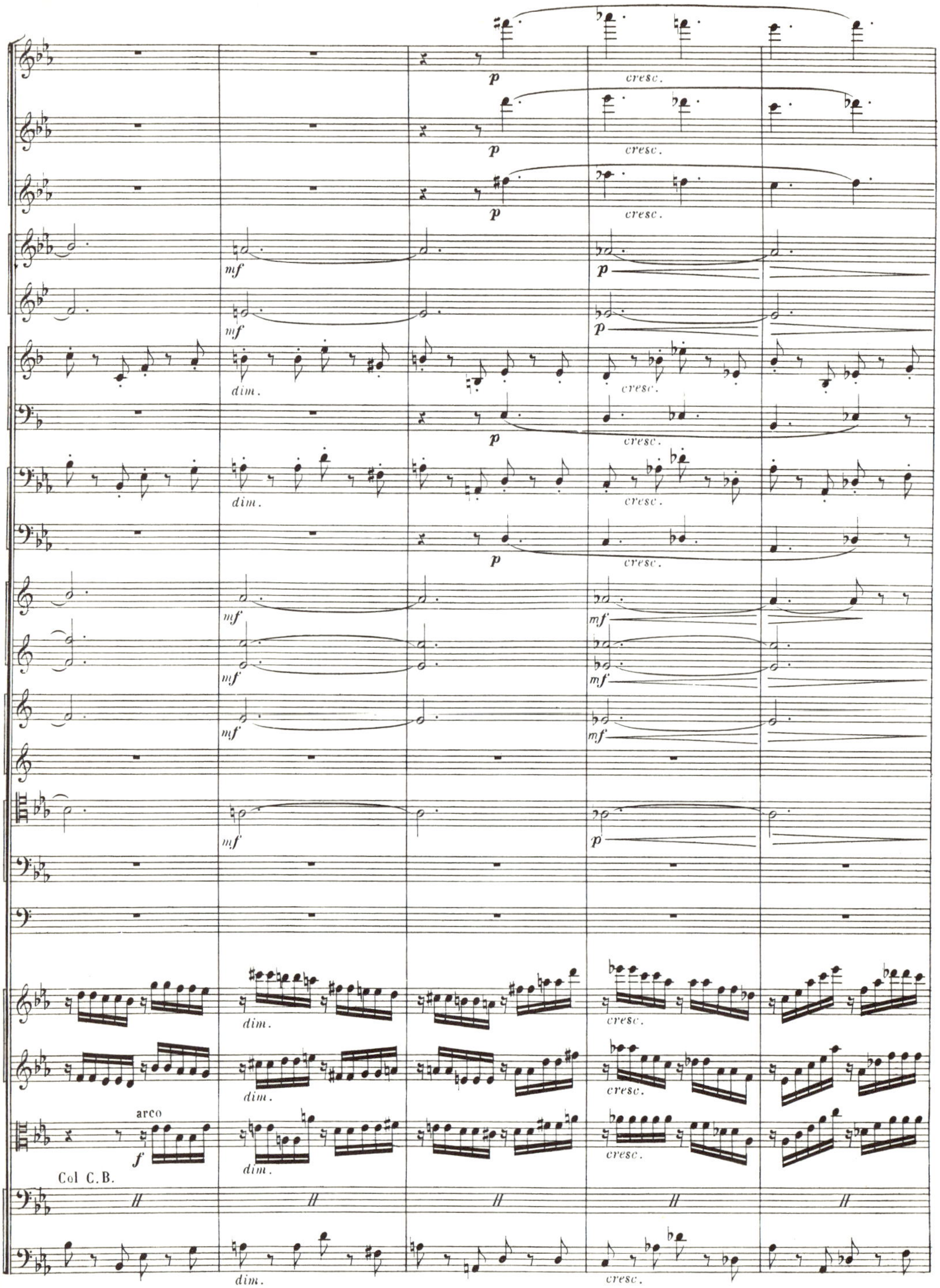
p
cresc.
mf
dim.
arco
f
Col C.B.

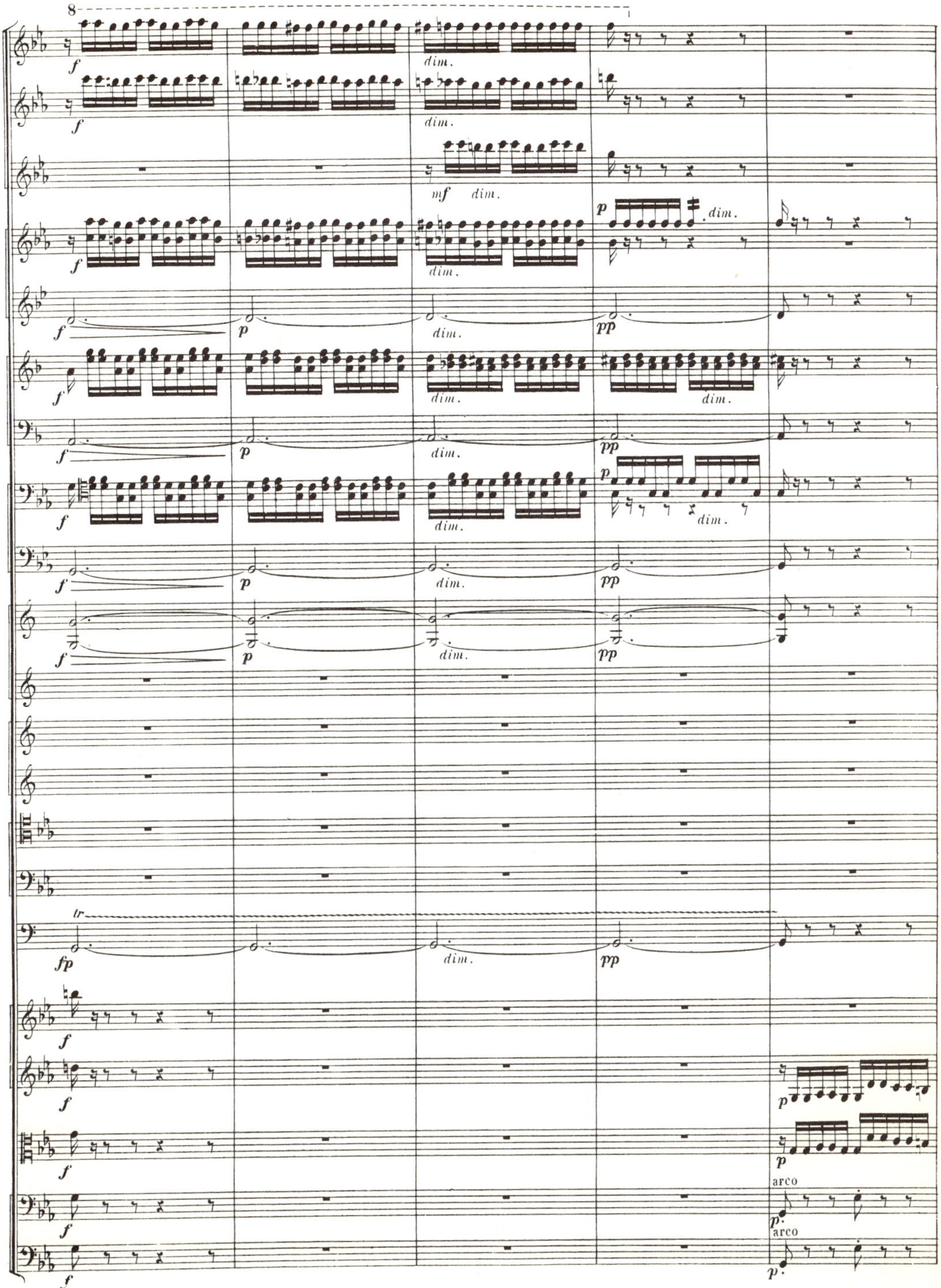
8
f
dim.
mf
p
pp
fp
tr
arco

Cor Ang.
mf espress.
Bons 1º
mf espress.
1er et 2e Cors
pp
Timb.
pp
Velles et C.B.
C
1re Fl.
mf espress.
Hb. 1º
mf espress.
Cor Ang.
Cl. 1º
mf espress.
Cl. B.
mf espress.
Bons
sf
1er et 2e Cors
p
3e Tromp.
p
Timb.
p
C
Div.

1re Fl.
2e Fl.
Petite Fl.
Hb
Cor Ang.
Cl.
Cl. B.
Bons
C. Bon
Cors
Tromp.
Tromp.
Tromb.
Timb.
sf
mf
f
p
2o
1o

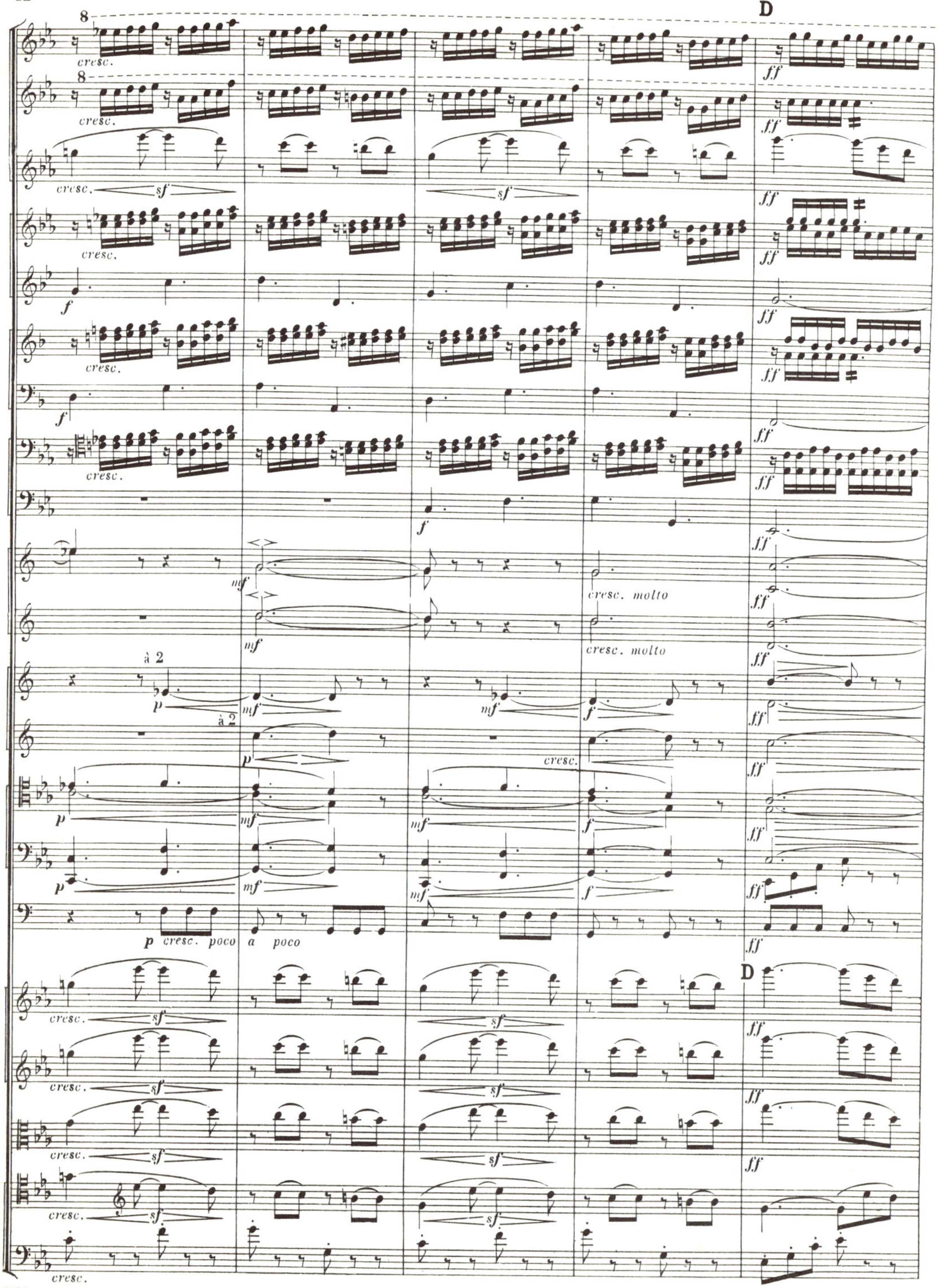
D
8
cresc.
sf
f
ff
mf
cresc. molto
à 2
p
cresc. poco a poco

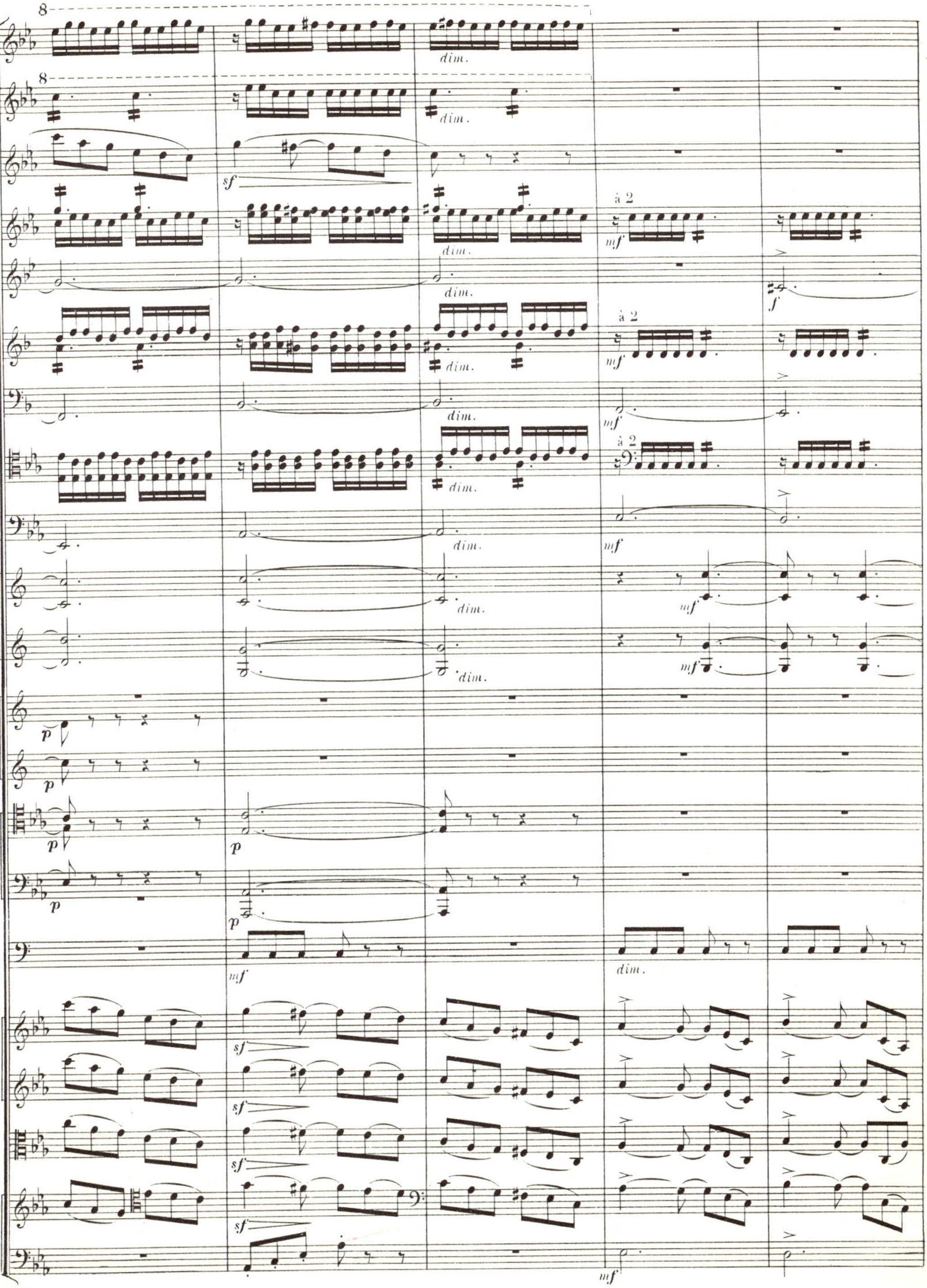

8
dim.
sf
à 2
mf
f
p

1º
dim.
dim.
dim.
1º
legg.
p
dim.
p
p legg.
dim.
1º
dim.
dim.
dim.
4º
mf
dim.
pp
dim.
p
dim.
p
dim.
p
dim.
dim.
p

Cl.
Bons
pp
Timb.
p
pizz.
Velles et C.B.
E
1re Fl.
2e Fl.
Grande Fl.
Hb 1º
Cor Ang.
Cl.
Bons sempre pp
3e et 4e Cors
ppp
Div.
arco
pizz.

1re Fl.
pp
F
2e Fl.
pp
3e Fl.
pp
Hb
pp
Cl.
pp
Cl.B.
pp
Bons
p
3e et 4e Cors
3e
p
F
p espress.
pp
p
pp
p
pp
arco
p
Bons
3e et 4e Cors
mf
Velles et C.B.
p

1er Fl.
p espress
f
2e Fl.
p
f
3e Fl.
p
f
Hb.
Cor Ang.
p espress.
f
Cl.
p
f
Cl. B.
p
mf
Bons
à 2
p
mf
C. Bon
p
mf
Cors
Tromp.
Tromb.
Timb.
sempre p
sempre p

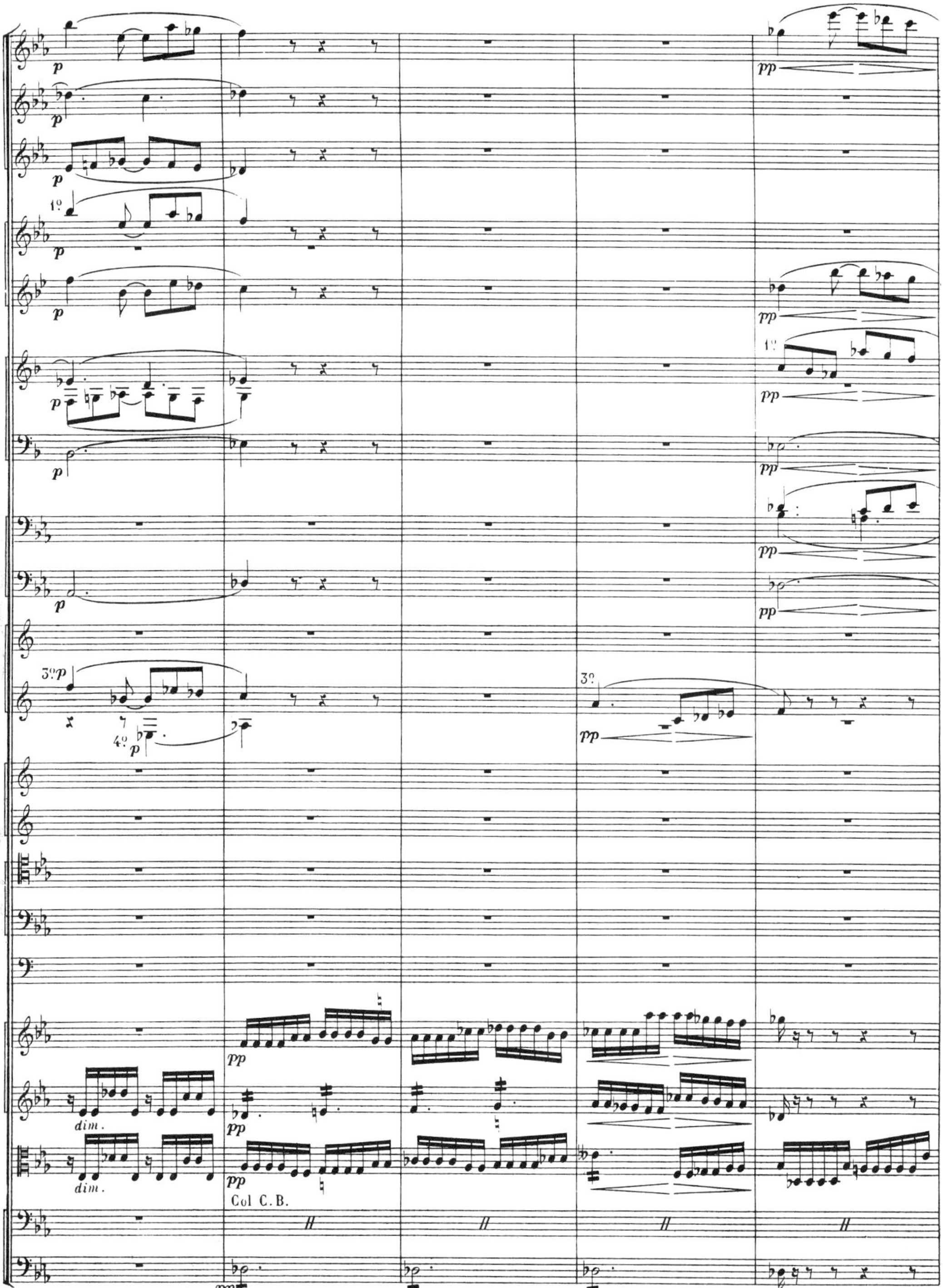
p
pp
1º
3º p
4º p
3º
dim.
Col C.B.

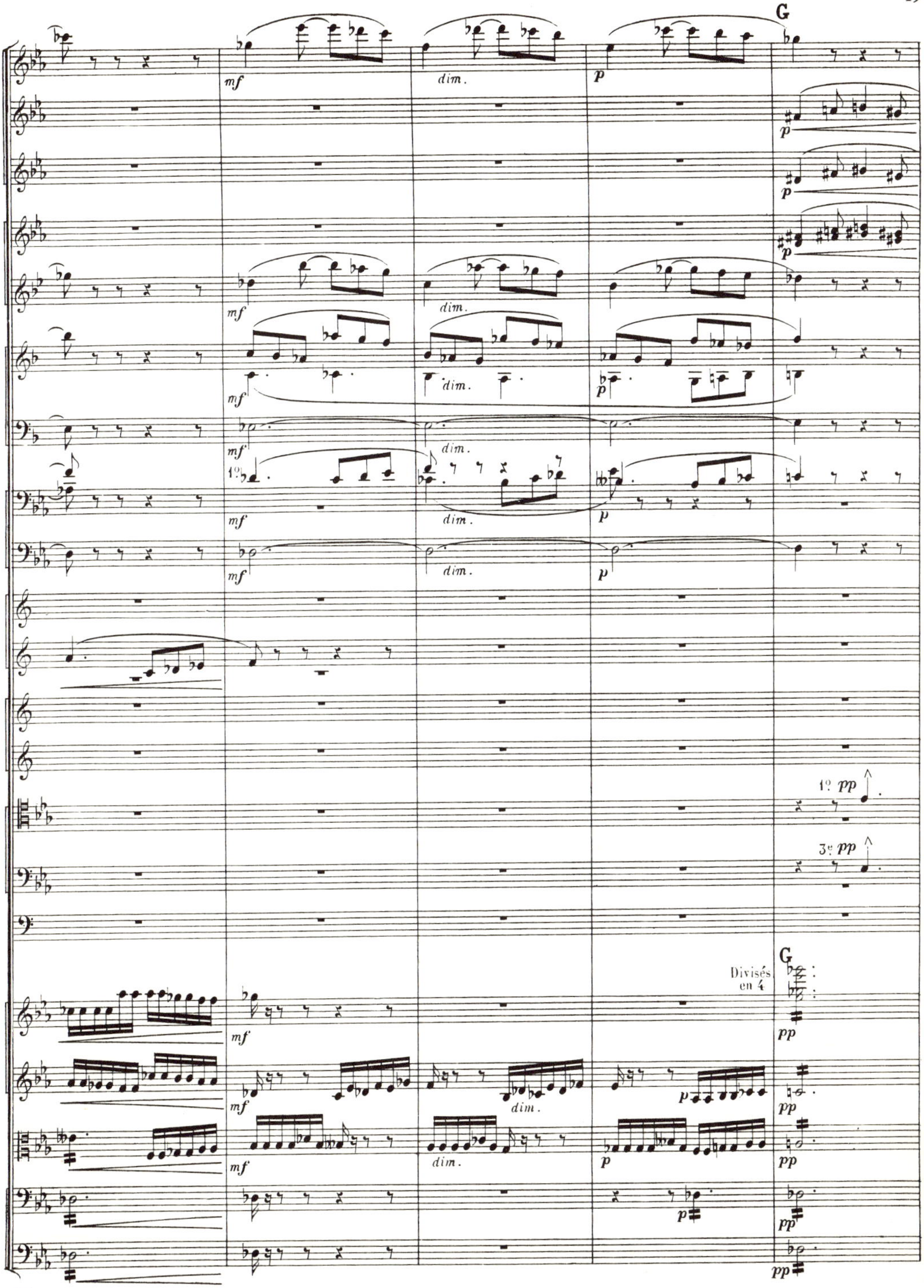
G
mf
dim.
p
1º
1º pp
3º pp
Divisés
en 4
pp

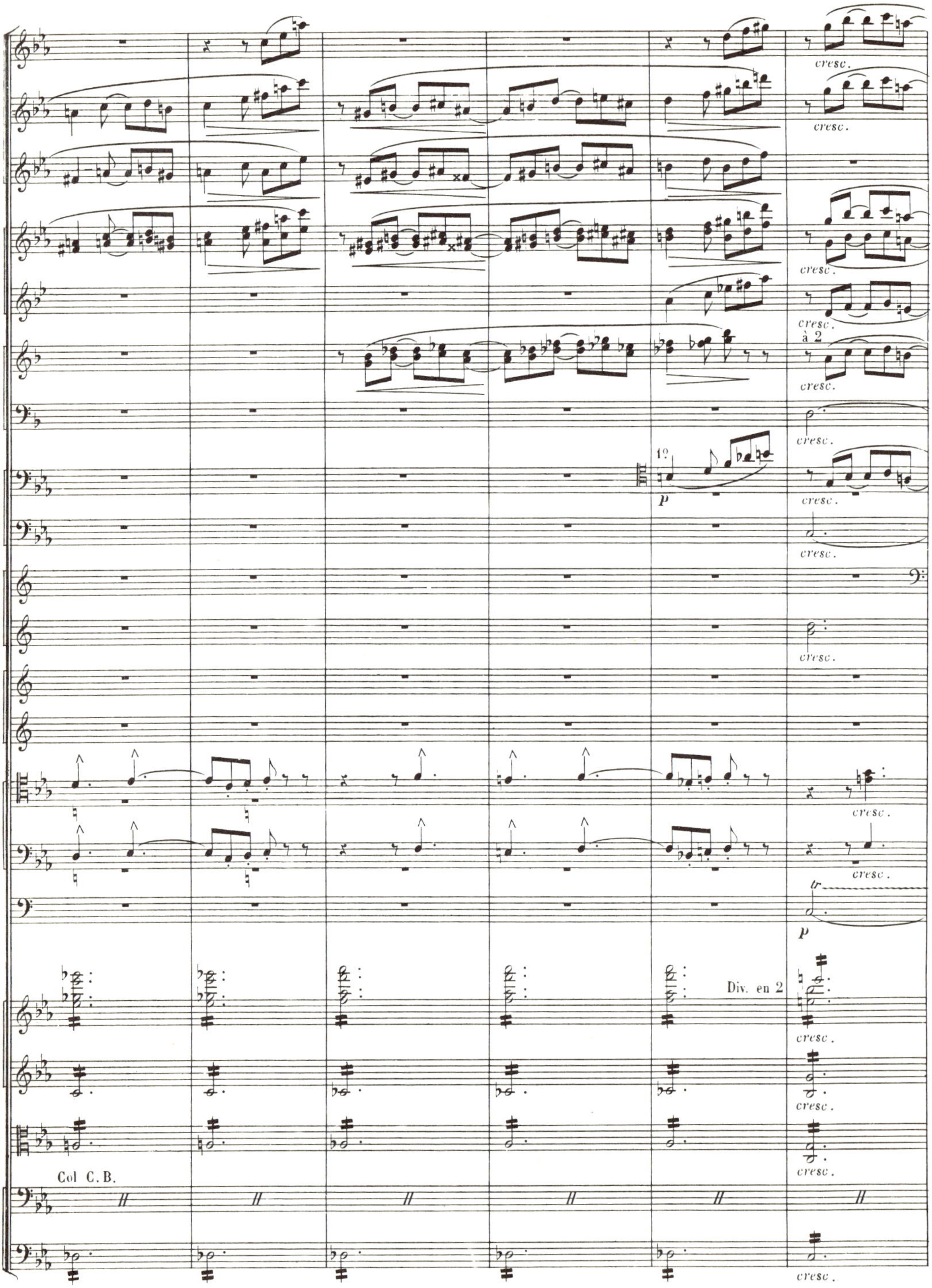
cresc.
à 2
1º
p
tr
Div. en 2
Col C.B.

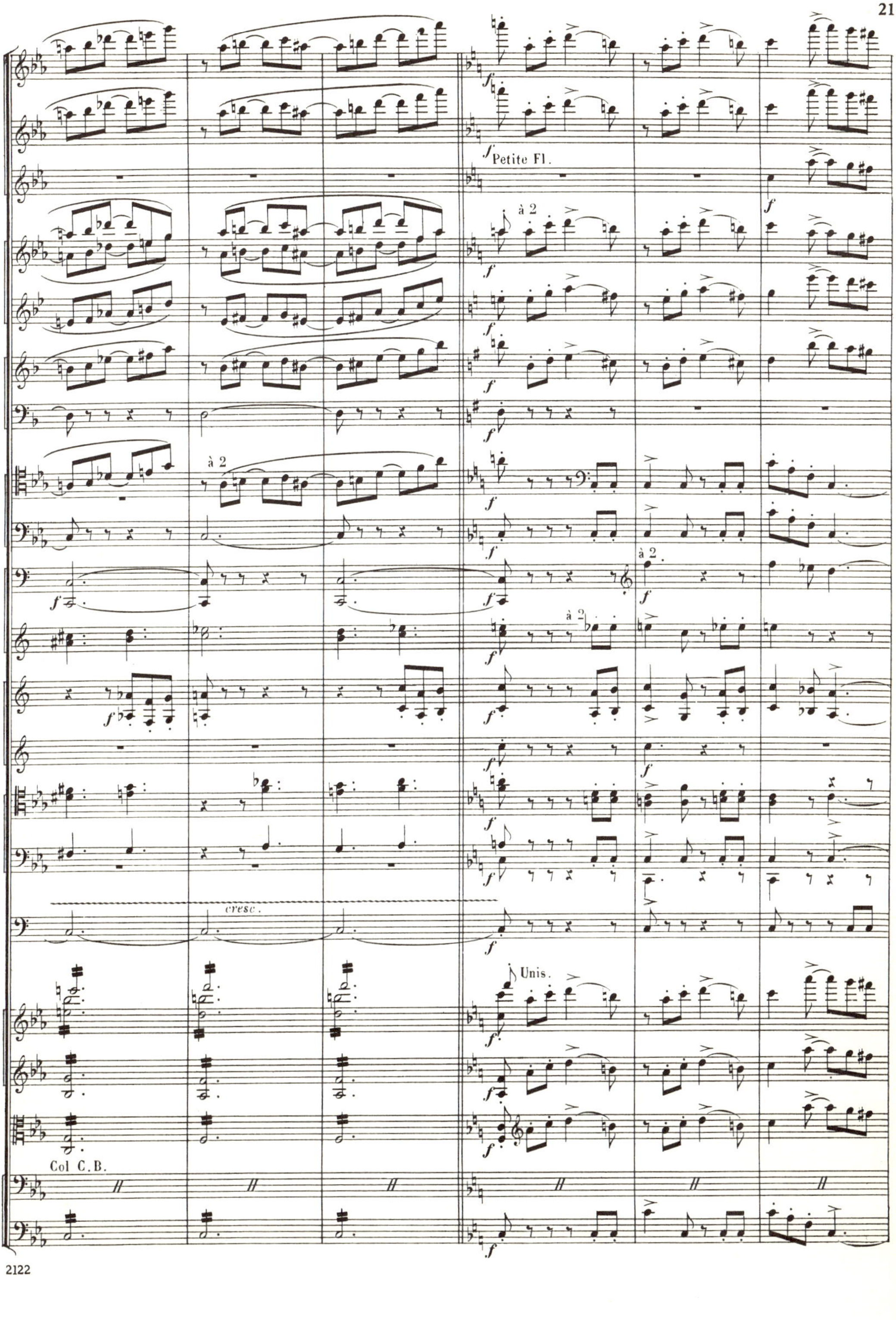
Petite Fl.
à 2
à 2
à 2
à 2
cresc.
Unis.
Col C.B.

Col C.B.

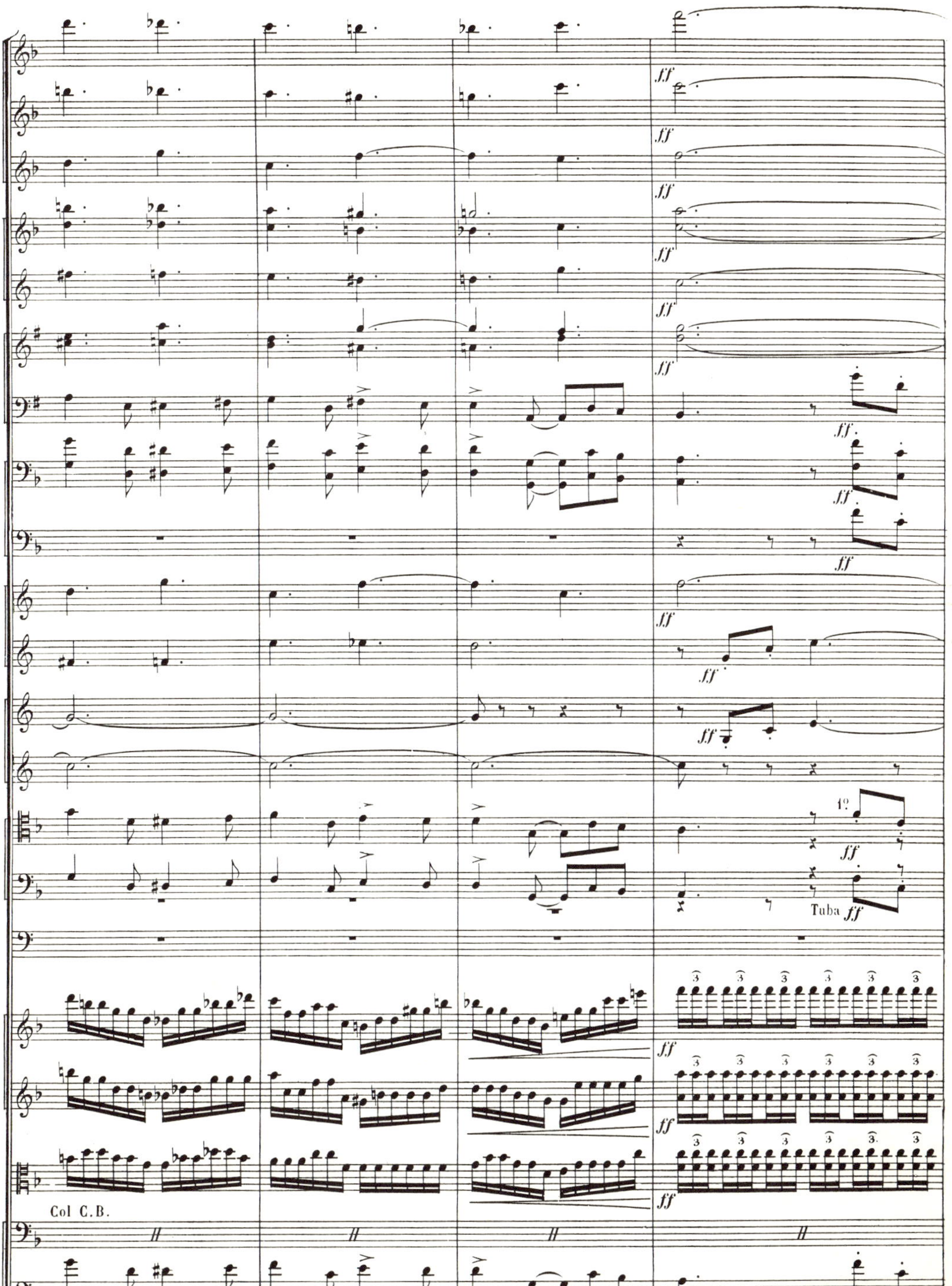
ff
Col C.B.
1º
Tuba

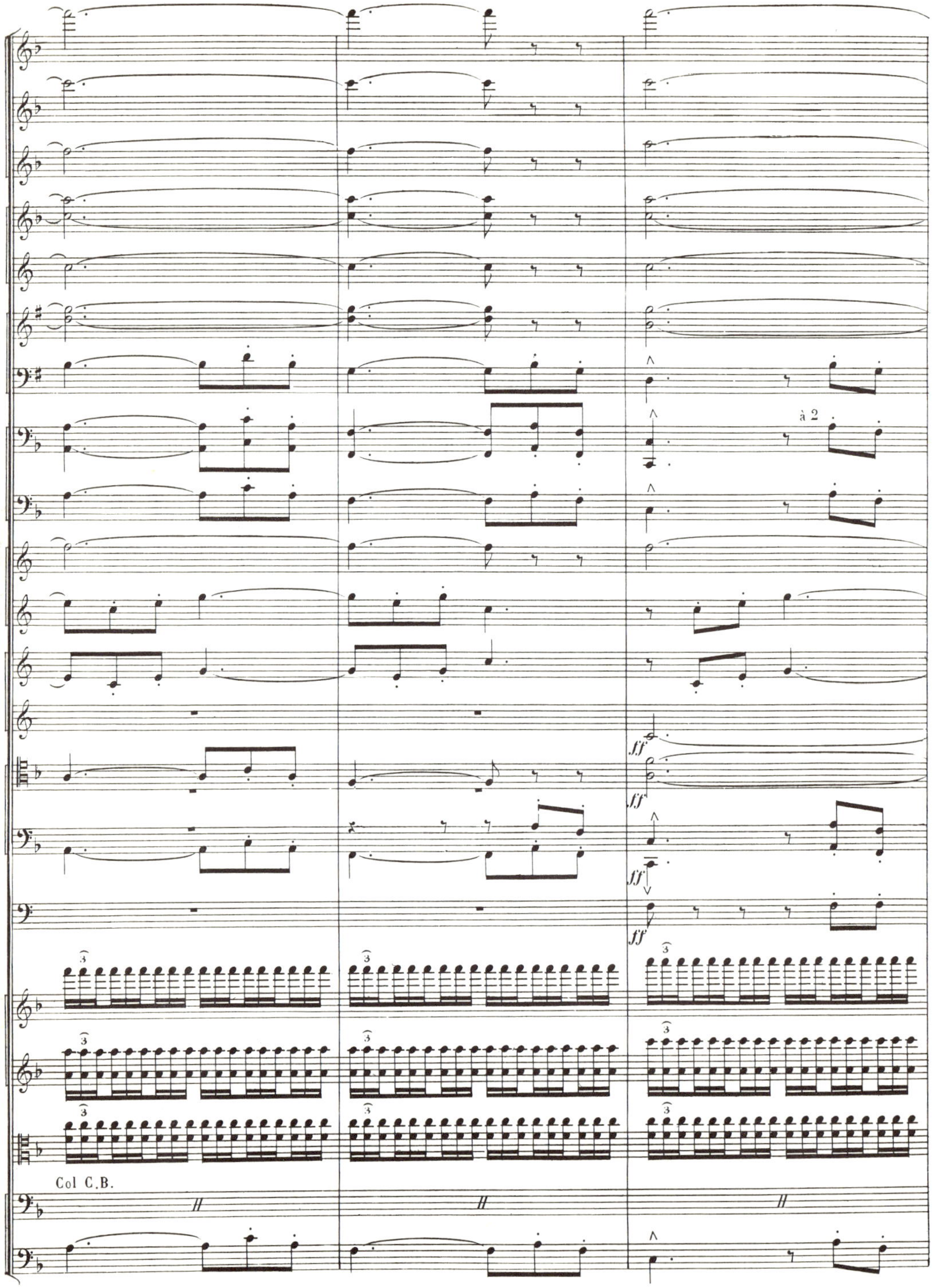
à 2
ff
Col C.B.

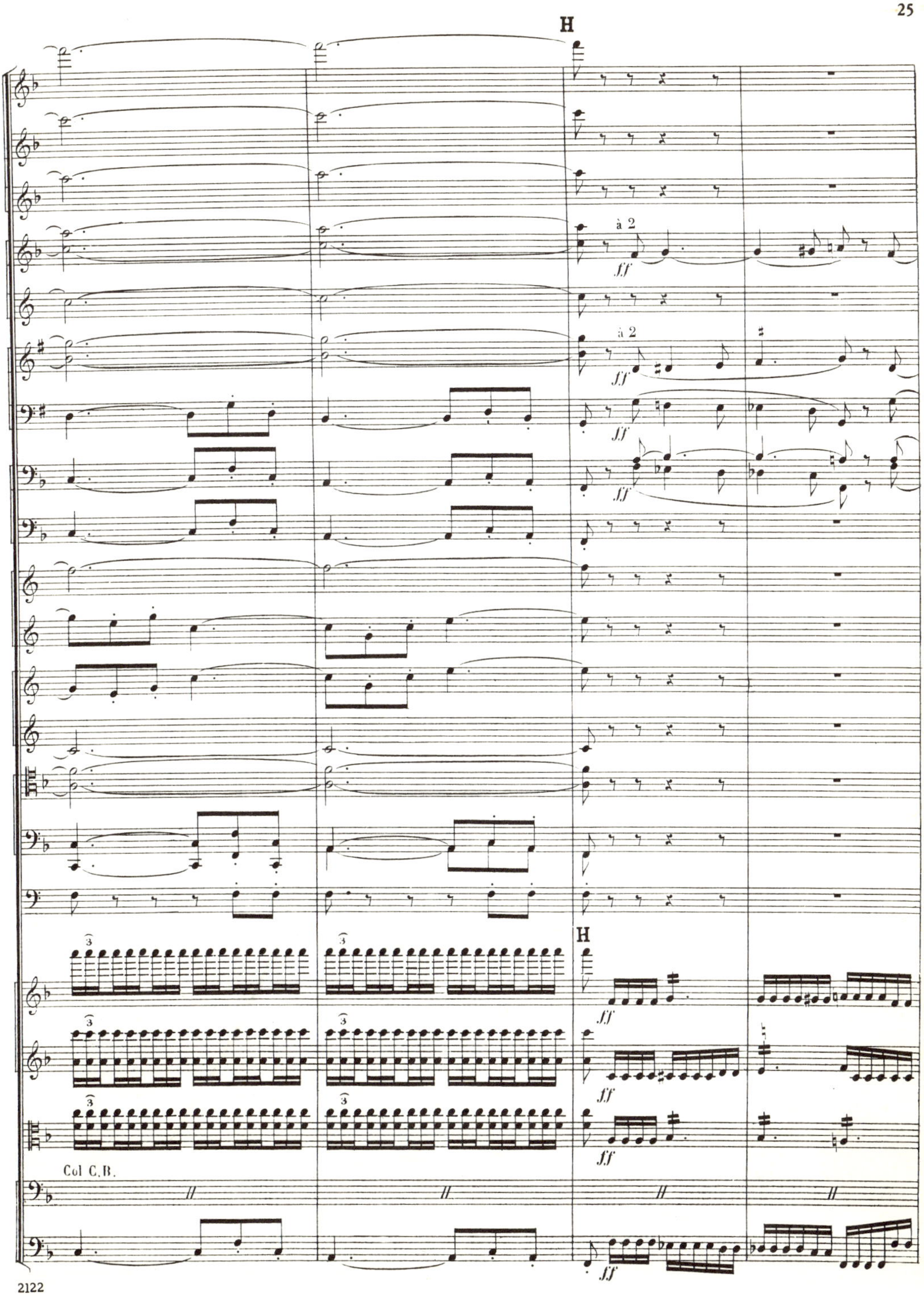
H
à 2
ff
à 2
ff
ff
ff
H
ff
ff
ff
Col C.B.
ff

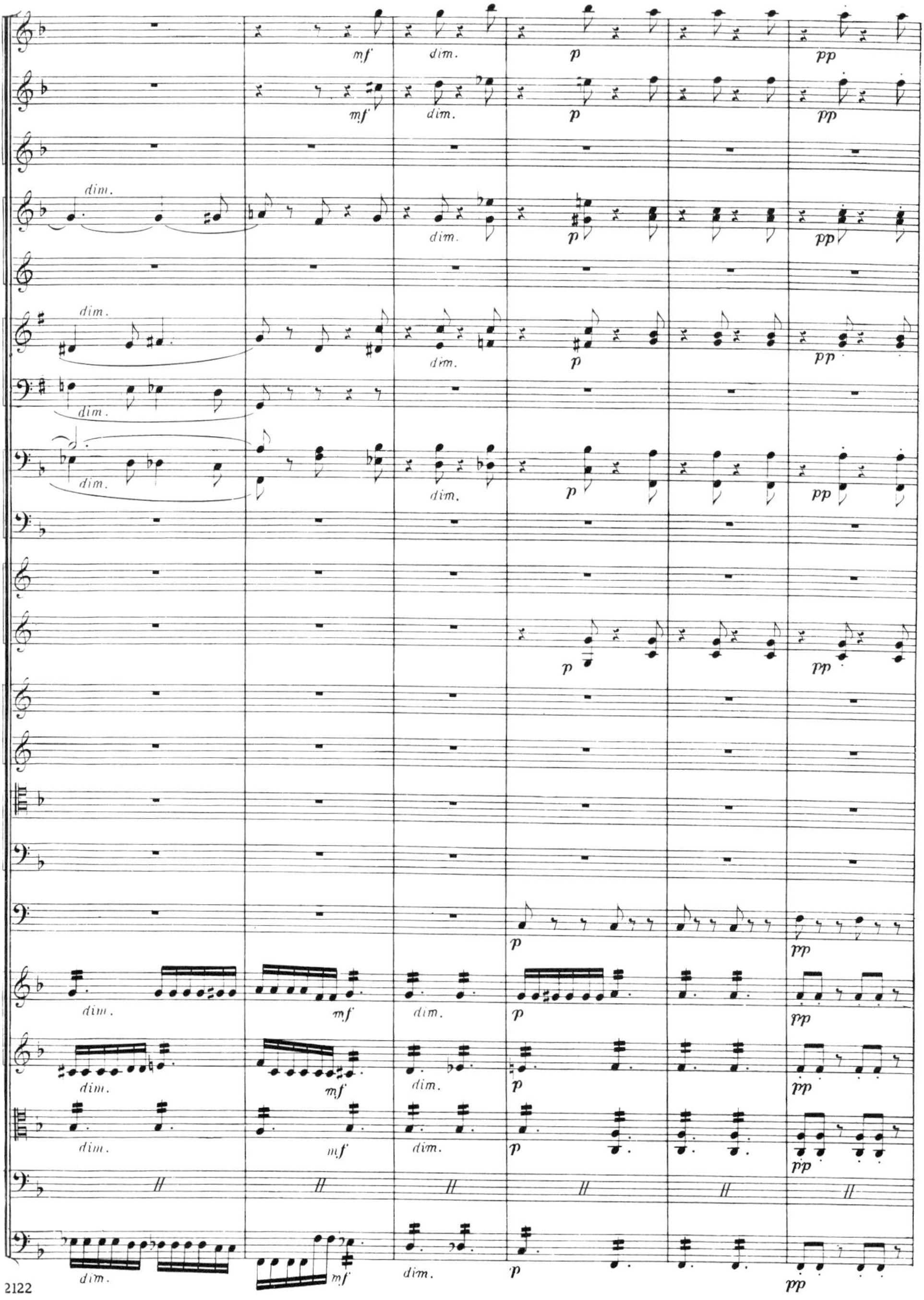

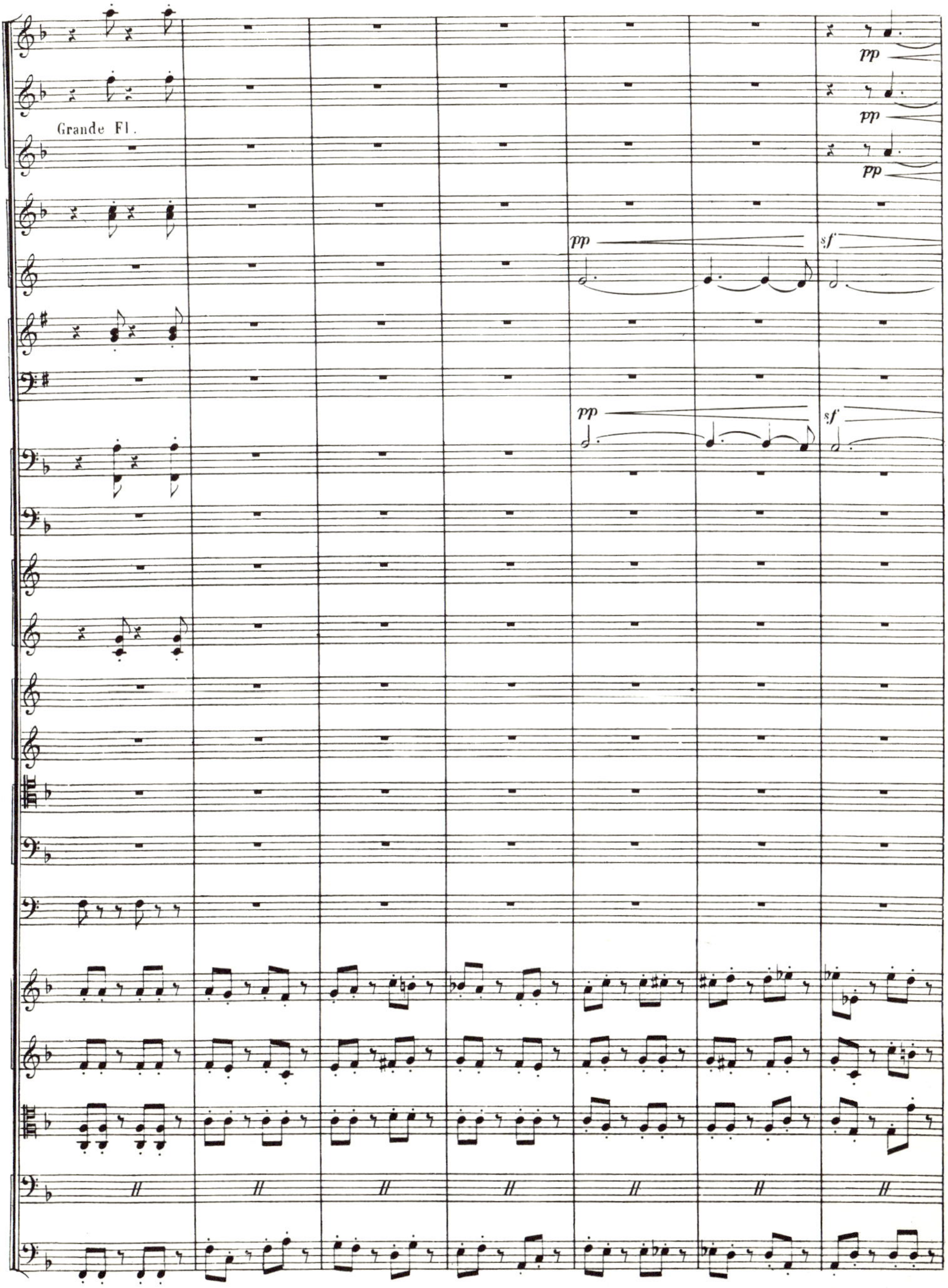
Grande Fl.
pp
pp
pp
pp
sf
pp
sf

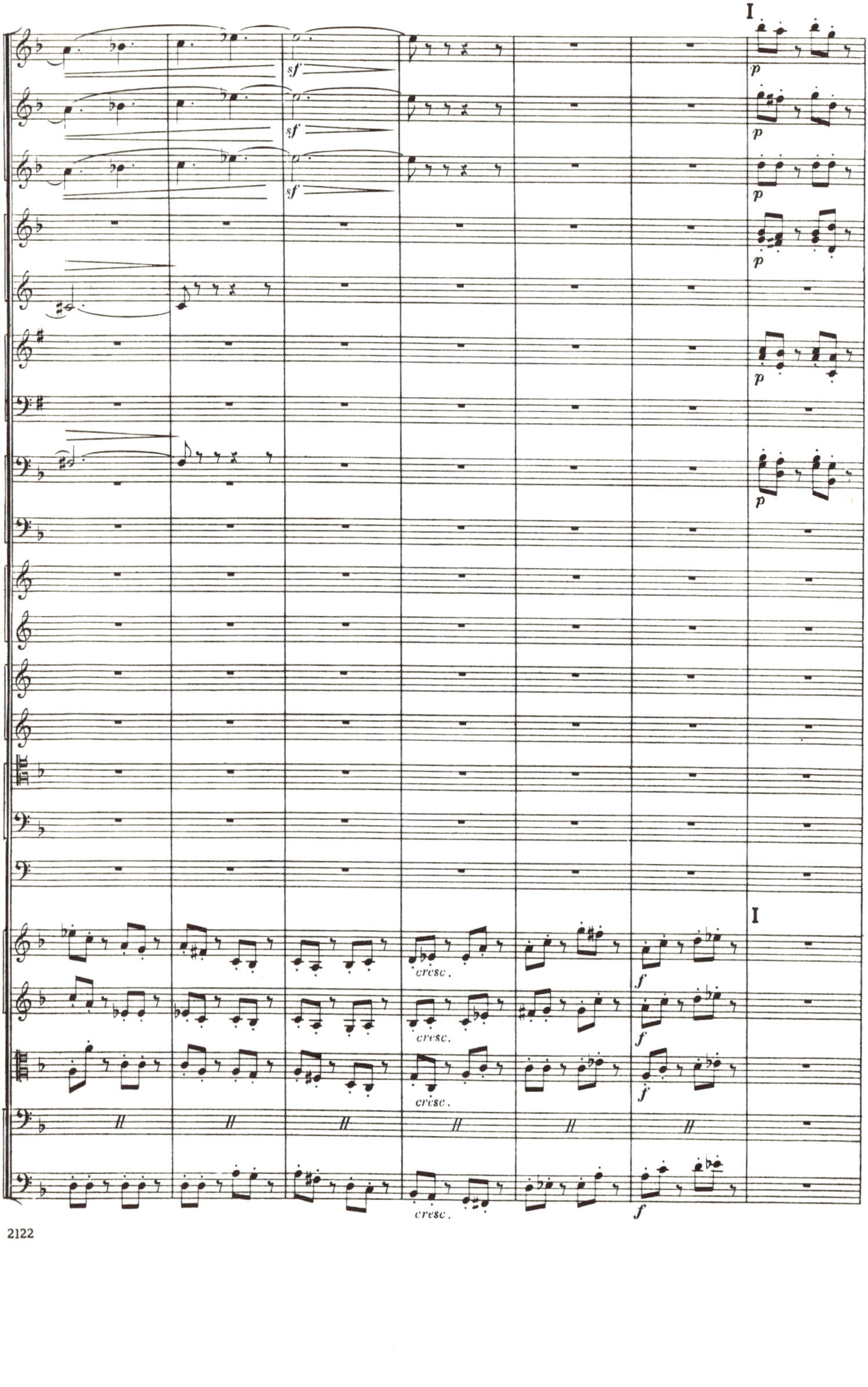
I
sf
sf
sf
p
p
p
p
p
p
I
cresc.
cresc.
cresc.
cresc.
f
f
f
f

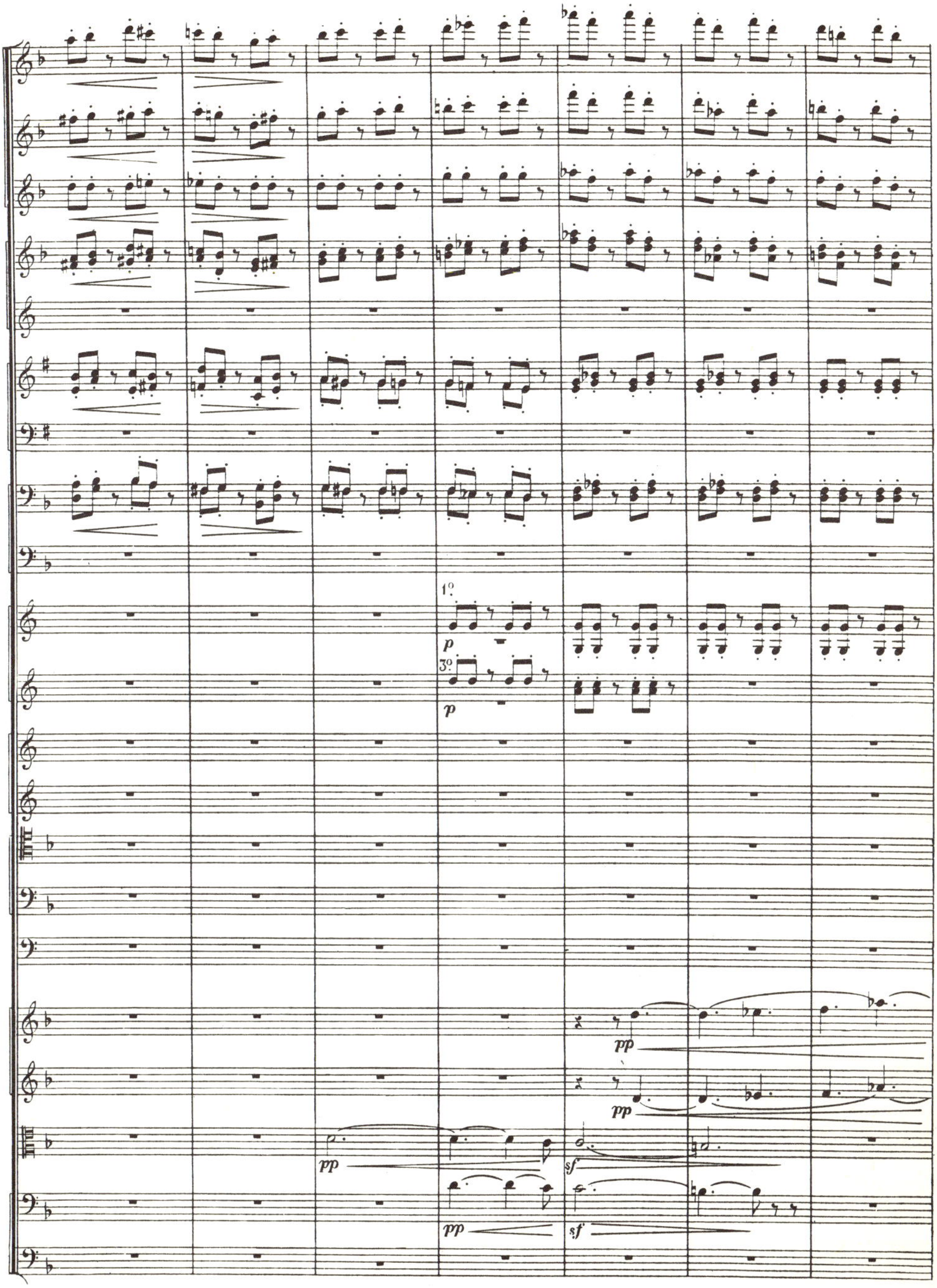
1º
p
3º
p
pp
pp
pp
pp
sf
sf

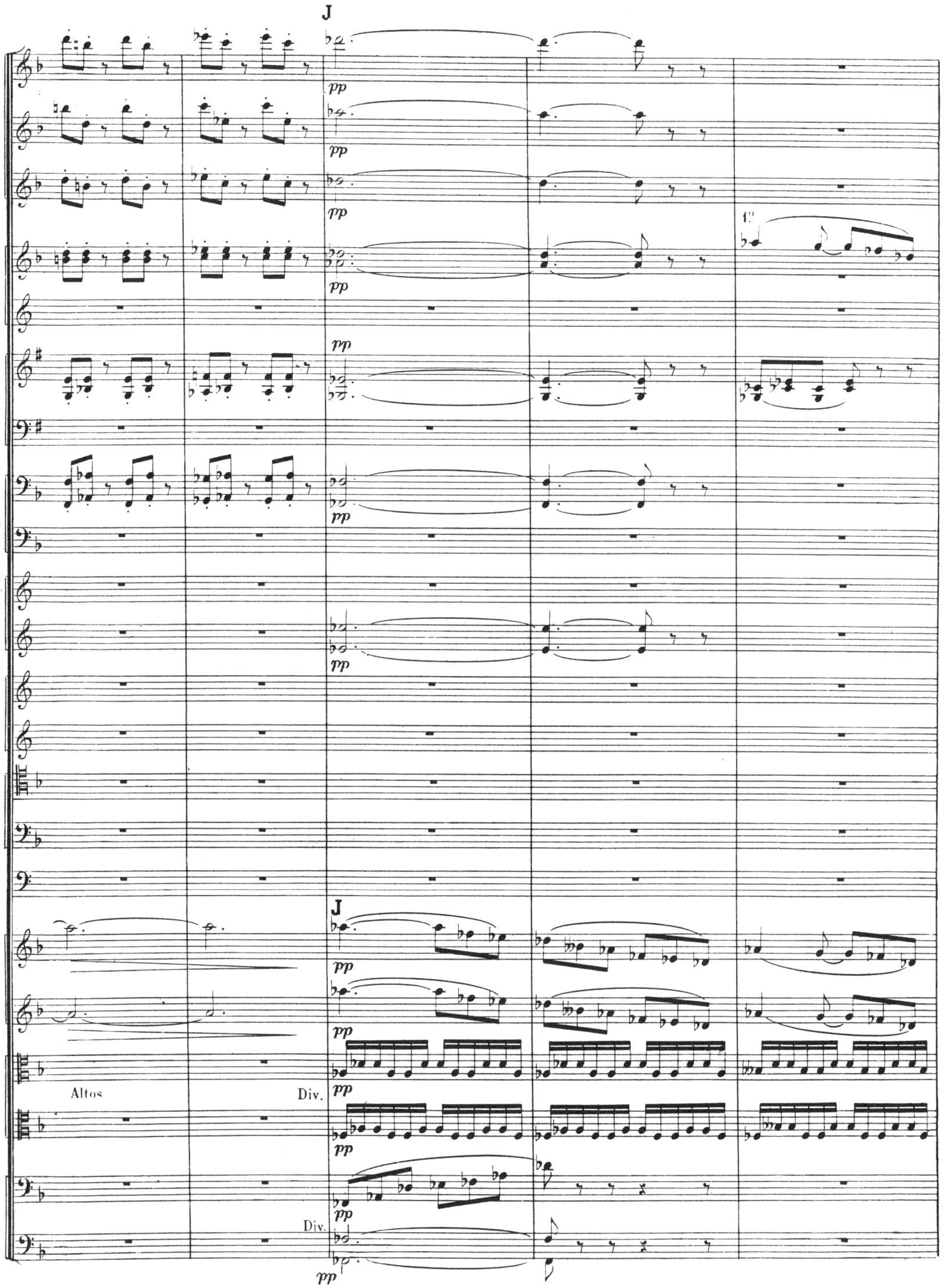
J
pp
pp
pp
pp
pp
pp
pp
1?
J
pp
pp
pp
Altos
Div.
pp
pp
Div.
pp

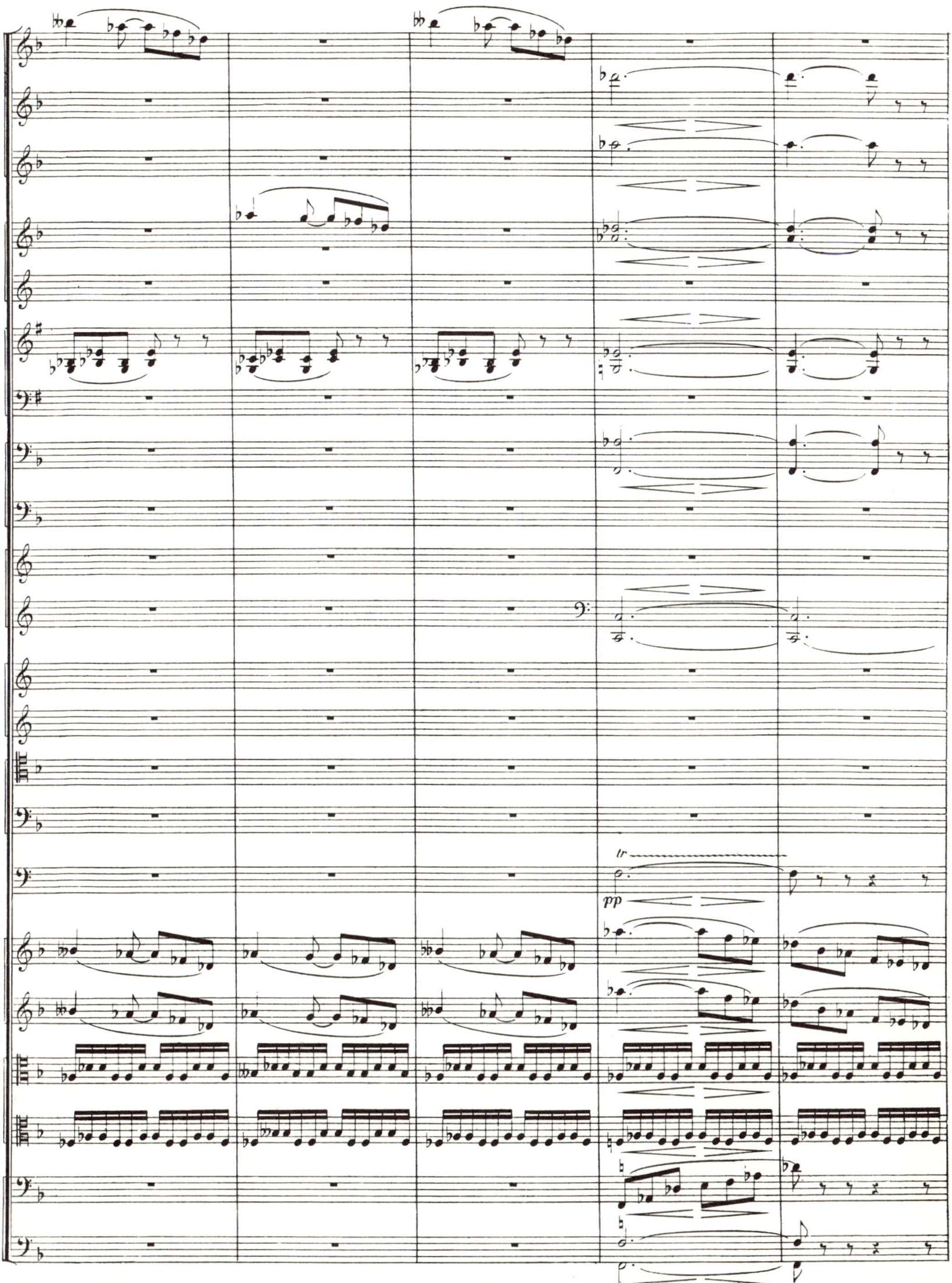
tr
pp

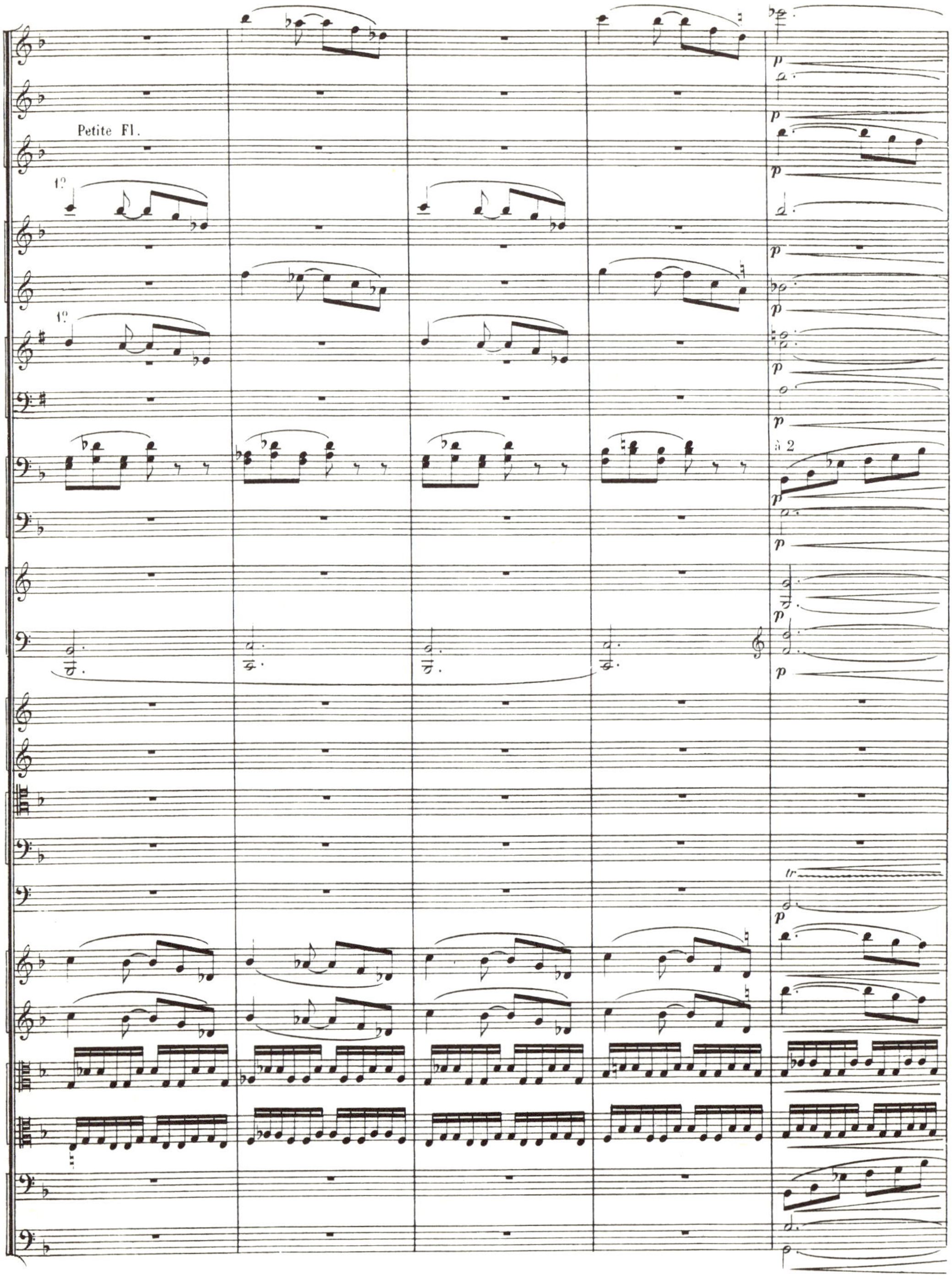
Petite Fl.
1º
1º
à 2
tr

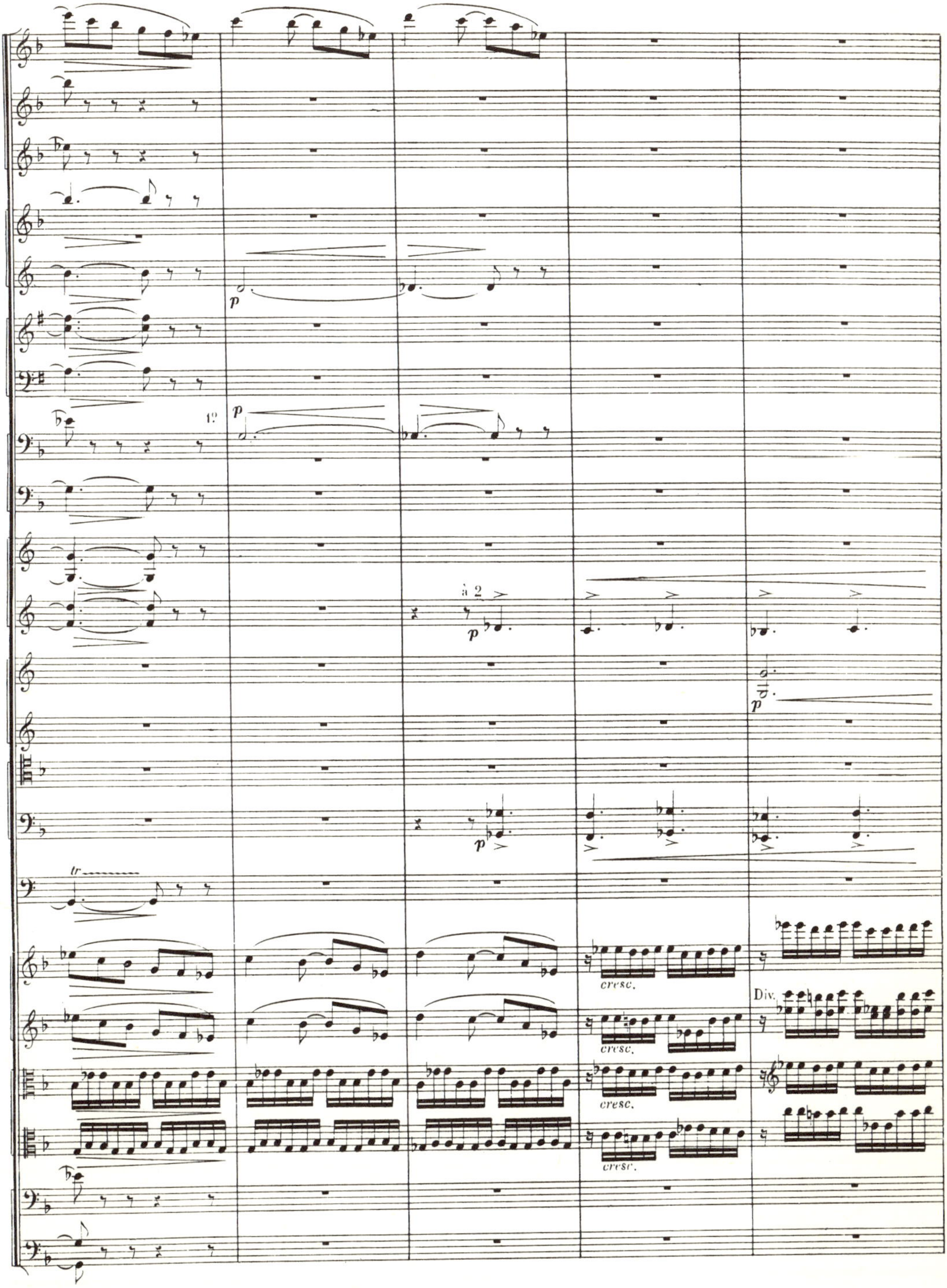
tr
1º
p
à 2
cresc.
Div.

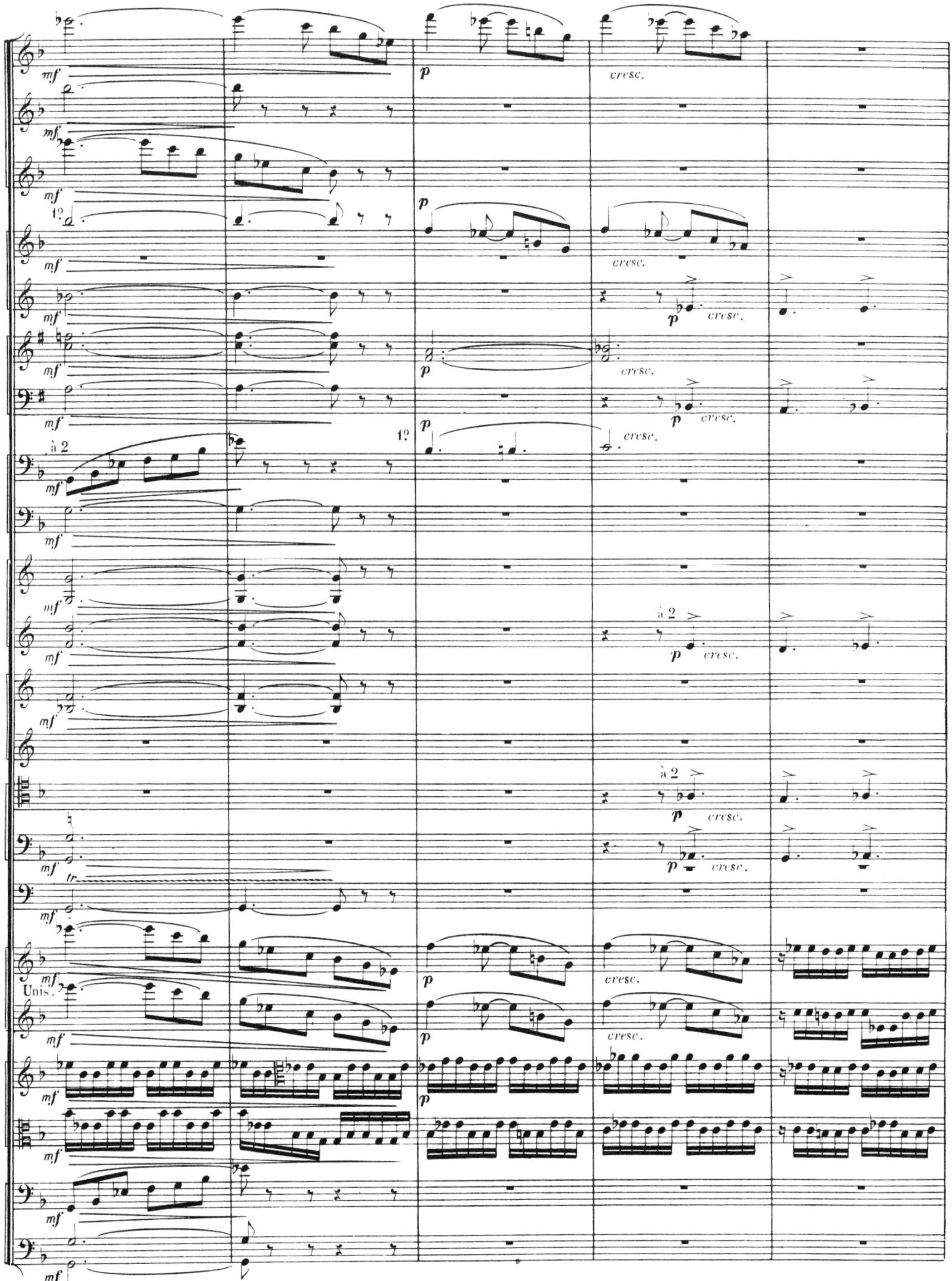
mf
p
cresc.
1º
à 2
Unis.
tr

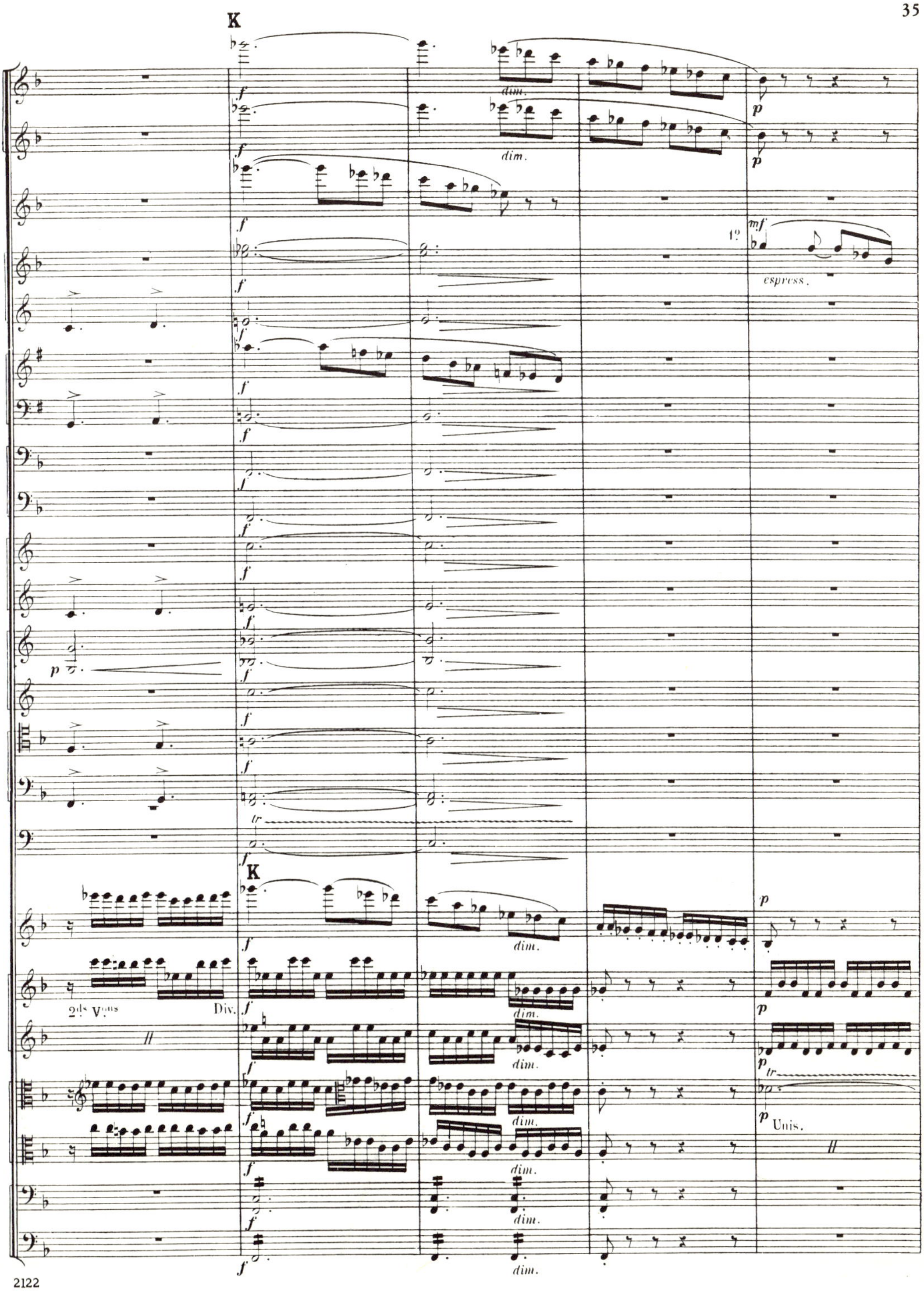
K
f
dim.
p
1º
mf
espress.
tr
K
2ds Vons
Div.
Unis.

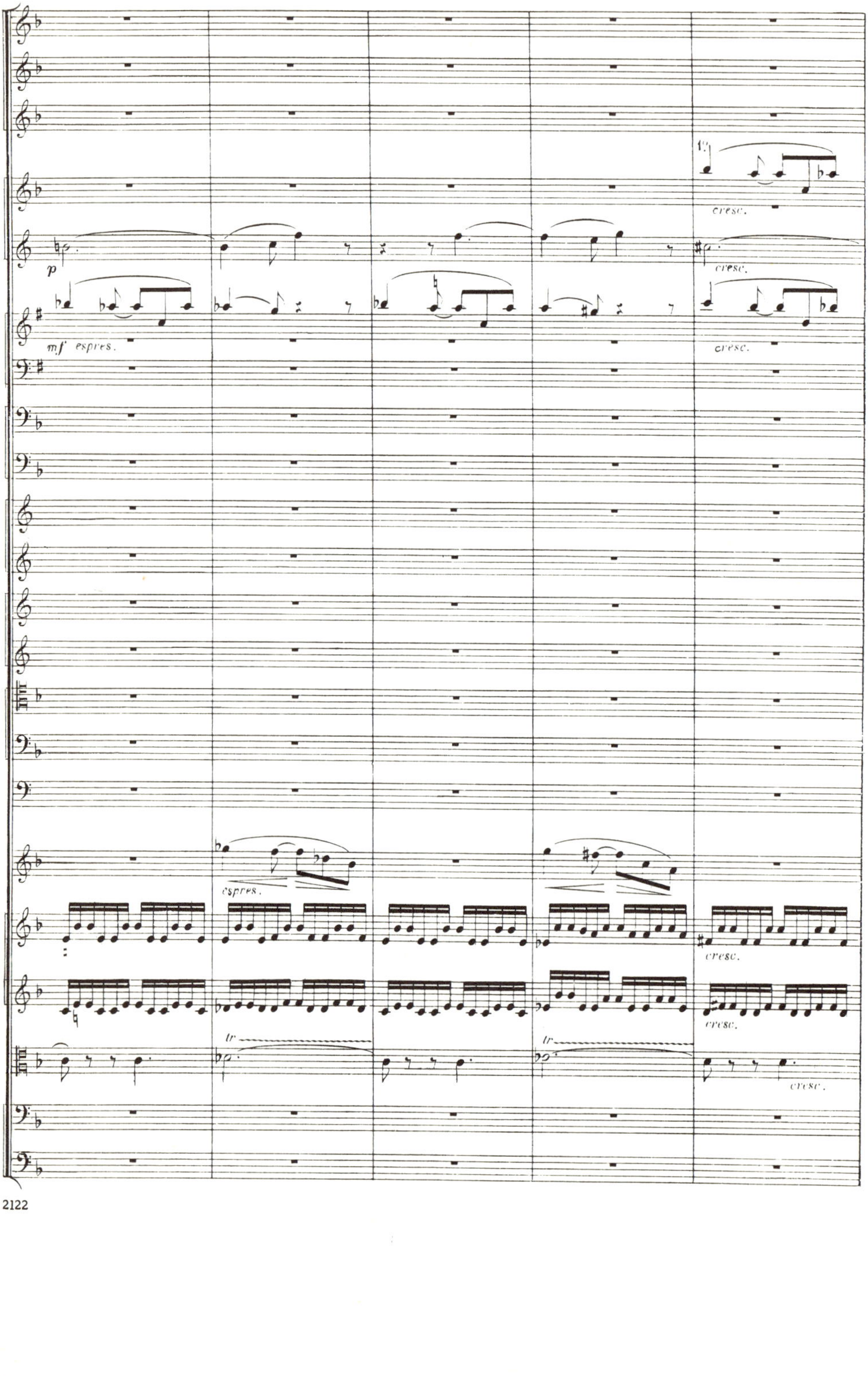
cresc.
p
cresc.
mf espres.
cresc.
espres.
cresc.
cresc.
tr
tr
cresc.

cresc. molto
cresc. molto
cresc. molto
cresc. molto
ff
à 2
1º cresc. molto
p
mf
cresc. molto
cresc. molto
cresc. molto
cresc. molto
p cresc. molto

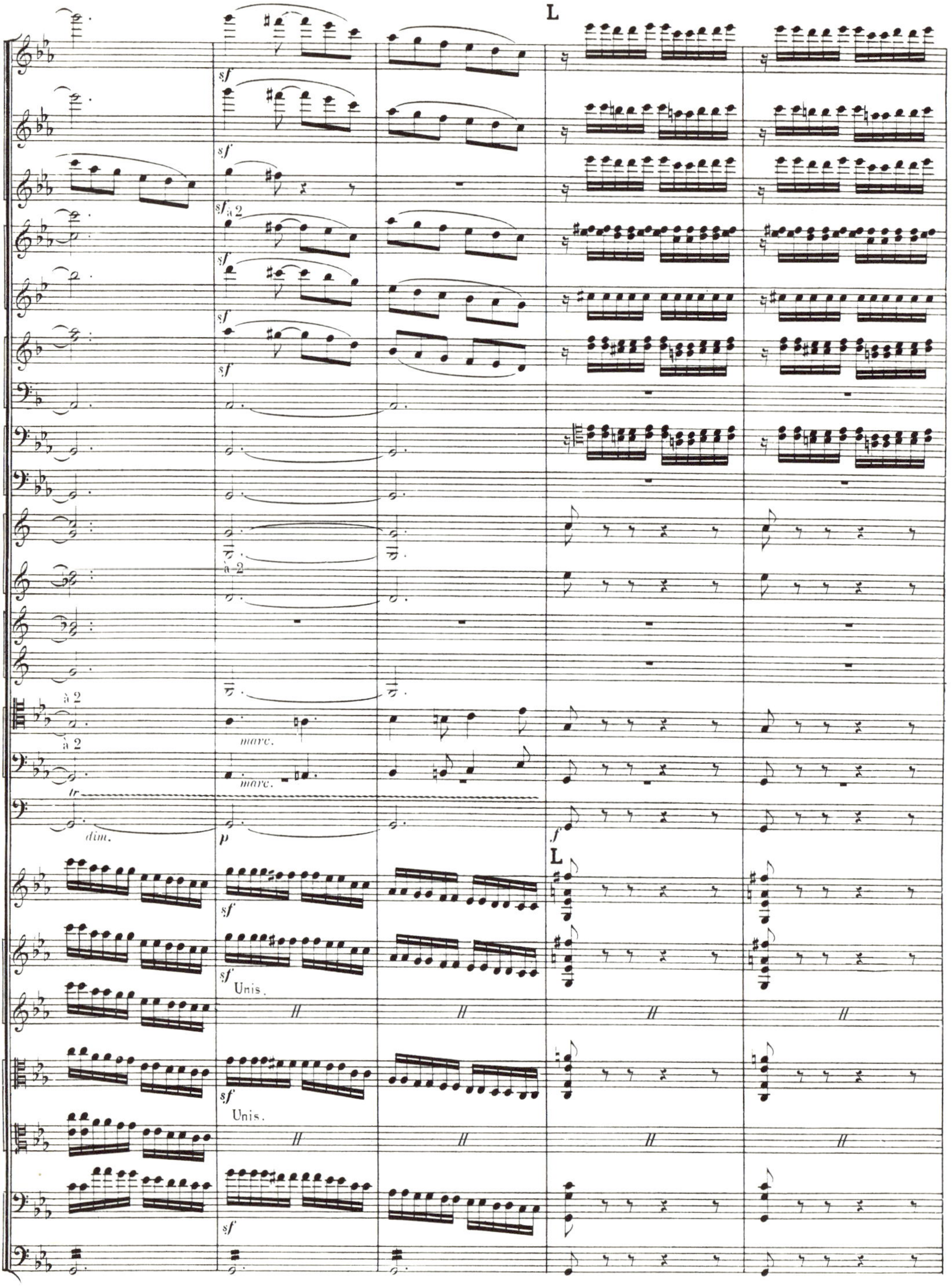
L
sf
a 2
marc.
tr
dim.
p
f
Unis.

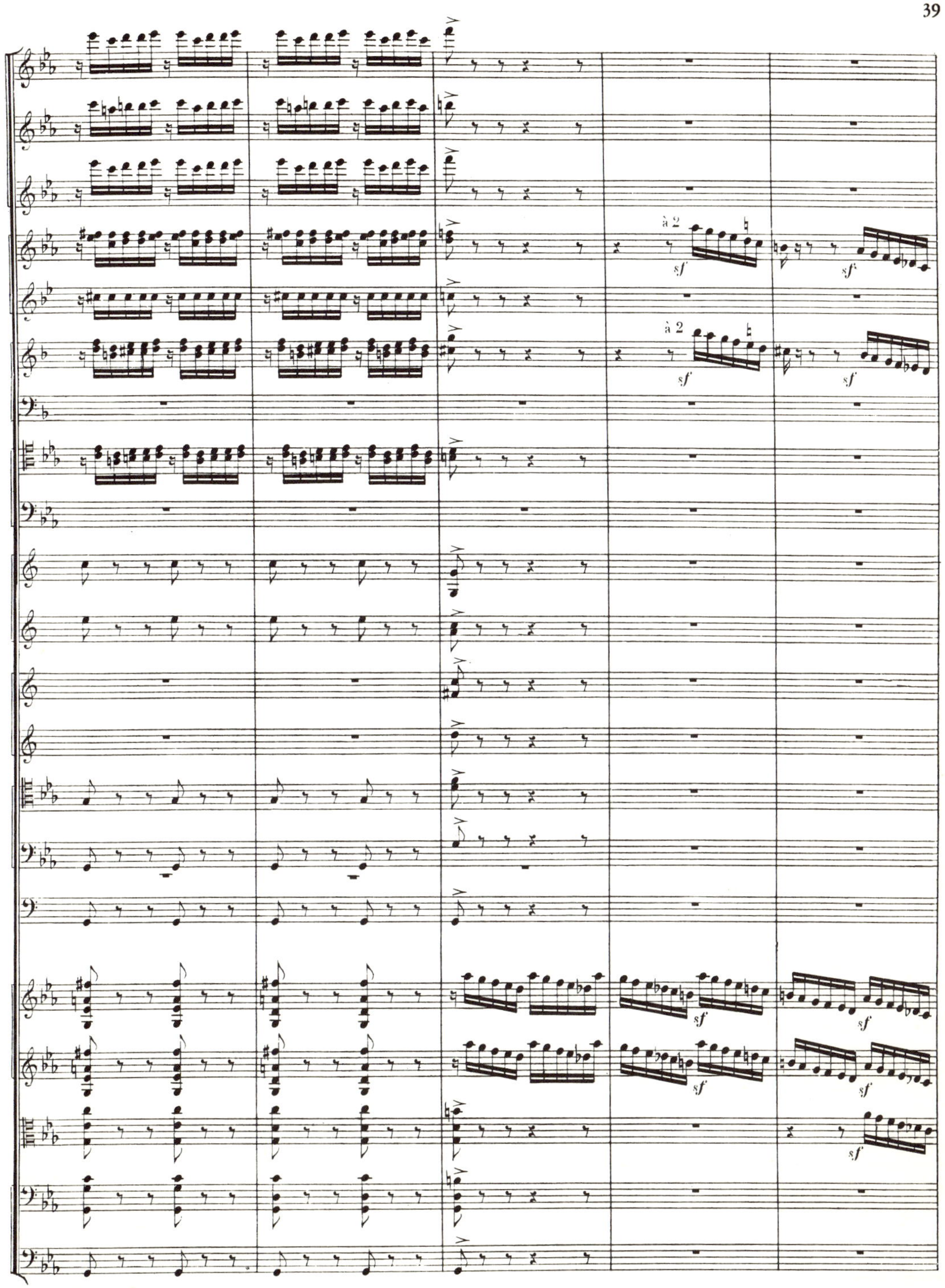

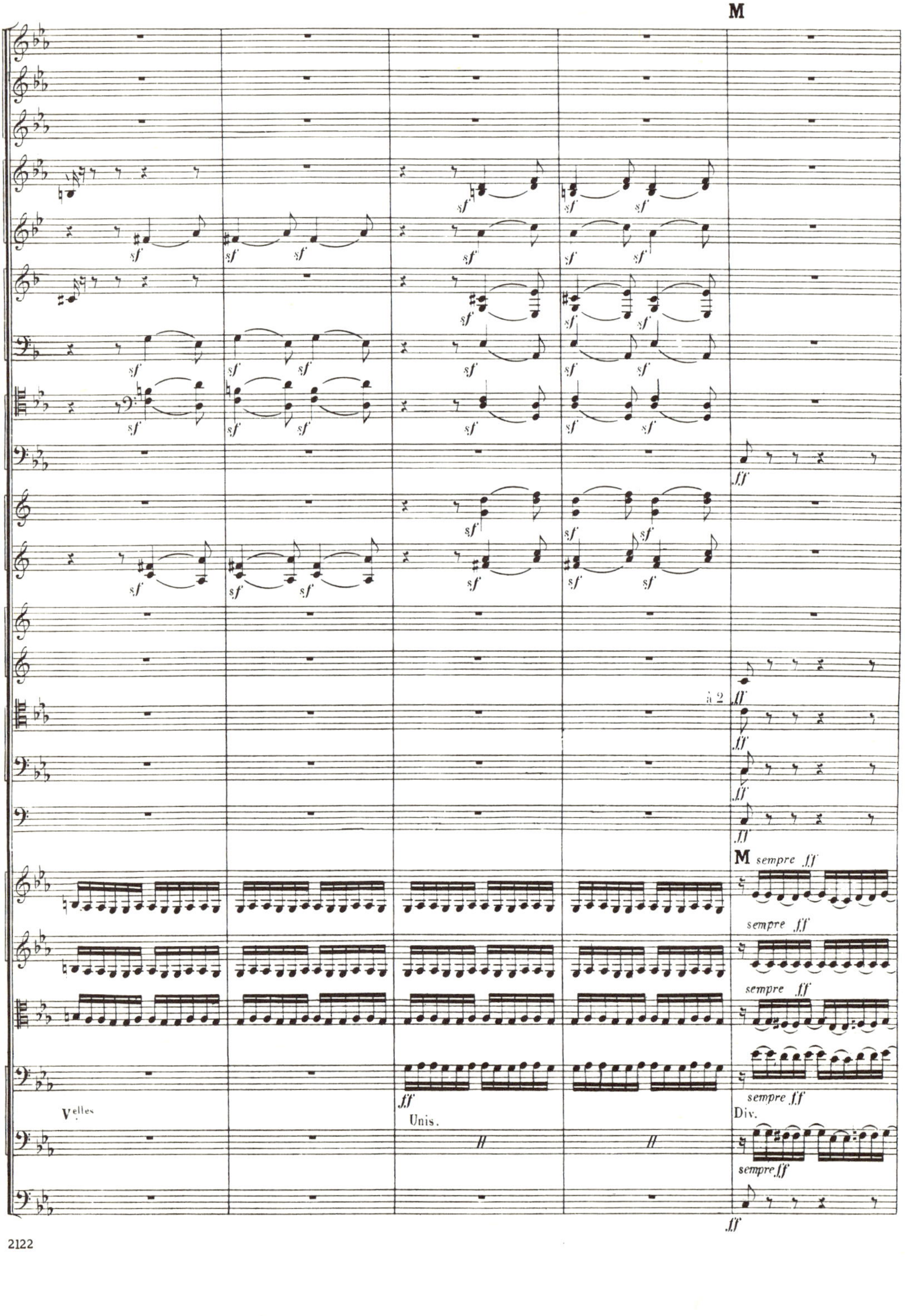
M
sf
ff
à 2
sempre ff
Velles
Unis.
Div.

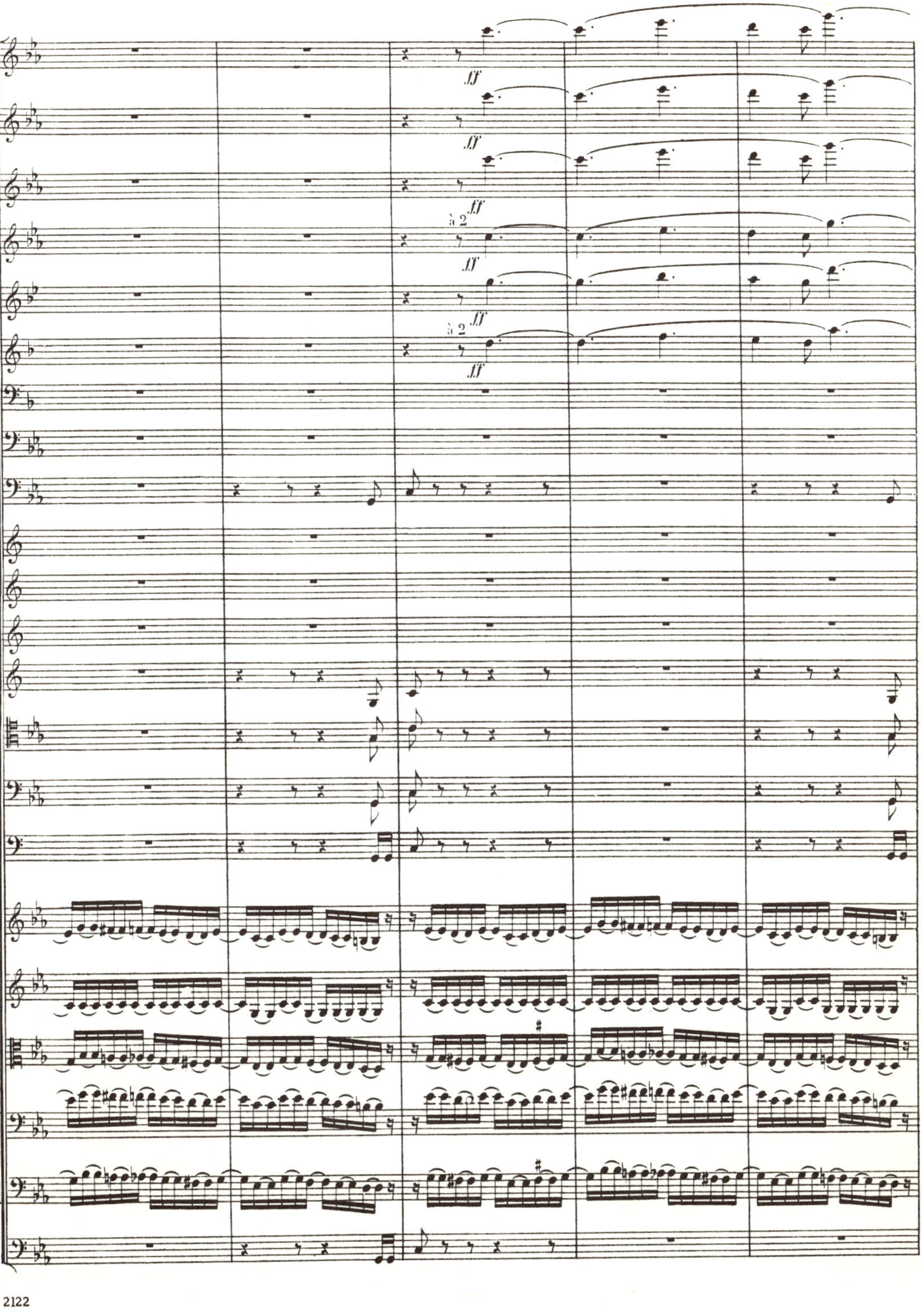
ff
ff
ff
à 2
ff
ff
à 2
ff

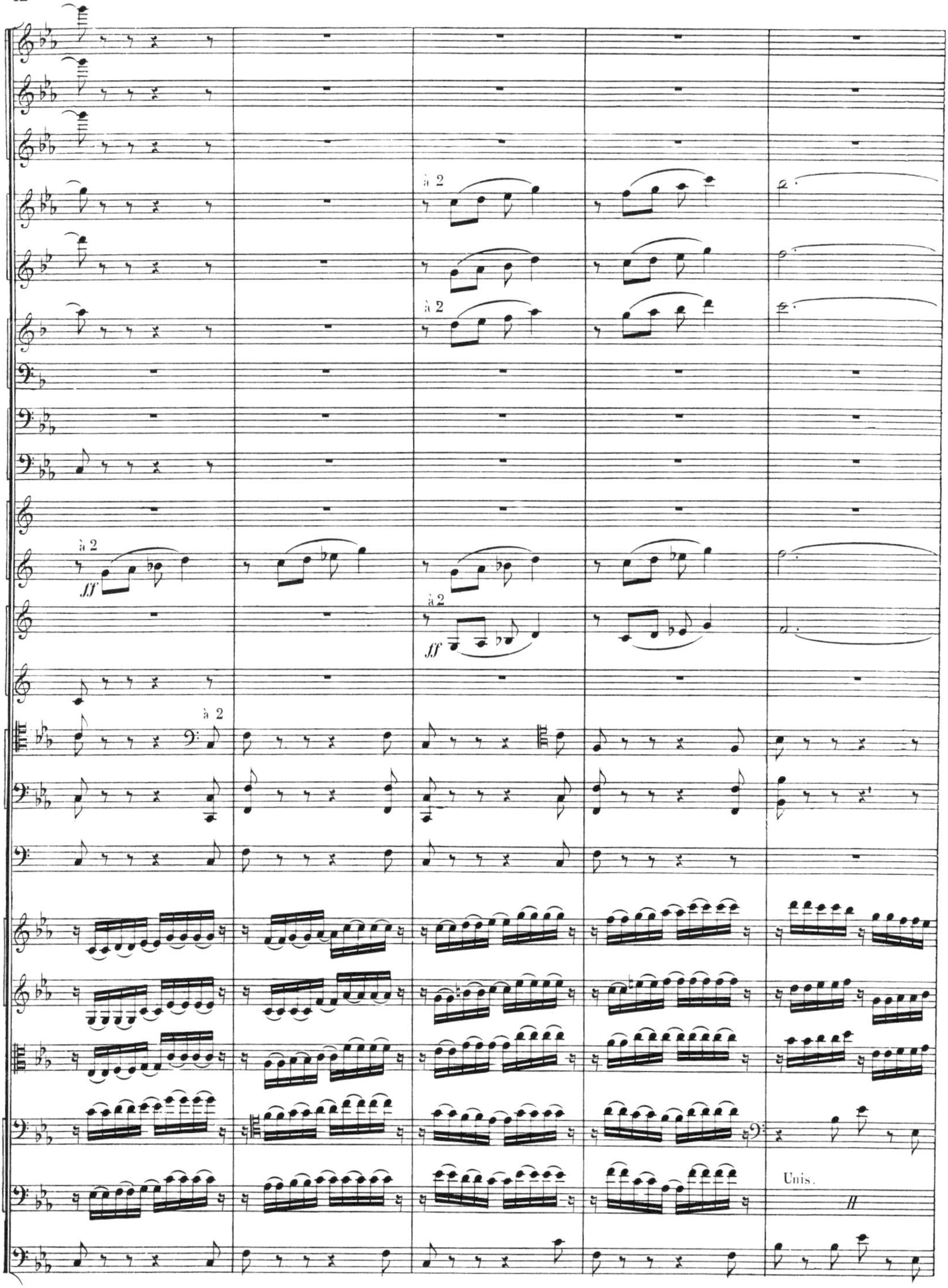
à 2
à 2
à 2
ff
à 2
ff
à 2
Unis.

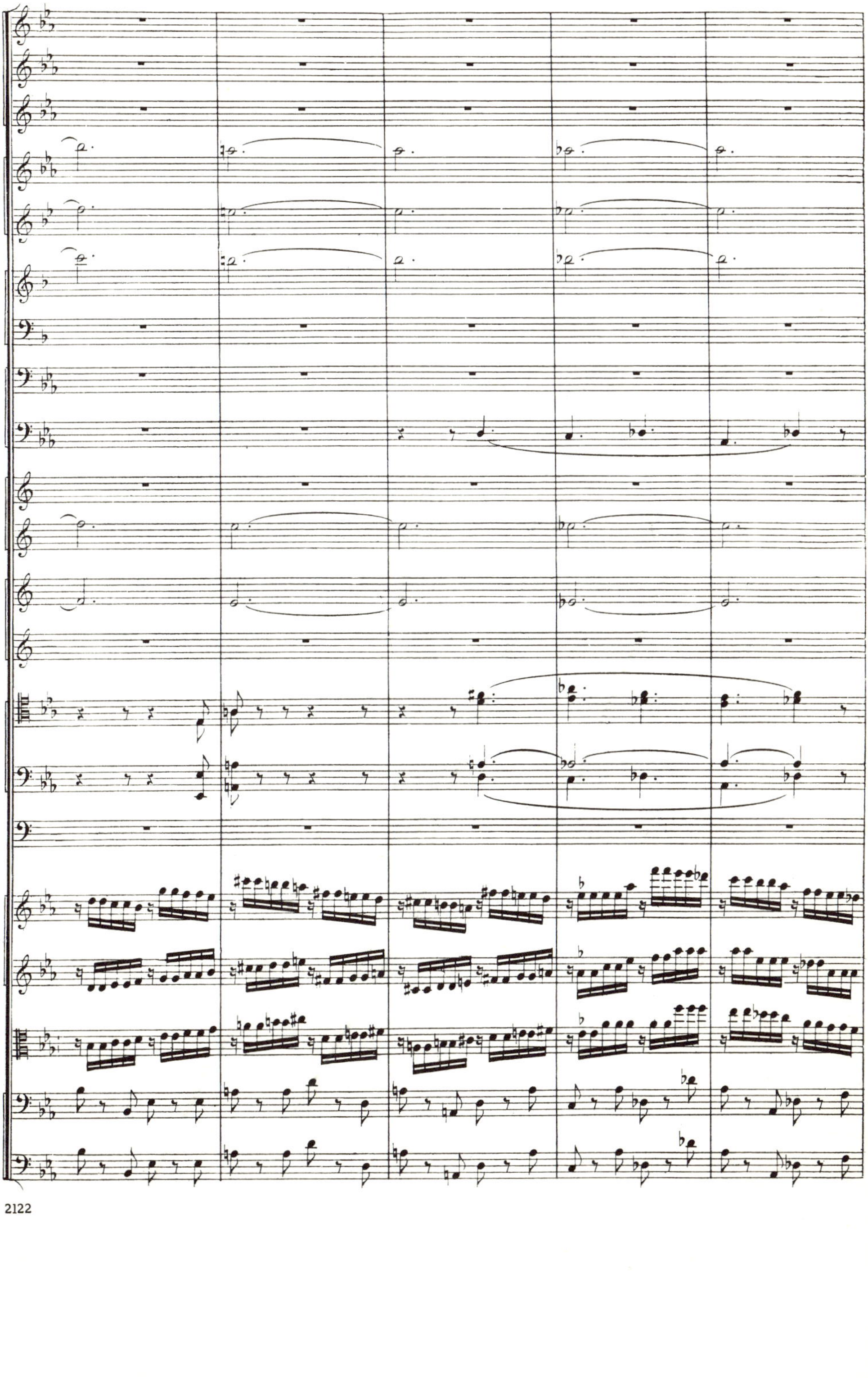

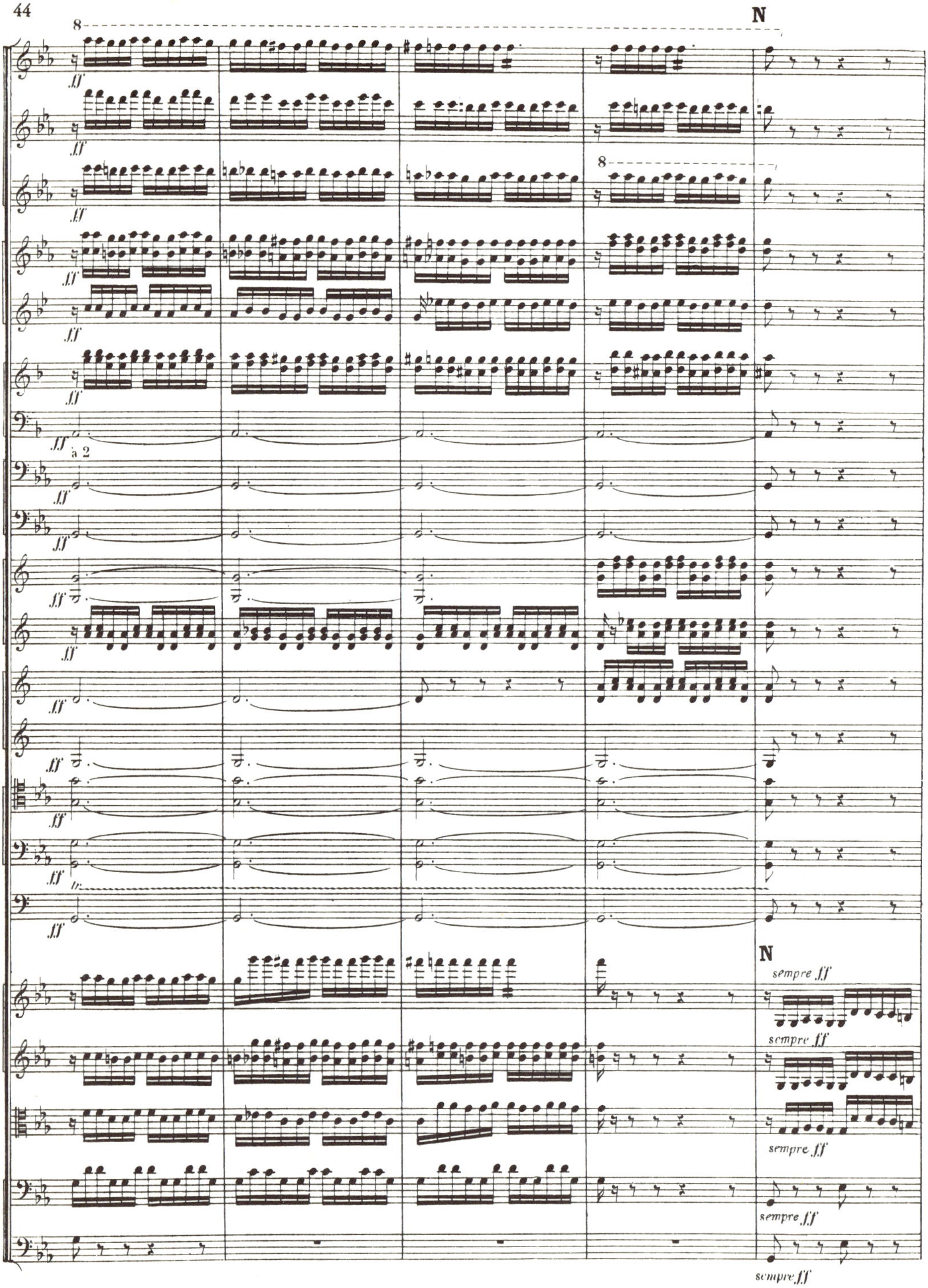
8
N
ff
à 2
tr
8
N
sempre ff

sempre ff
à 2 sempre ff
sempre ff
à 2
sempre ff
à 2 sempre ff
Col C.B.

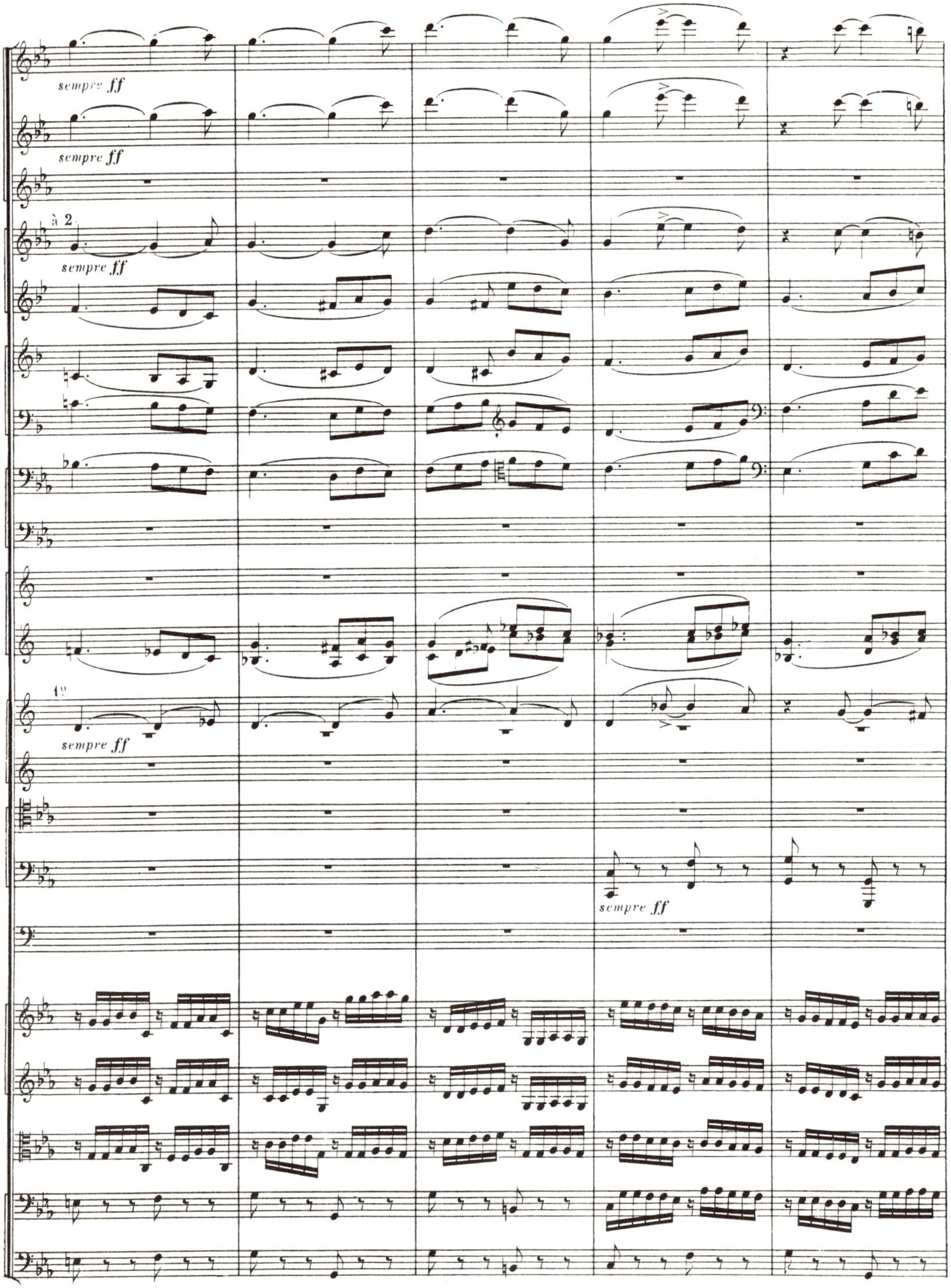
sempre ff
sempre ff
à 2.
sempre ff
1º
sempre ff
sempre ff

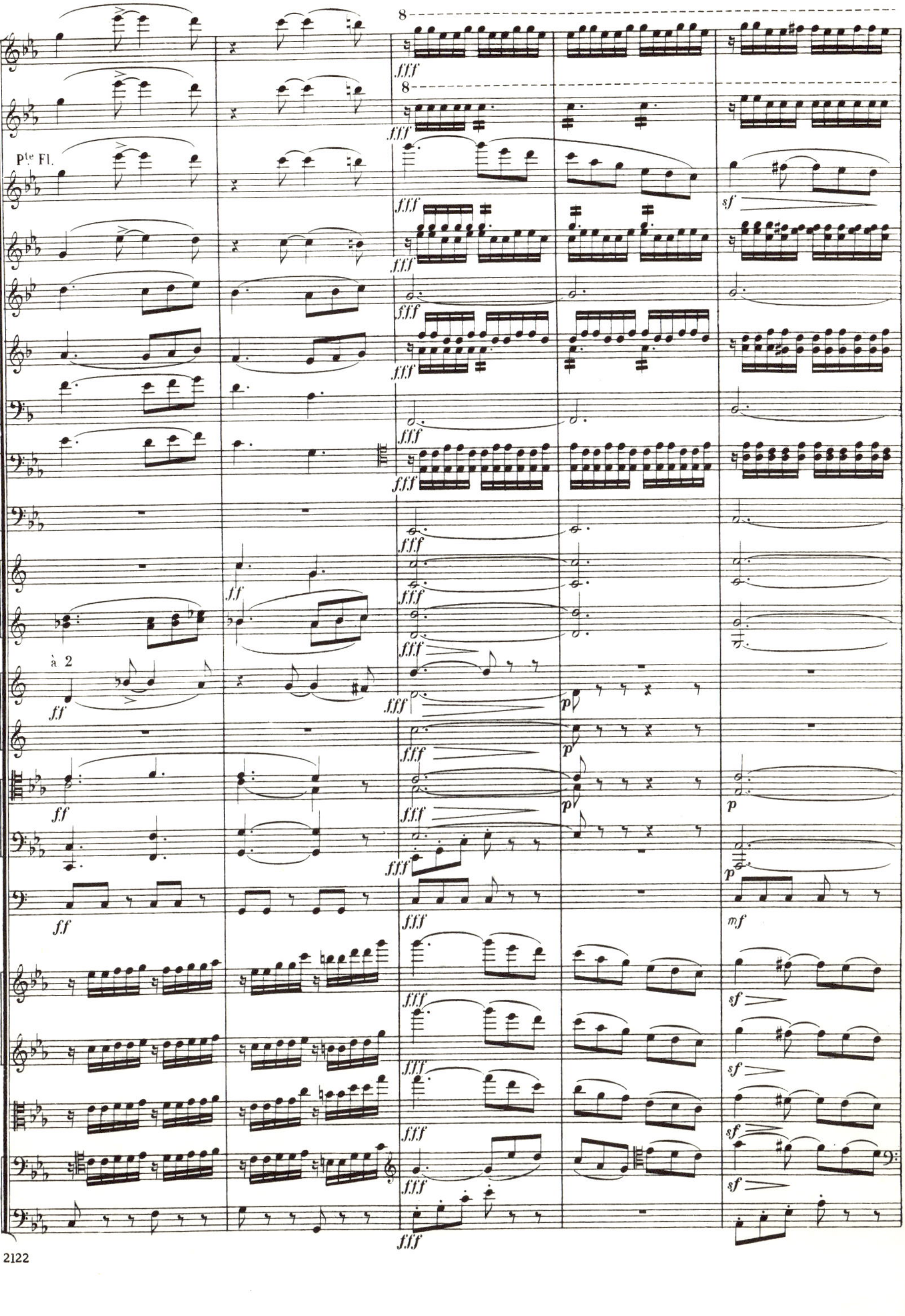

8
Pte Fl.
à 2

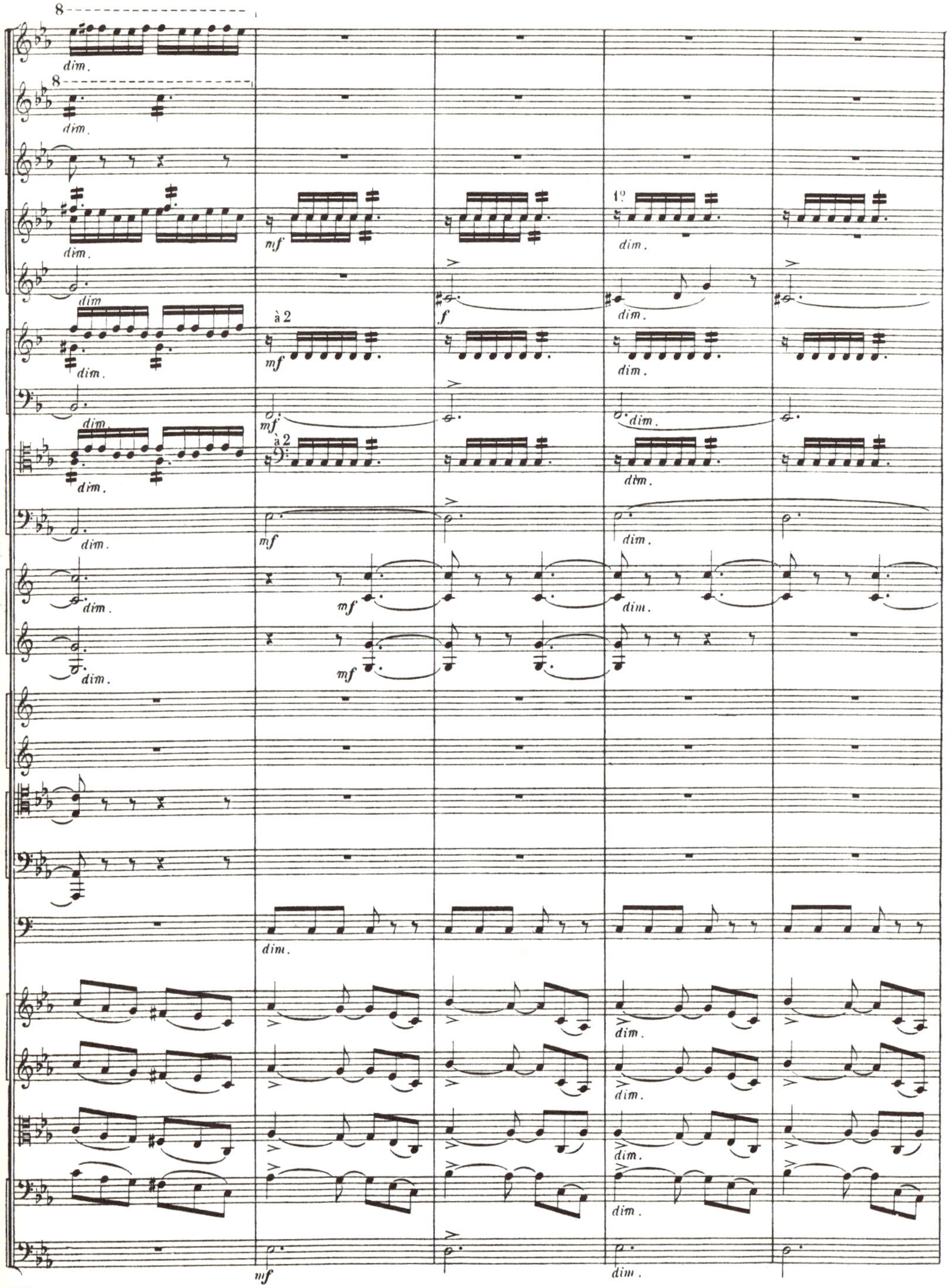
8
dim.
1º
mf
f
à 2

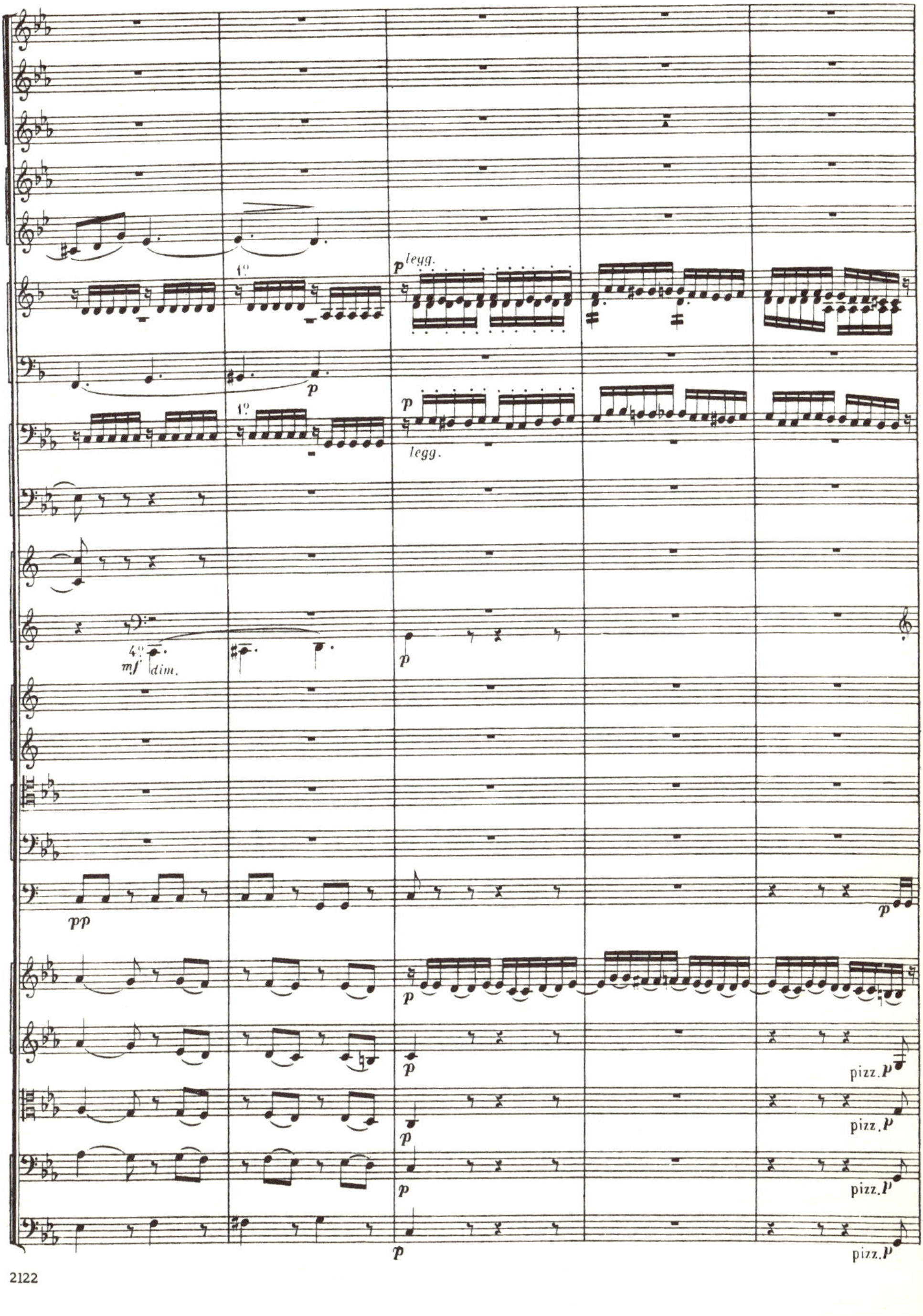
legg.
1º
p
4º
mf
dim.
pp
pizz.

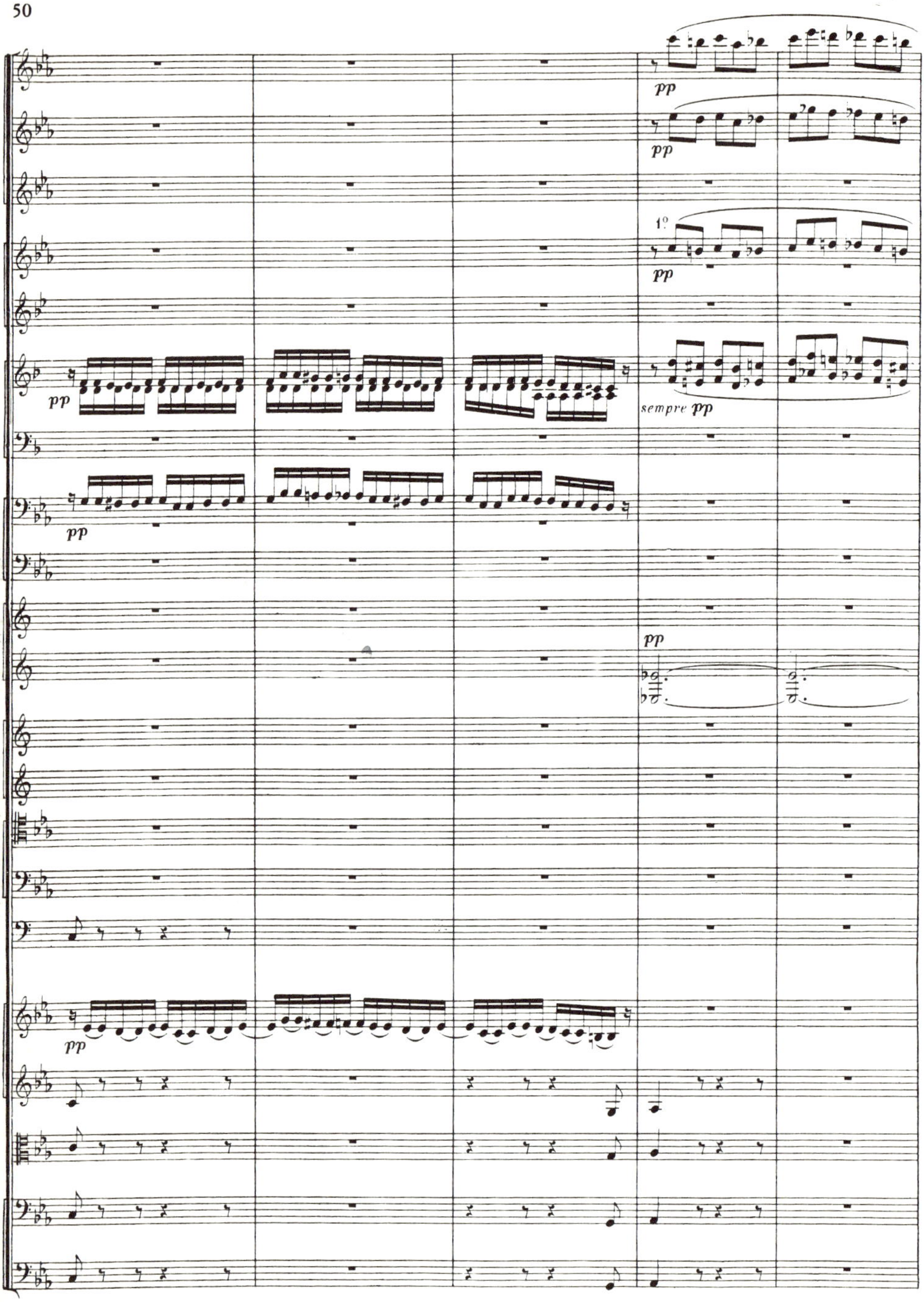
pp
pp
1º
pp
pp
sempre pp
pp
pp
pp

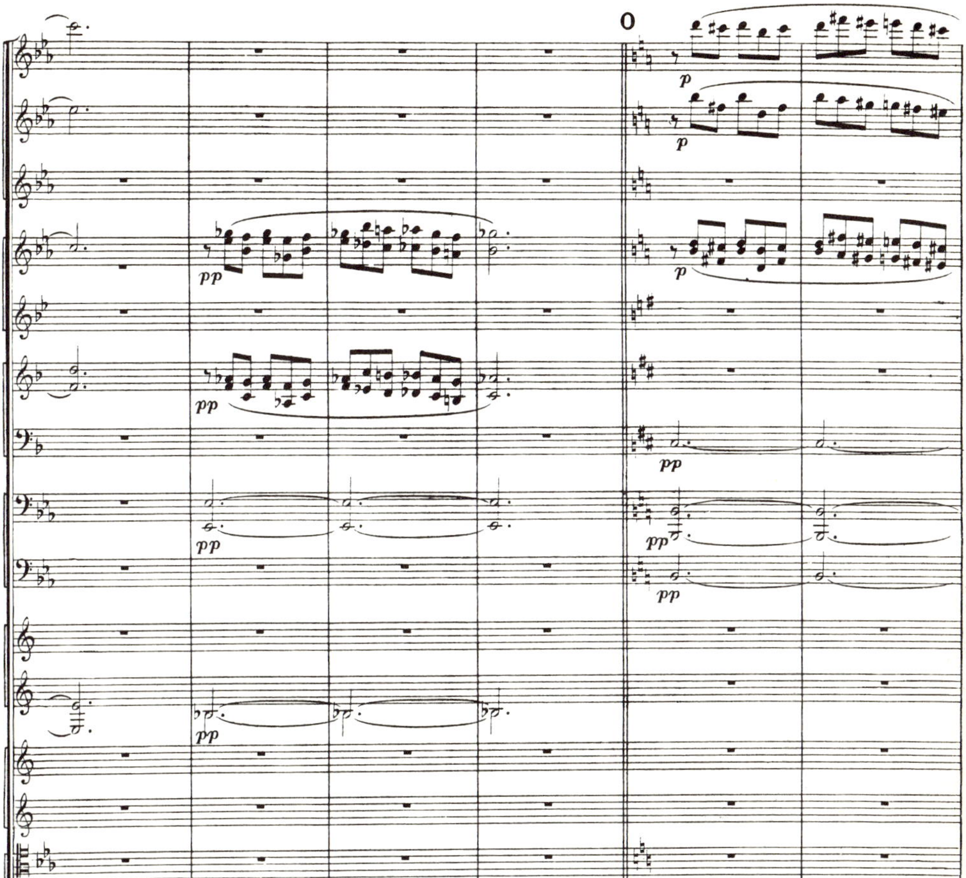
O
p
pp
Div.
arco
(pizz)

1re Fl.
2e Fl.
Hb
Cl. B.
Bons
C.Bons
Velles et C. B.
dim.
dim.
dim.
1re Fl.
Hb
3e et 4e Cors
pp
pp
pp
Unis
arco
sempre pp
sempre pp
sempre pp
sempre pp
Velles
C.B.

1re Fl.
2e Fl.
Grande Fl.
3e et 4e Cors
sempre pp
sempre pp
sempre pp
4e
pp
sempre pp
sempre pp
sempre pp
Div.
pizz.
arco
1re Fl.
2e Fl.
3e Fl.
P
P
p
p
p
Unis.
p

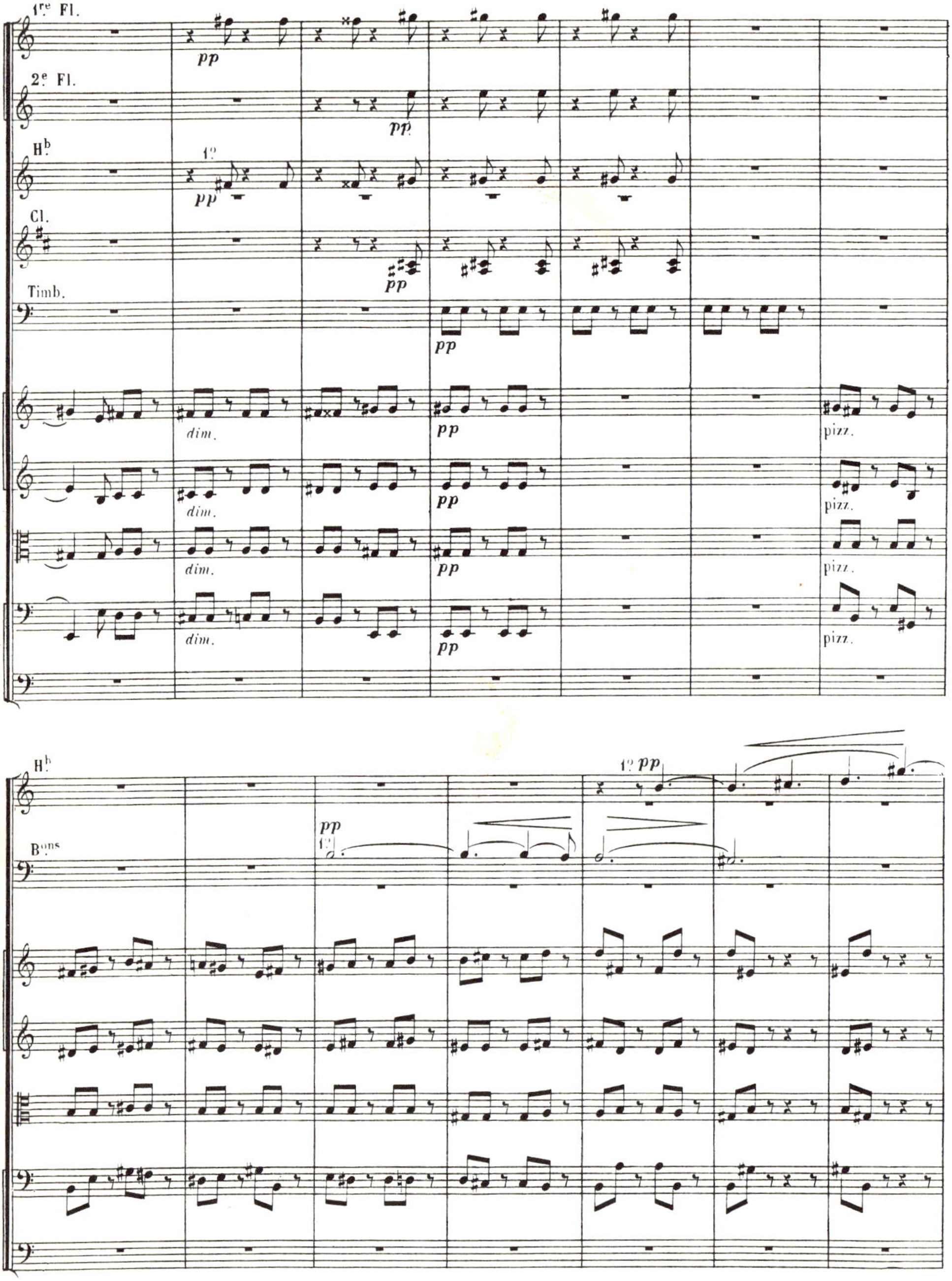
1re Fl.
2e Fl.
Hb.
Cl.
Timb.
pp
1o
dim.
pizz.
Bons

2122

pp
Q
Cl.
1º p
poco cresc.
3e et 4e Cors
3º
1er et 2e Tromb.
1º
Q
1ers Vons Div.
2ds Vons Div.
Altos Div.
Velles Div.
C. B.

1re Fl.
2e Fl.
3e Fl.
Hb.
Cor Ang.
Cl.
Cl. B.
Bons
1o
C. Bon
Cors
Tromp.
Tromb.
Timb.
Orgue
Ped.
R
R
p
pp
Unis.

2122

pp
mf
dim.
pp
Cl.
1° p
2e et 3e Cors
3° p
1er et 2e Tromb
1°
p
Orgue
sans nuance
pp
Vons
Altos Div.
Velles
C. B. Div.
sans nuance aux Contrebasses

59

2122

poco cresc.
poco cresc.
Velles et C.B.
pp
pp
T
Orgue
pp
T
pp
Velles
pp
C.B.

poco cresc.
dim.
8
cresc.
cresc.
dim.
cresc.
dim.
cresc.
dim.
dim.
1re Fl.
2e Fl.
3e Fl.
Hb
1o
Cor Ang.
Cl.
Bons
pp
U
p
tr
Col C.B.
molto tranquillo
pizz. p

1re Fl.
2e Fl.
3e Fl.
Hb
Cor Ang.
Cl.
Cl. B.
Bons
C. Bon
Cors
Tromp.
Tromb.
Timb.
pp
Orgue
pizz.
p
pizz.
p
pizz.
p
Col C.B.

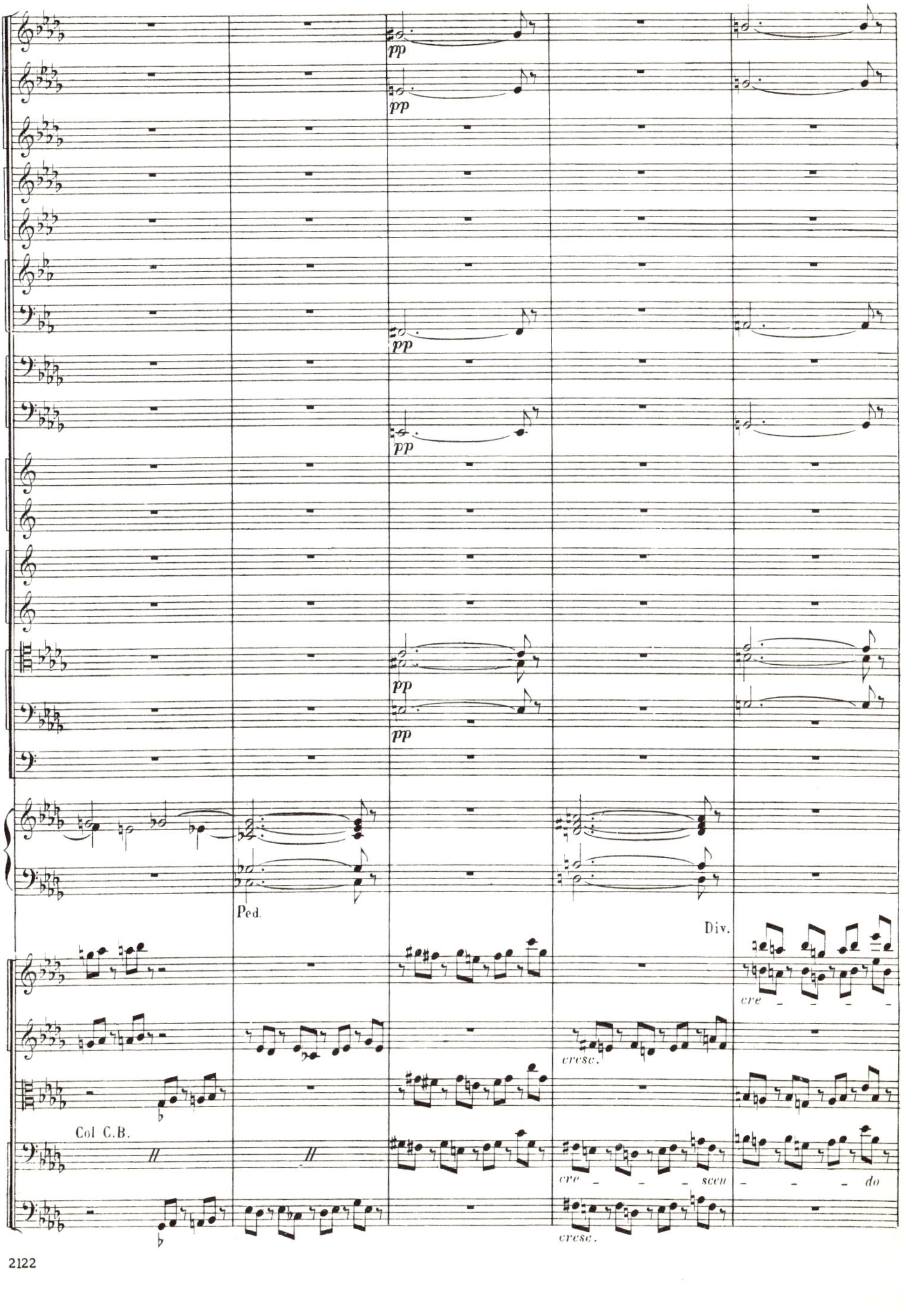
pp
pp
pp
pp
pp
pp
Ped.
Div.
cre
cresc.
Col C.B.
cre - - - scen - - - do
cresc.

V
p cresc.
p cresc.
pp
pp
p cresc.
pp
p cresc.
pp
p cresc.
pp
p
pp (voix céleste)
32 pieds
V
arco
p molto espressivo
cre - scen - do
(pizz.)
pp
cre - scen - do
pp
arco
p molto espressivo
cre - scen - do
Unis.
Div.
(pizz.)
pp
arco
p molto espressivo
Unis.
Div.
(pizz.)
pp
cre - scen - do
pp

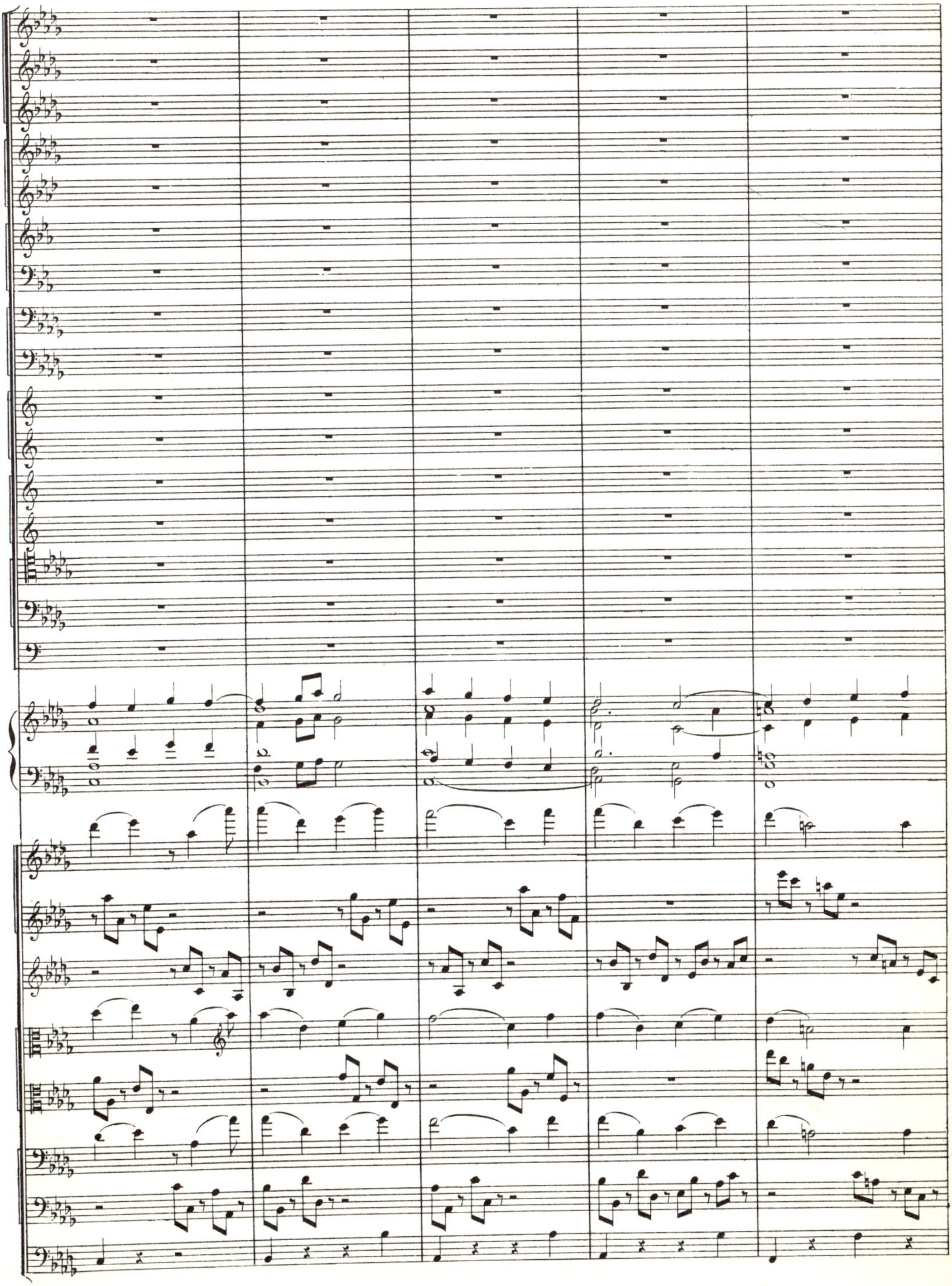

p 1º
1º
p
p
p
p
3º
p
poco cresc.
8
poco a poco cresc.
cresc.
cresc.
poco a poco cresc.
cresc.
poco a poco cresc.
cresc.
Div.
cresc.

p
p
p
dim.
pp
sf
sf
dim.
pp
dim.
pp
dim.
pp
pp
dim.
pp
8
f
sempre f
dim. molto
f
dim.
dim. molto
f
dim.
dim. molto
f
sempre f
dim. molto
f
dim.
dim. molto
dim. molto
sempre f
dim. molto
f
f
dim.
dim. molto
Unis.
f
dim.
dim. molto

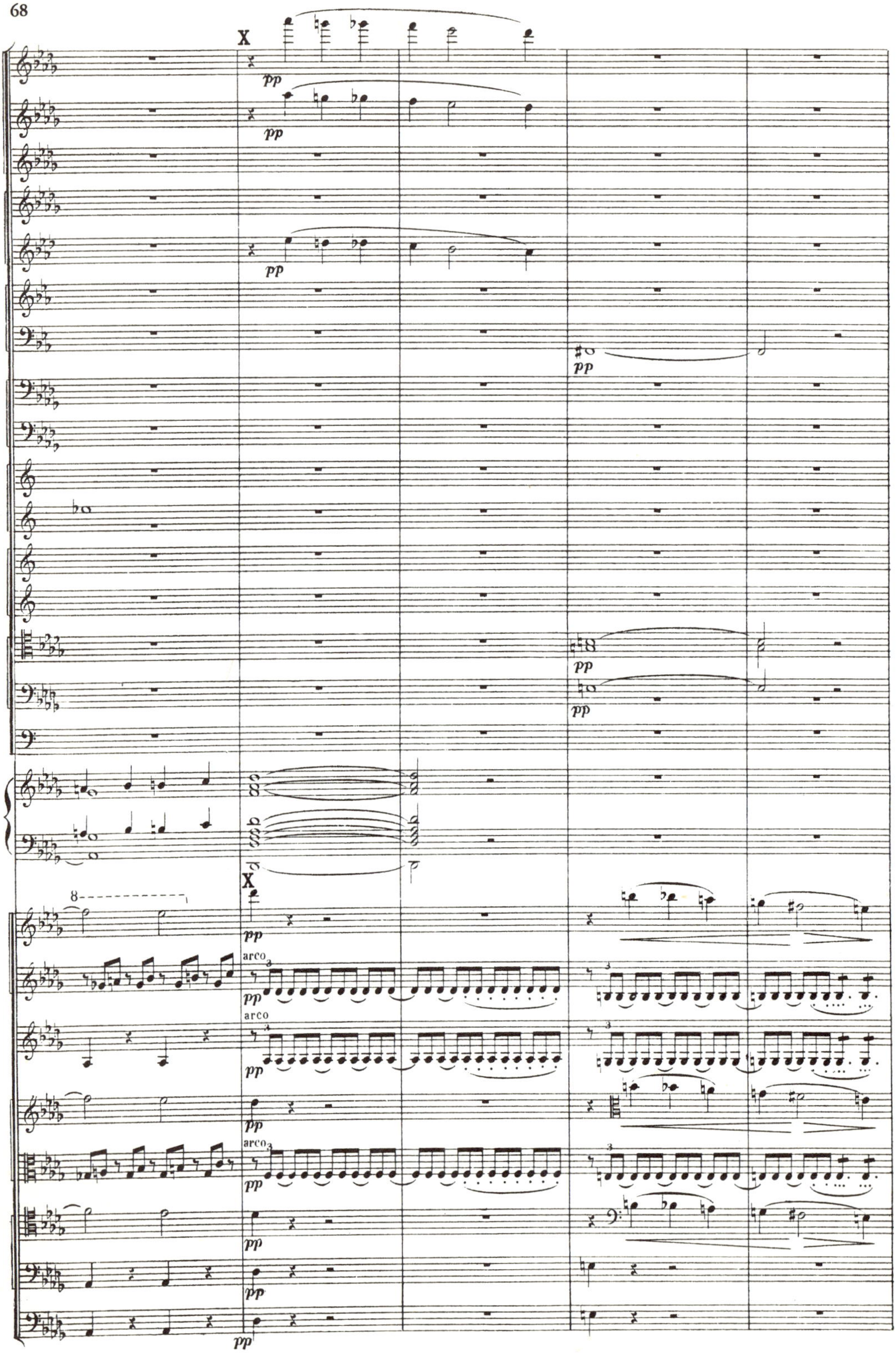
X
pp
pp
pp
pp
pp
pp
X
8
pp
arco
pp
arco
pp
pp
arco
pp
pp
pp
pp

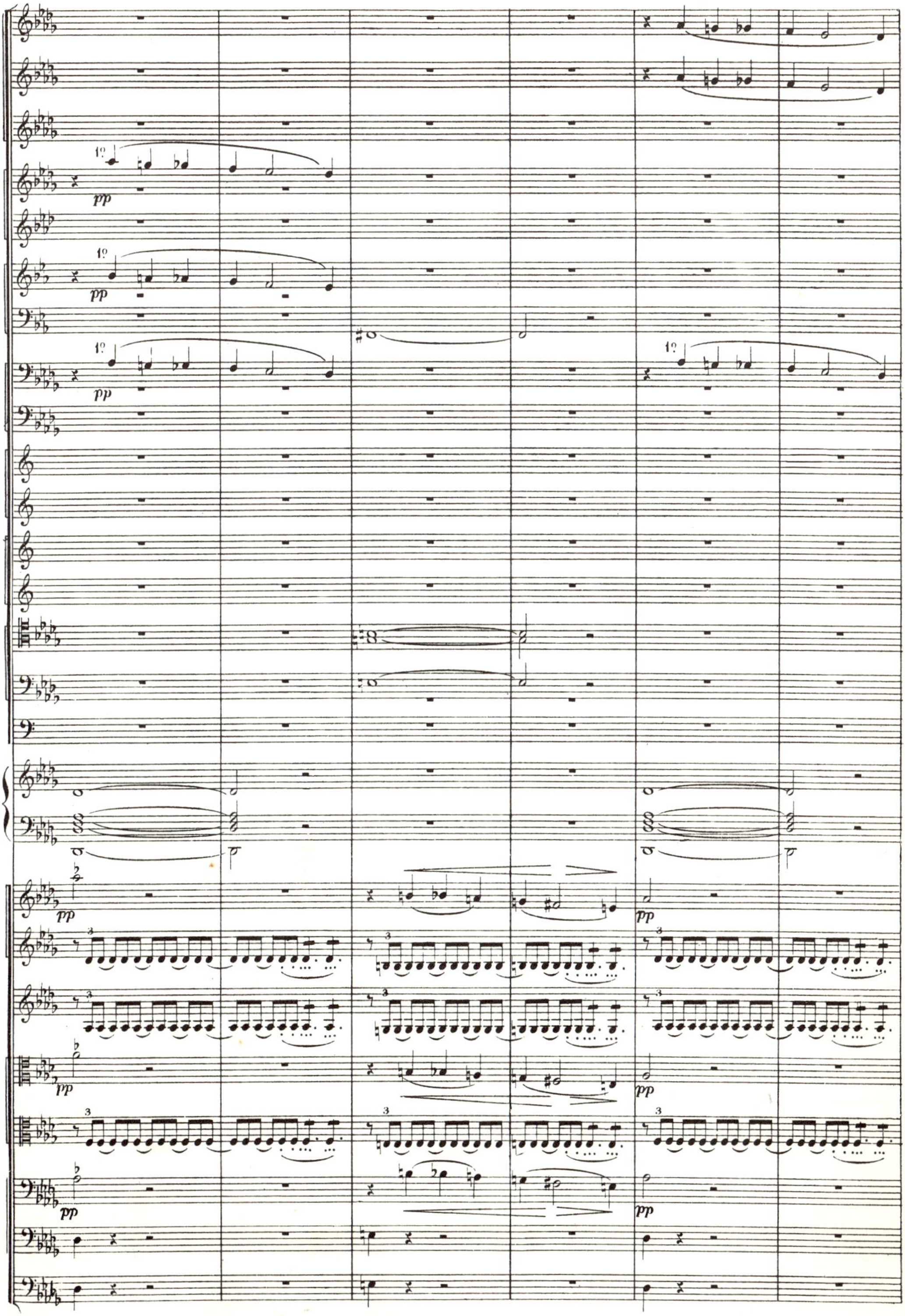
1º
pp

pp
2º
pp
pp
pp
pp
pp
morendo
cresc.
dim.
pp
pp
pp
Altos Unis.
espress.
pp
espress.
cresc.
dim.
pp
arco
espress.
pp
arco
pizz.
espress.
pp

II.

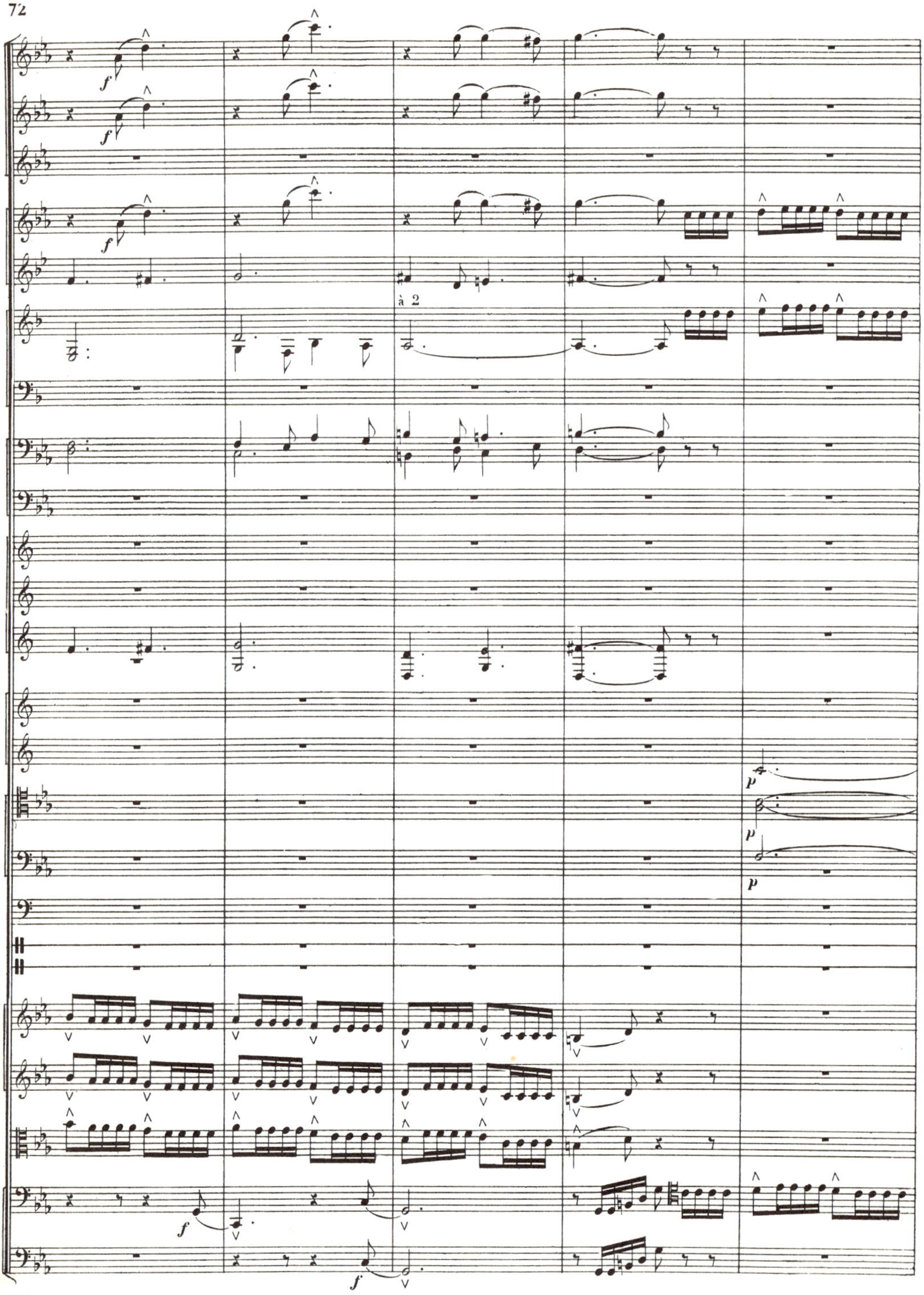
à 2

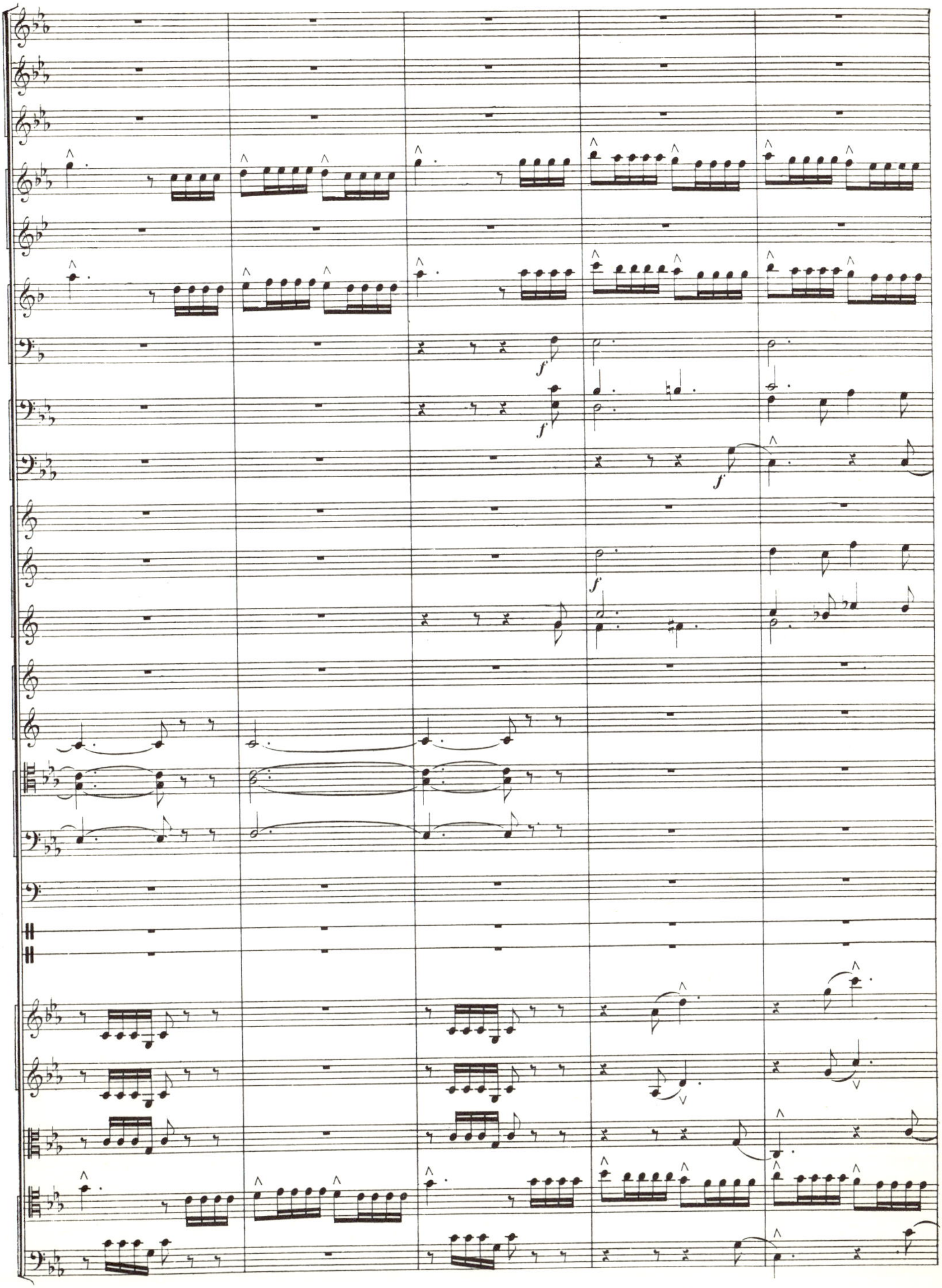

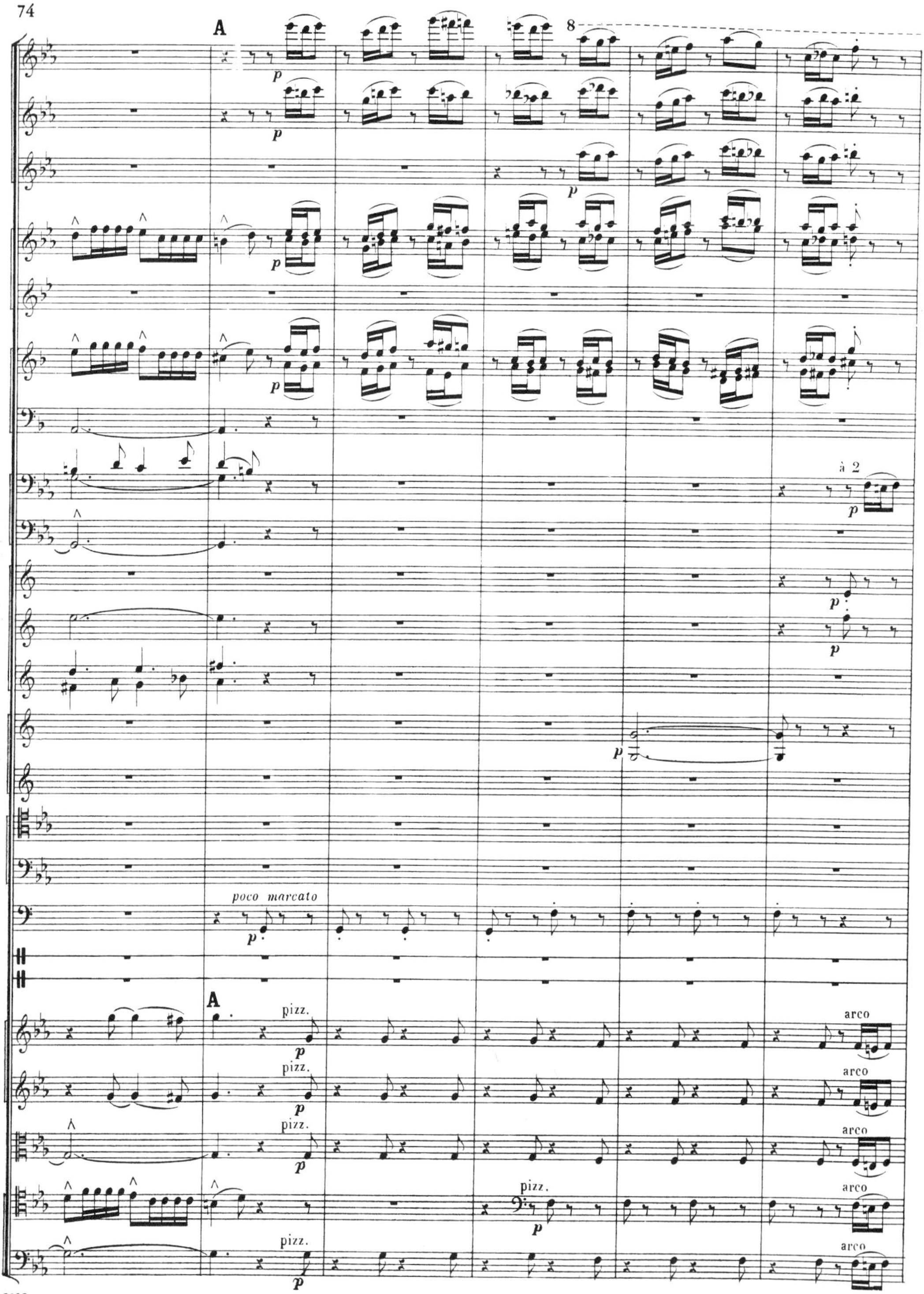
A
p
8
à 2
poco marcato
A
pizz.
arco

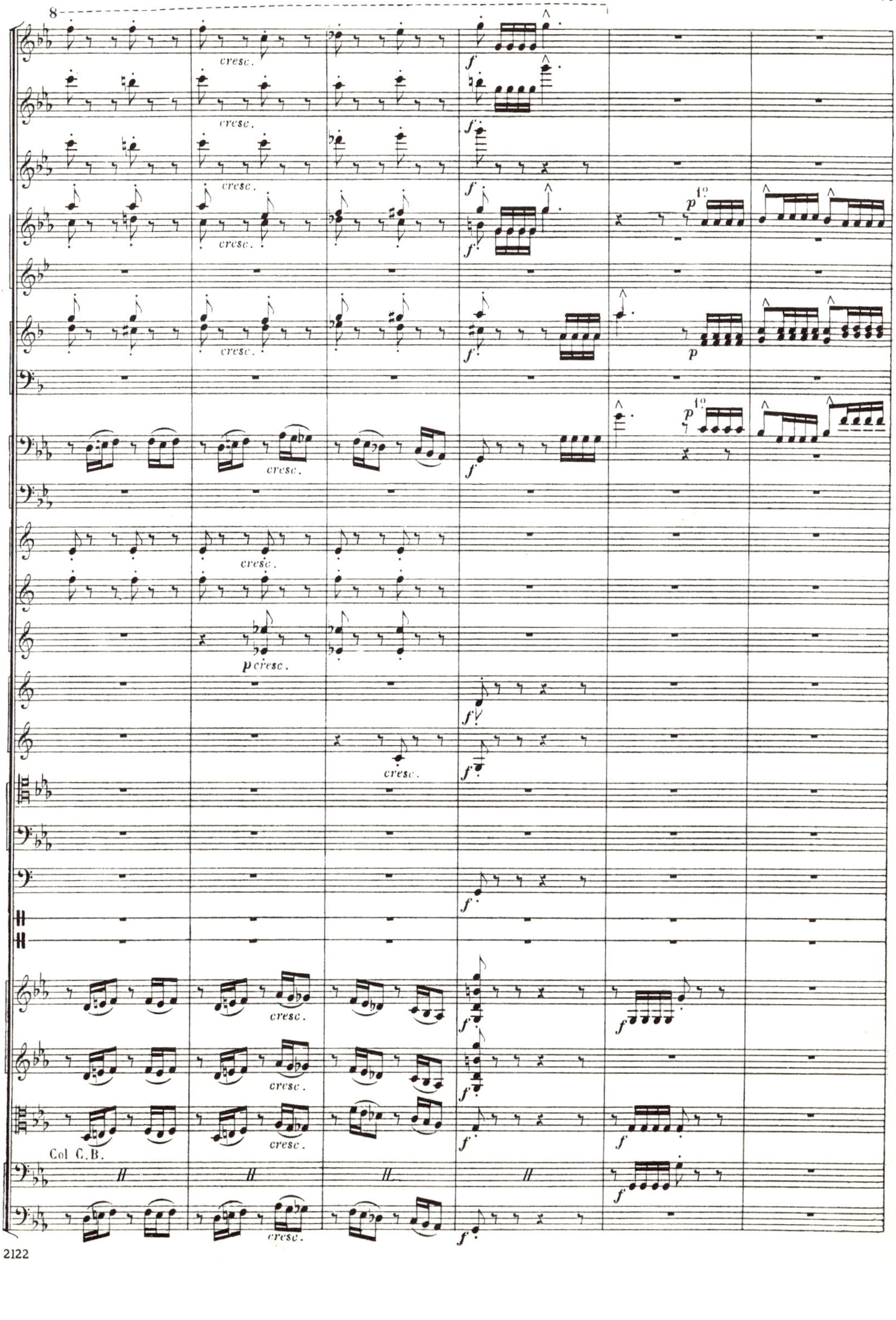
8
cresc.
f
p
1º
p cresc.
Col C.B.

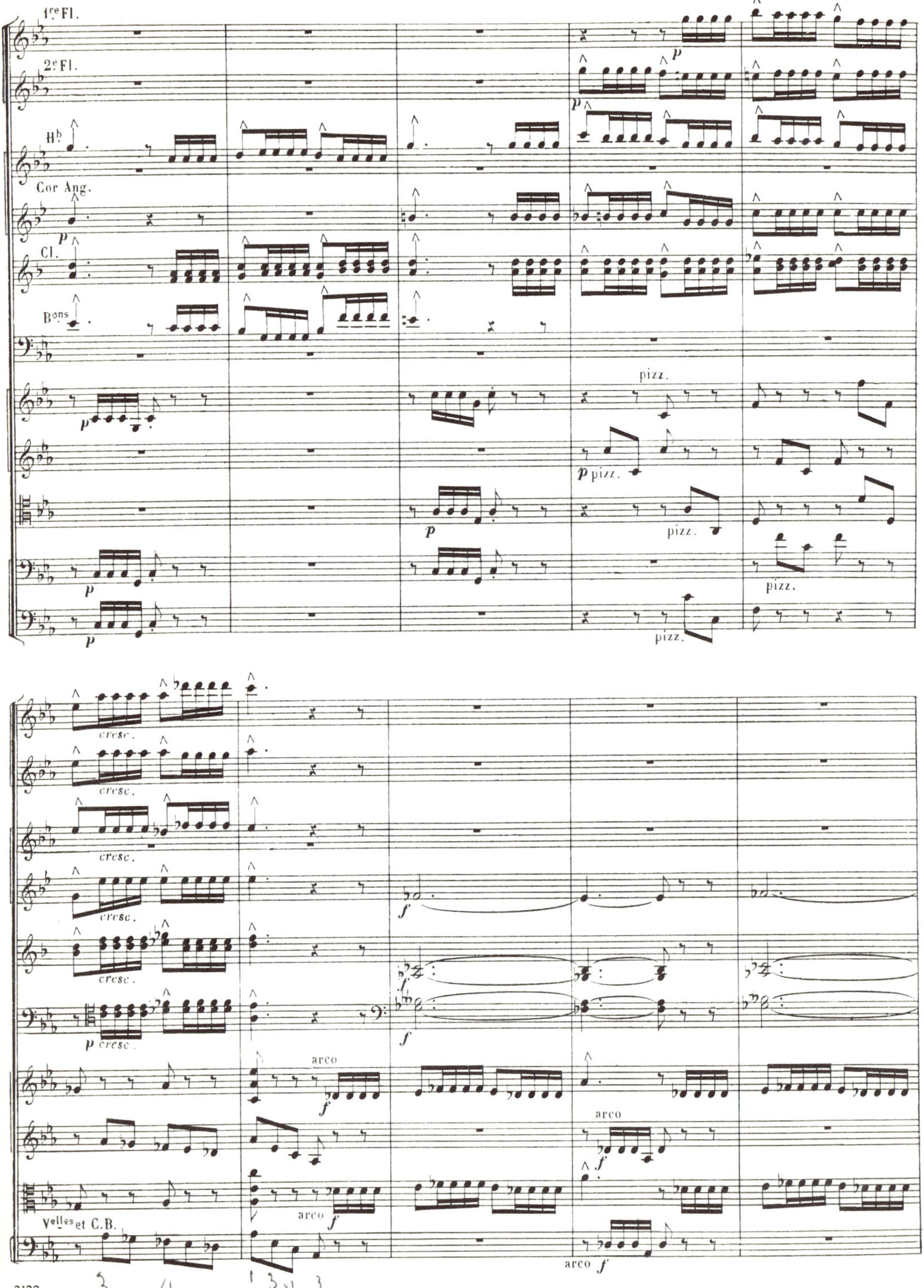
1re Fl.
2e Fl.
Hb.
Cor Ang.
Cl.
Bons
pizz.
arco
cresc.
Velles et C.B.

1re Fl.
B
2e Fl.
Pte Fl.
Hb.
à 2
Cor Ang.
Cl.
Cl.B.
Bons
C.Bon
Cors
3e
Tromp.
Tromb.
Timb.
B
Col C.B.

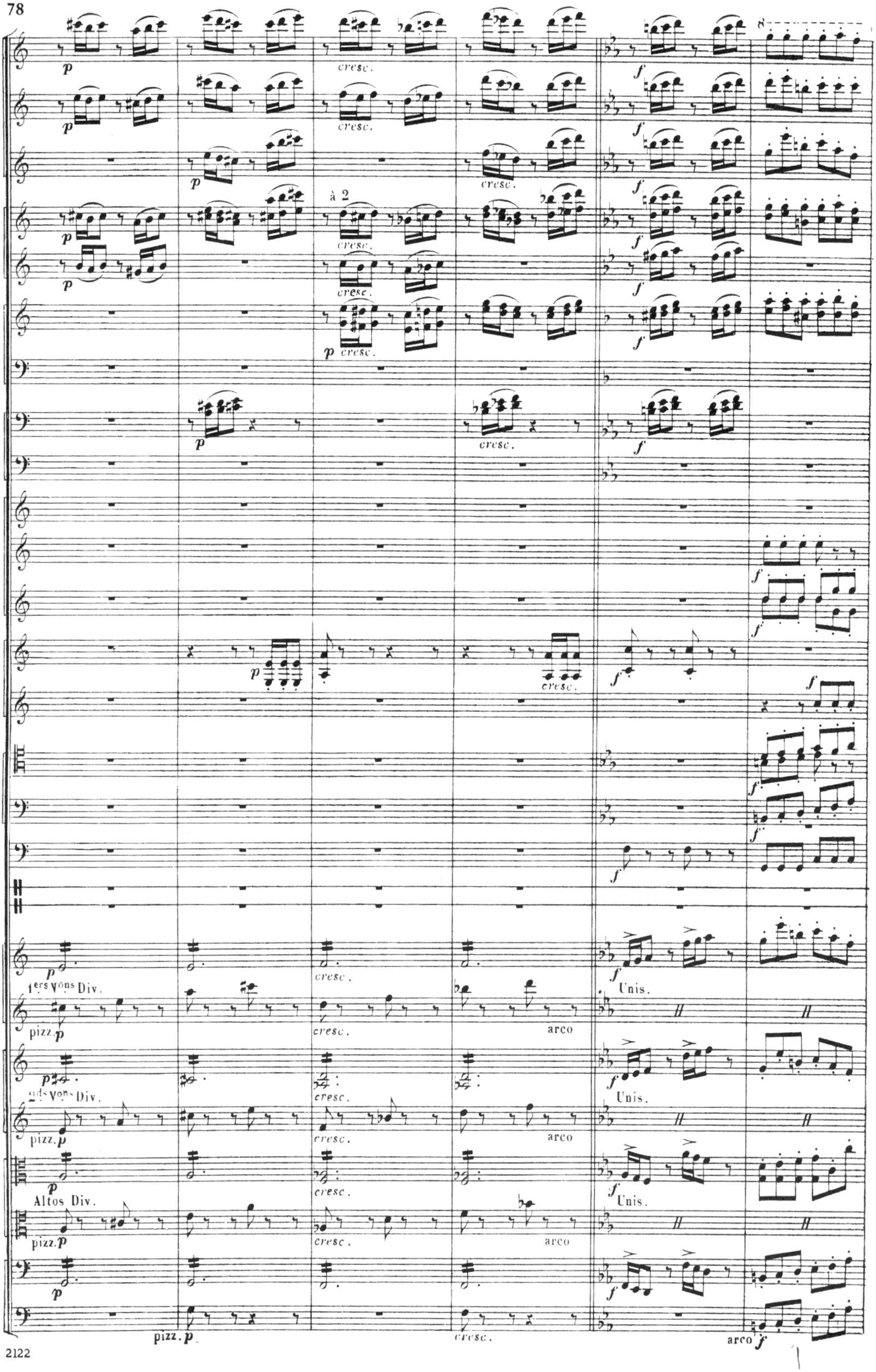
cresc.
à 2
1ers Vons Div.
pizz.
arco
Unis.
2ds Vons Div.
Altos Div.

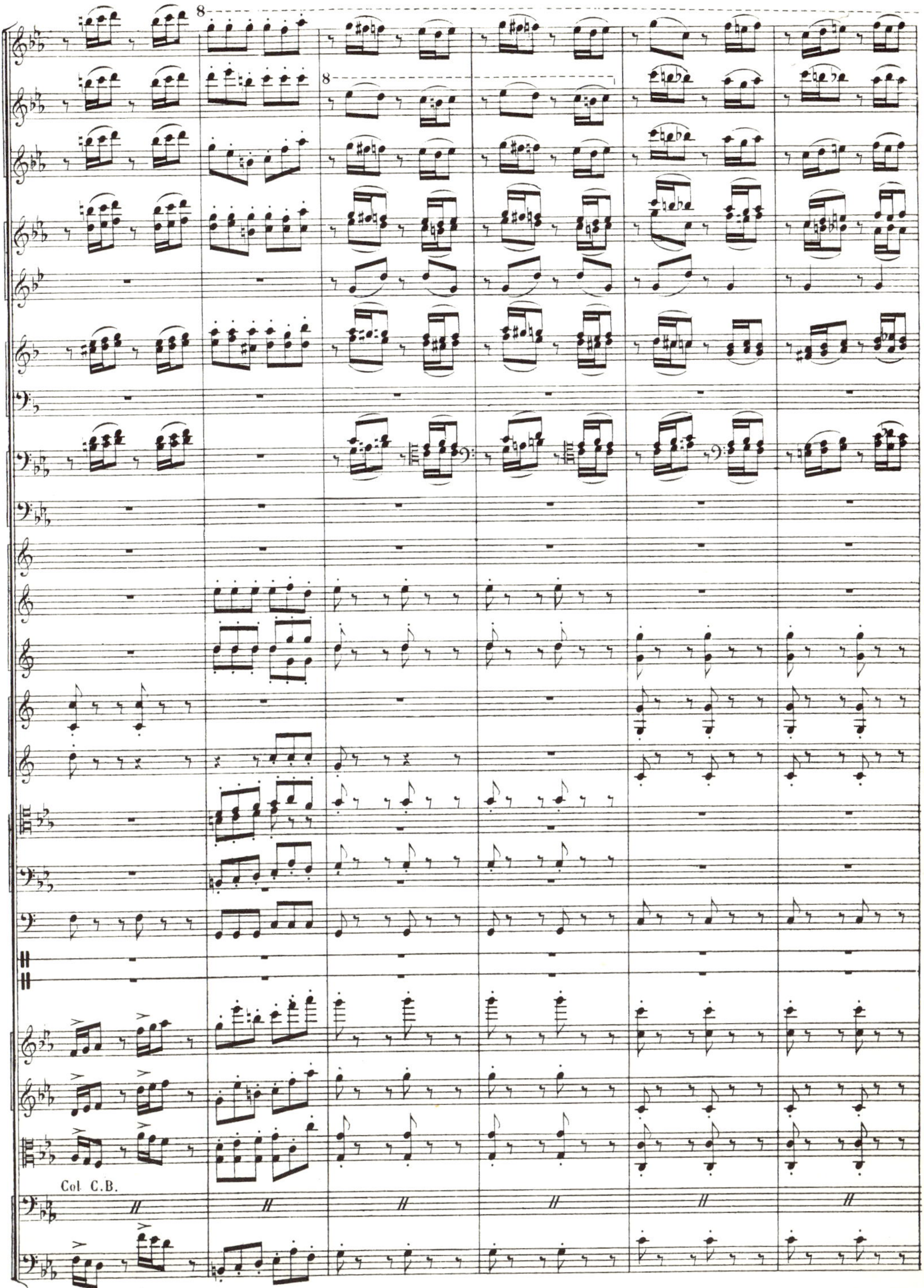

4 4 3

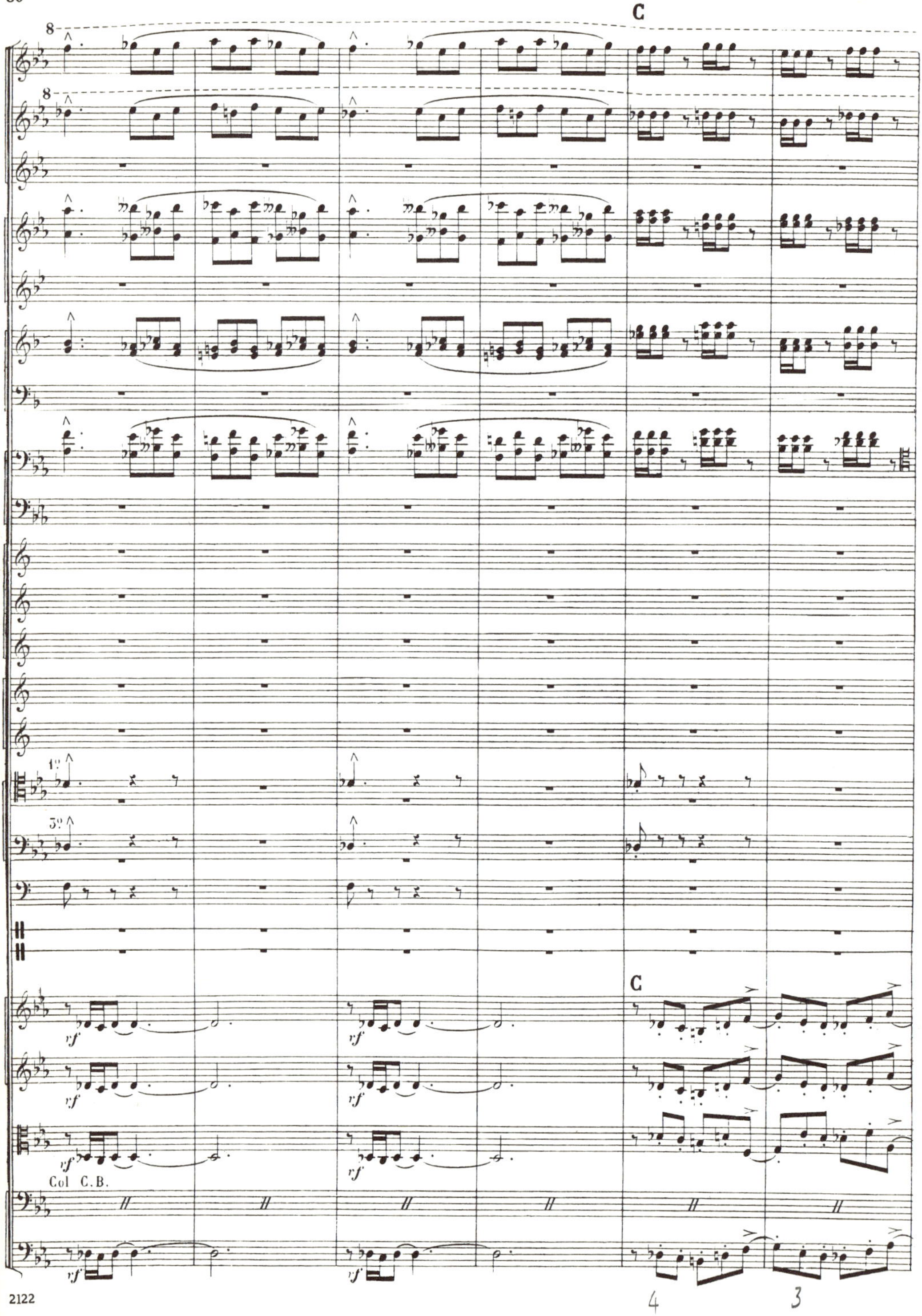
C
8
8
1º
3º
C
rf
rf
rf
rf
rf
rf
Col C.B.
rf
rf
4
3

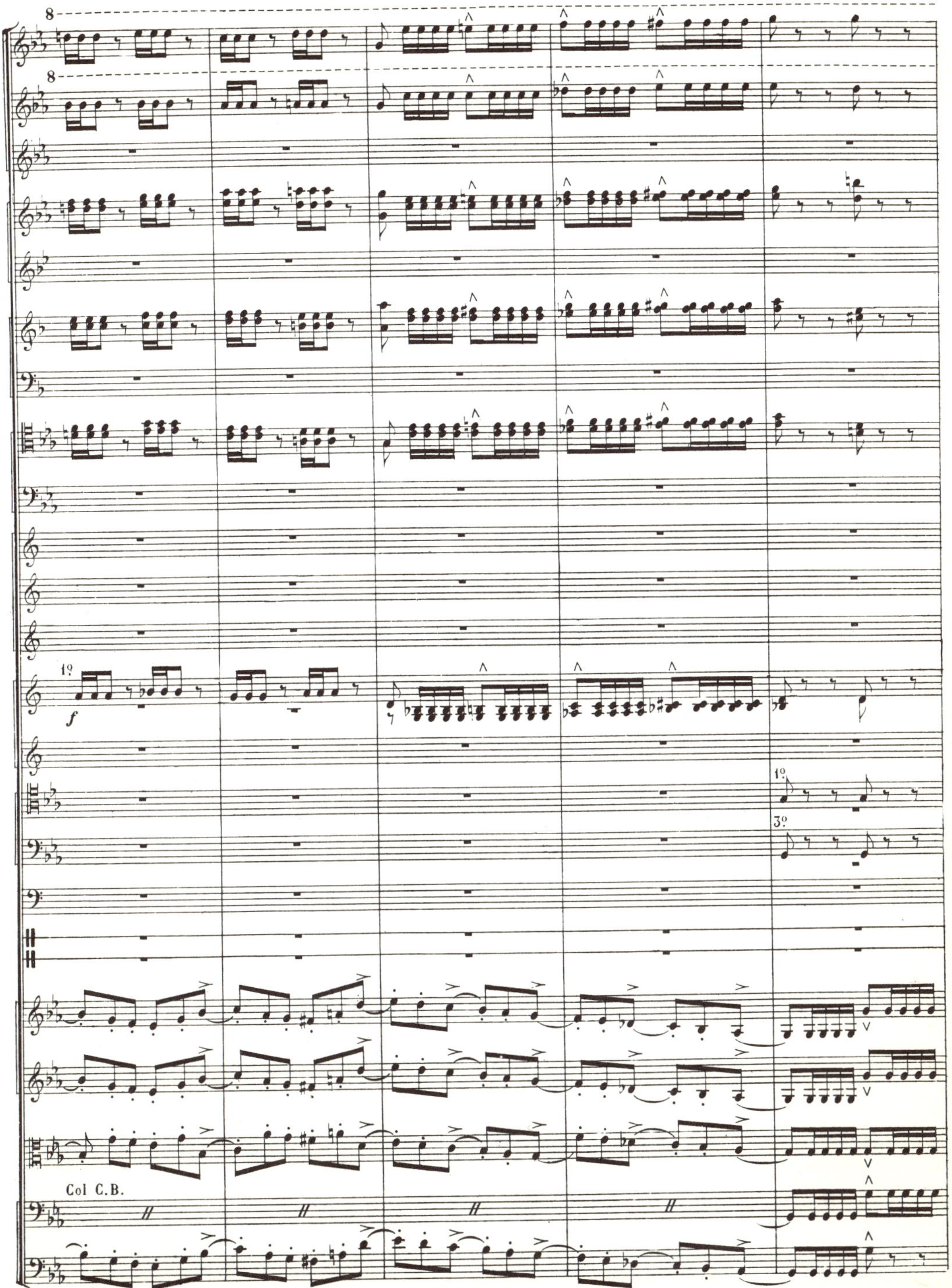
8
8
1º
f
1º
3º
Col C.B.

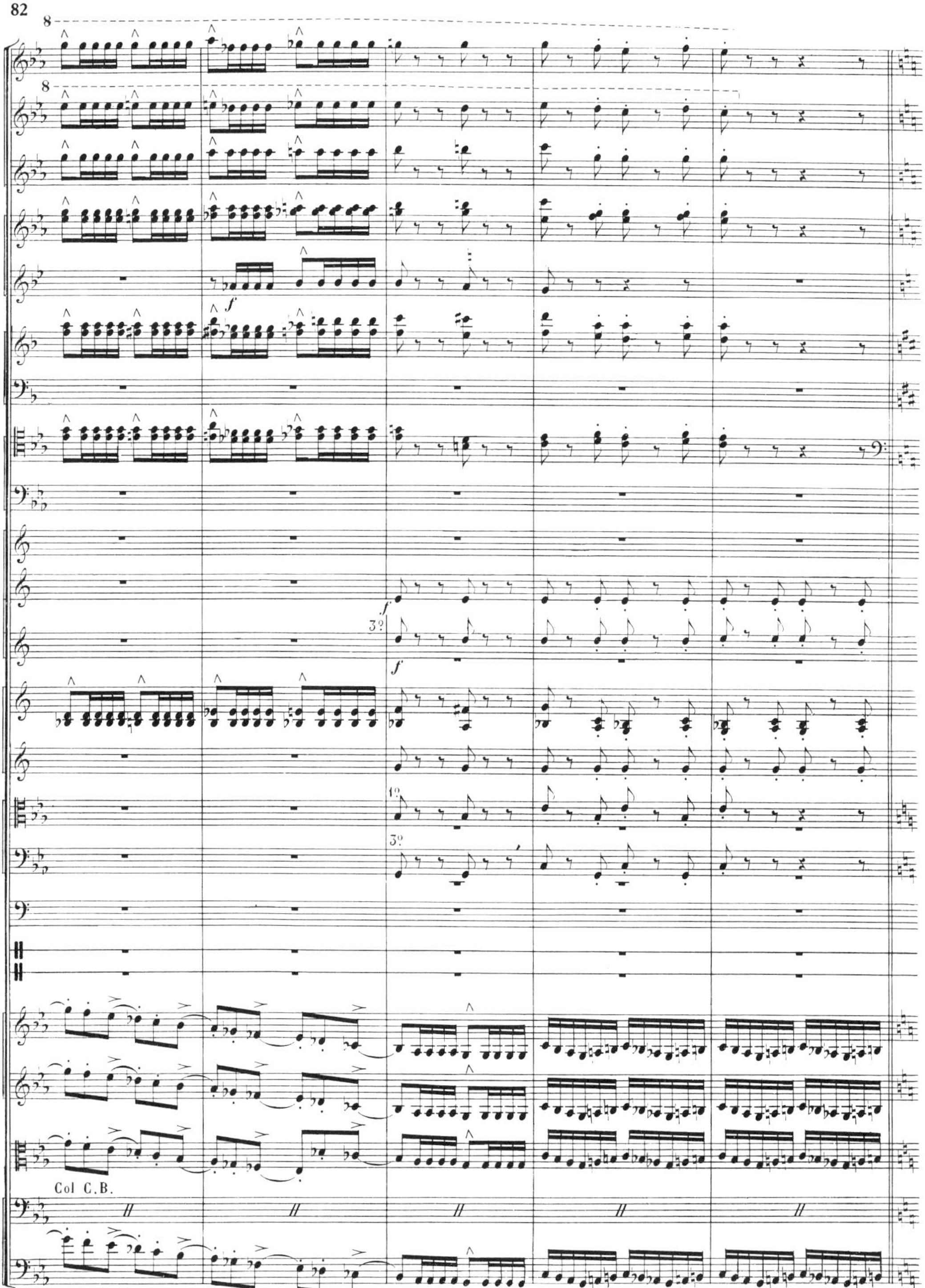
8
8
f
3º
f
1º
3º
Col C.B.

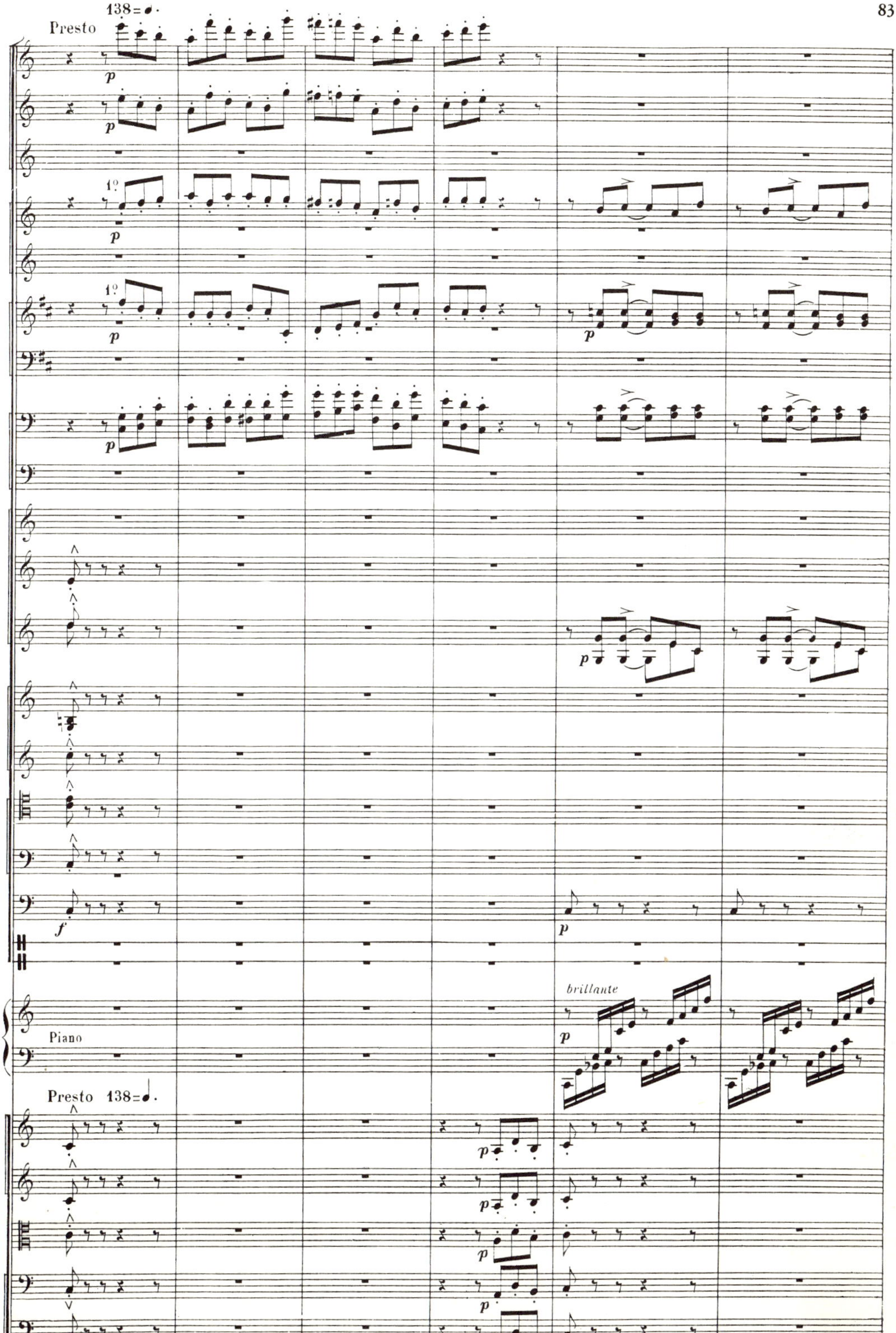
Presto 138=♩.
p
1º
brillante
Piano
Presto 138=♩.
f

D
(en MI♭-UT-LA♭)
Triangle
8
D
1ers Vons Div.
2ds Vons Div.
pizz.
Col C.B.
pizz.

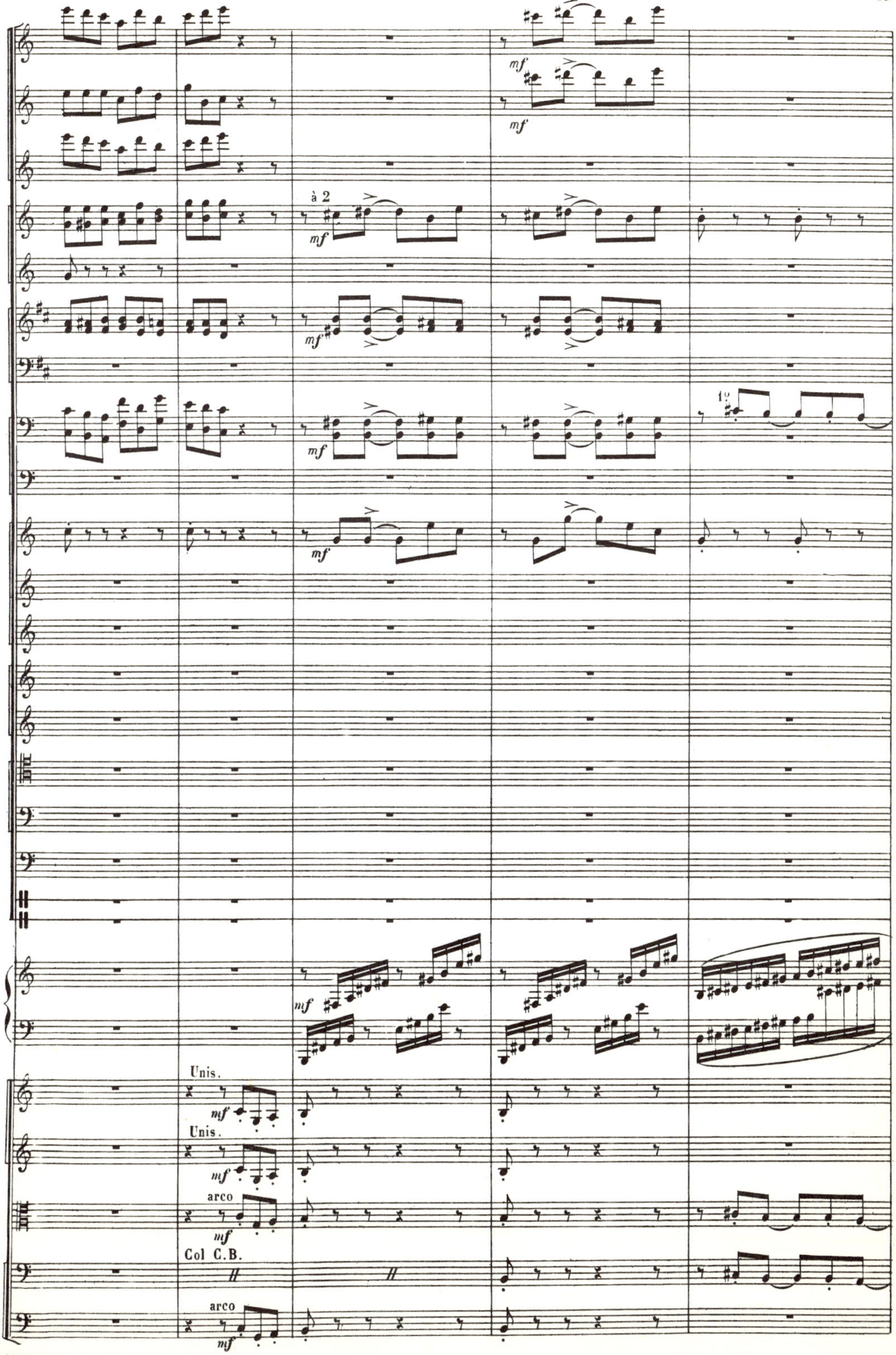
mf
mf
à 2
mf
mf
mf
1º
mf
mf
Unis.
mf
Unis.
mf
arco
mf
Col C.B.
arco
mf

E
p
à 2
5?
Triangle
une Cymbale frappée avec une baguette
mf
8
1ers Vons Div.
2ds Vons Div.
pizz.
Unis

cresc.
cresc.
1º
cresc.
1º
1º
p
cresc.
arco
p
cresc.
cresc.
arco
p
cresc.
cresc.
cresc.

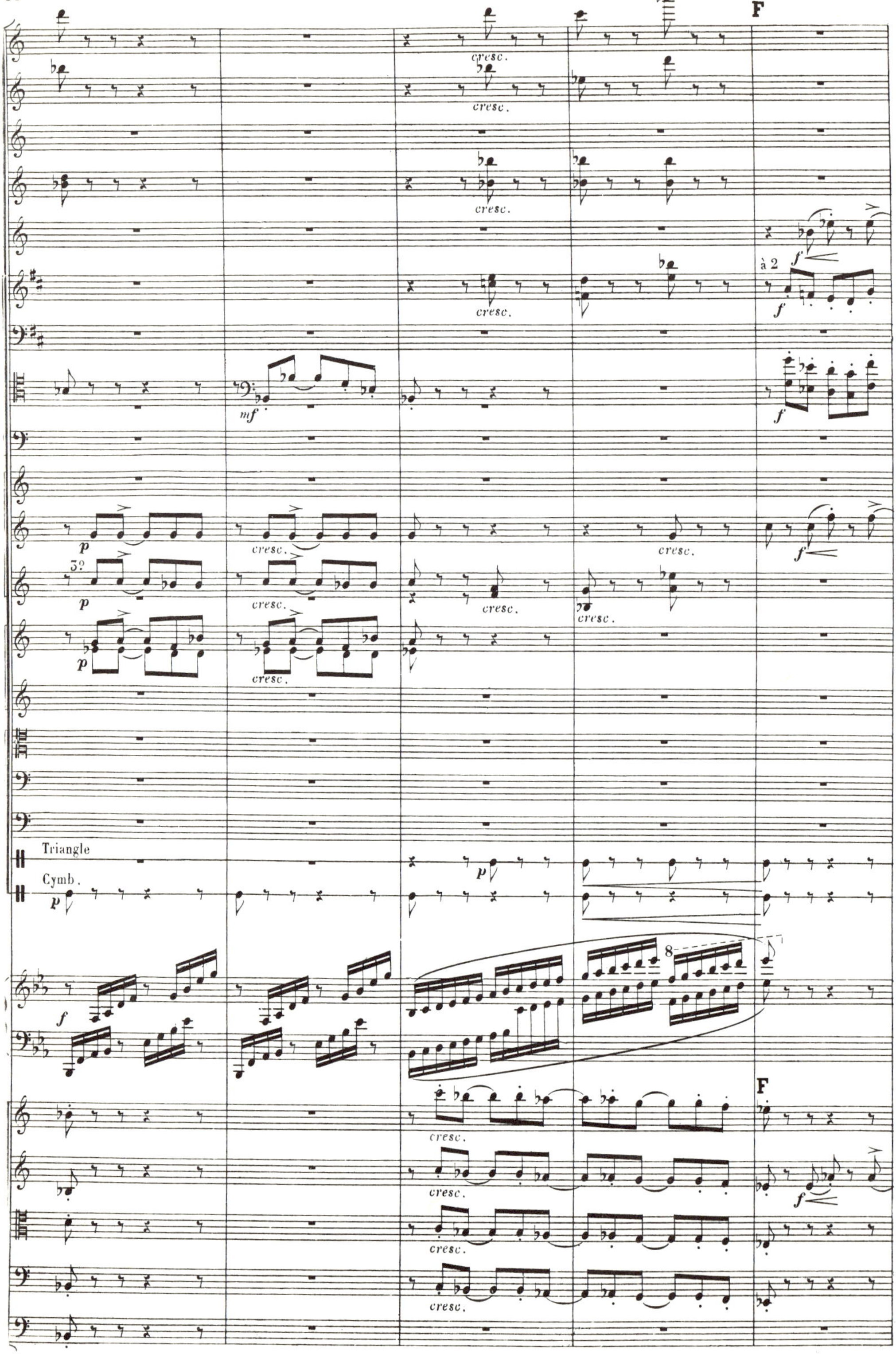
F
cresc.
à 2
f
mf
p
3?
Triangle
Cymb.
8

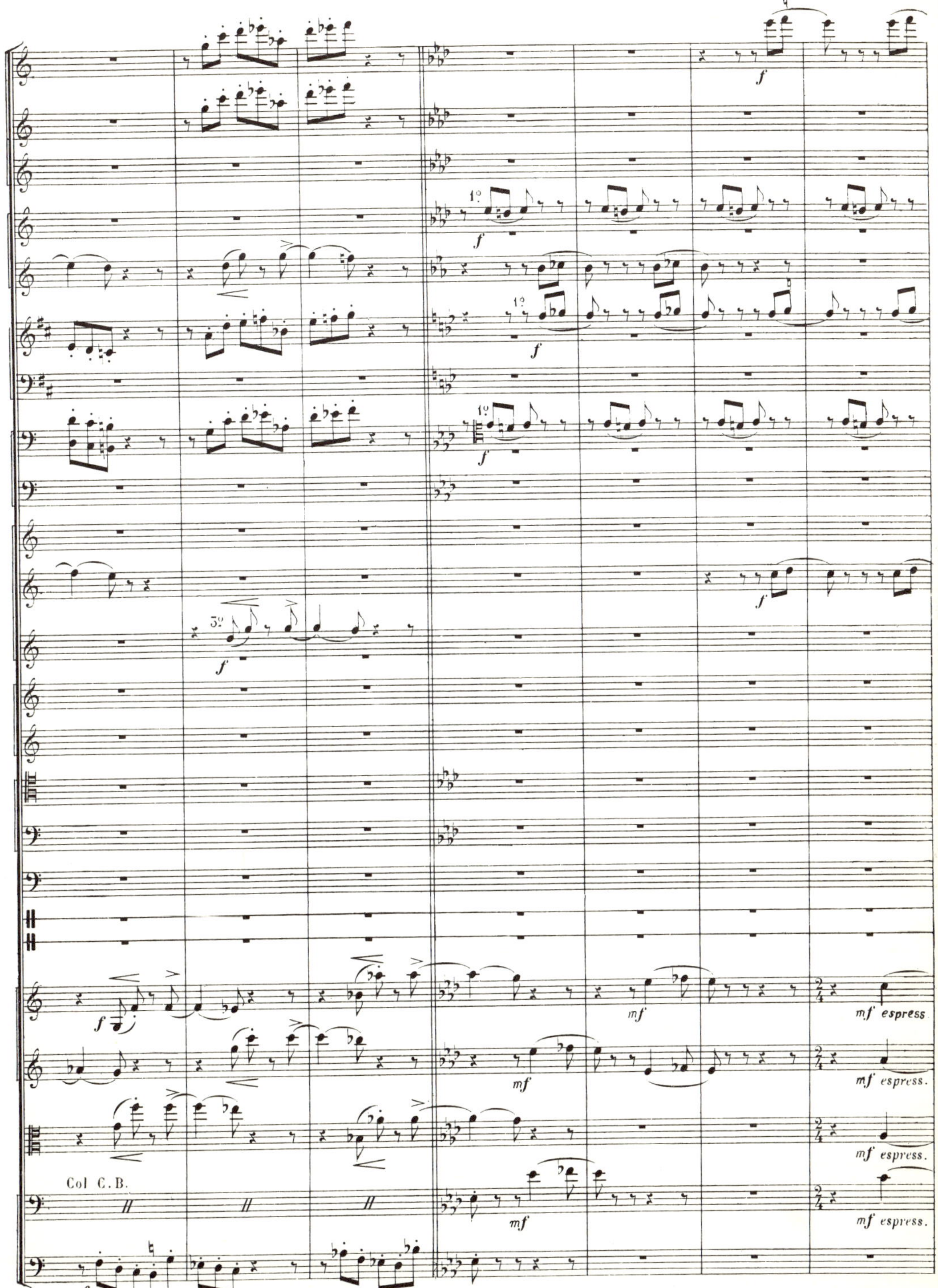
1º
3º
Col C.B.
mf espress.
mf espress.
mf espress.
mf espress.

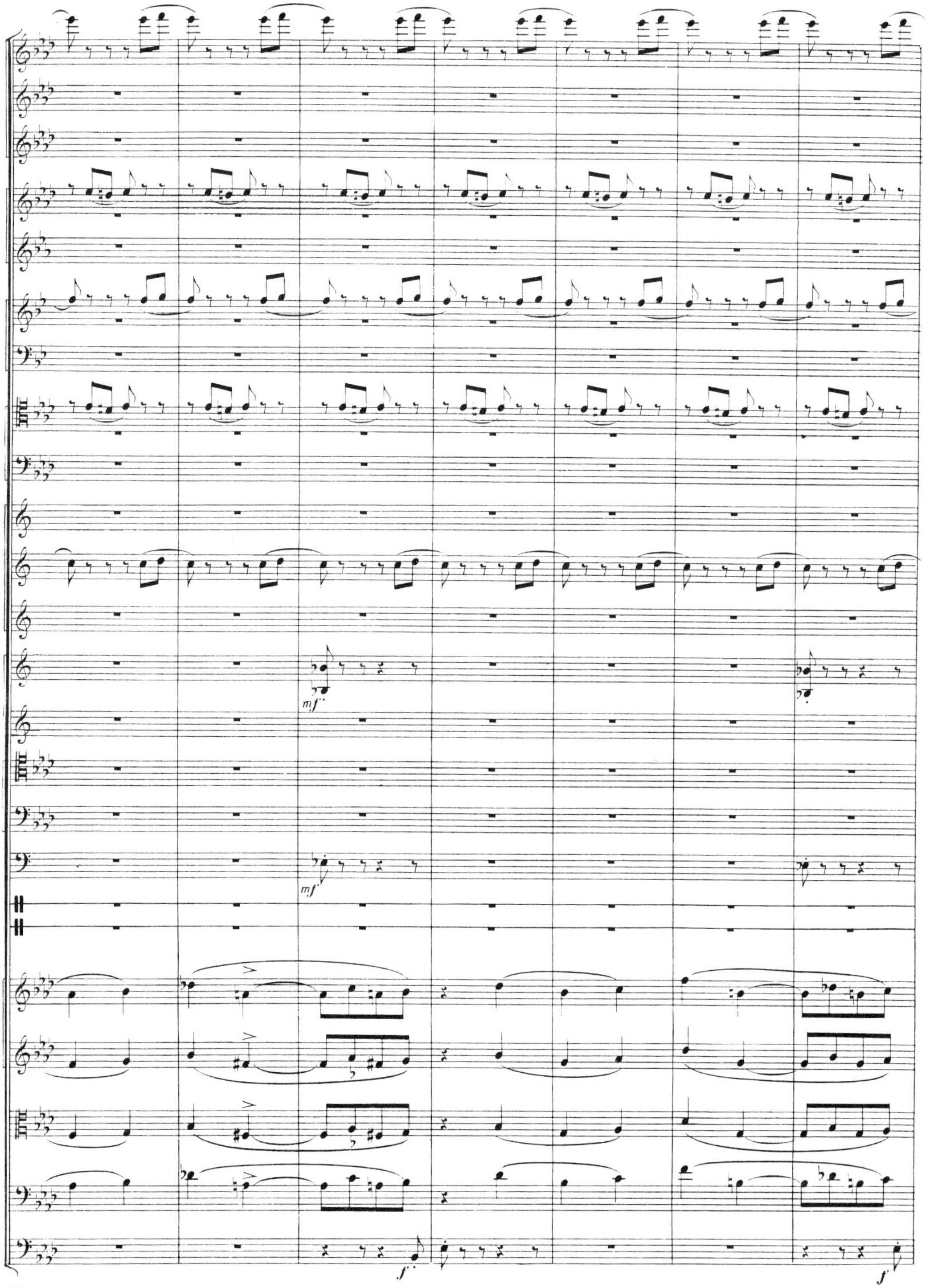
mf
mf
f
f

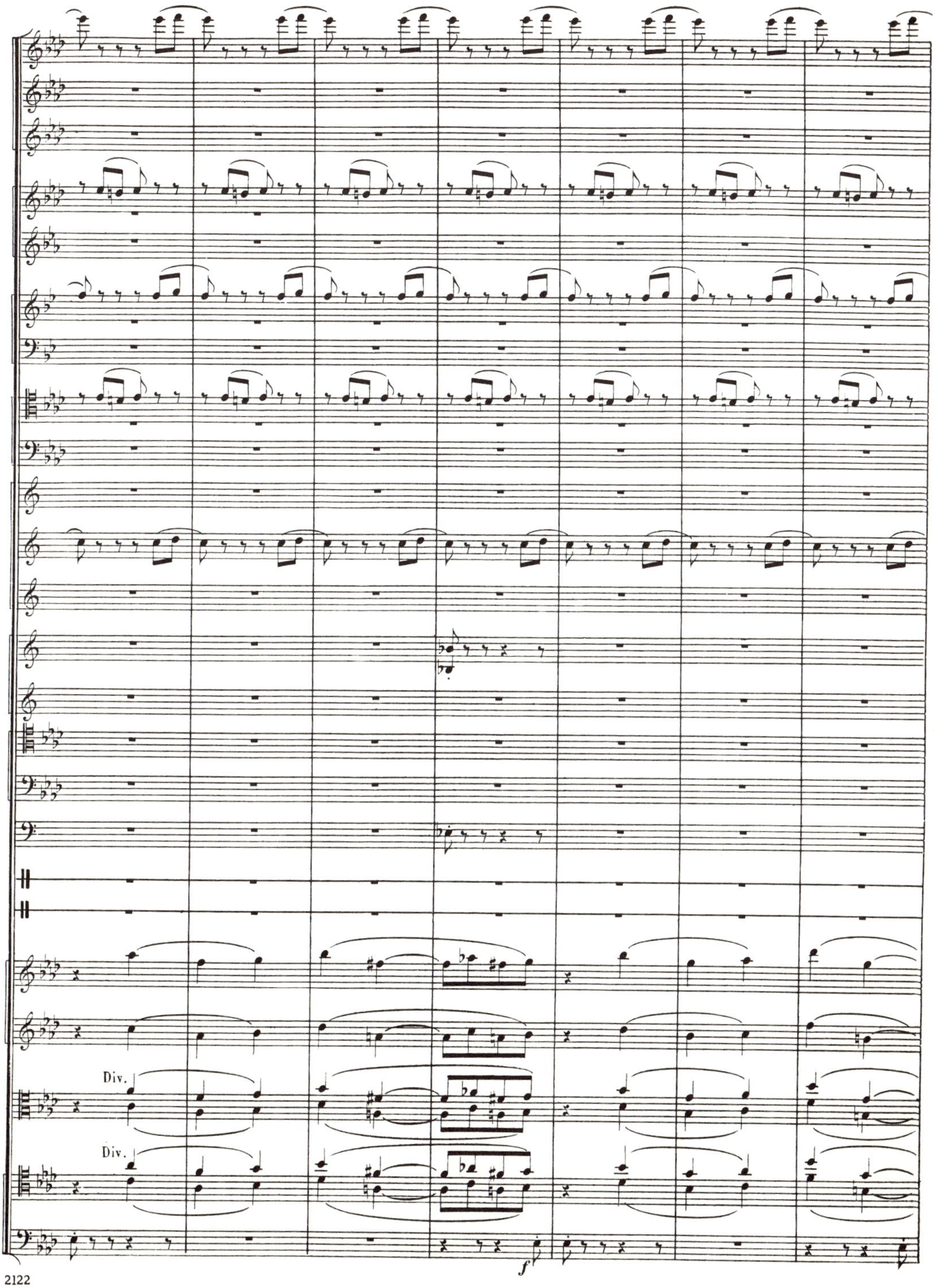
Div.
Div.
f

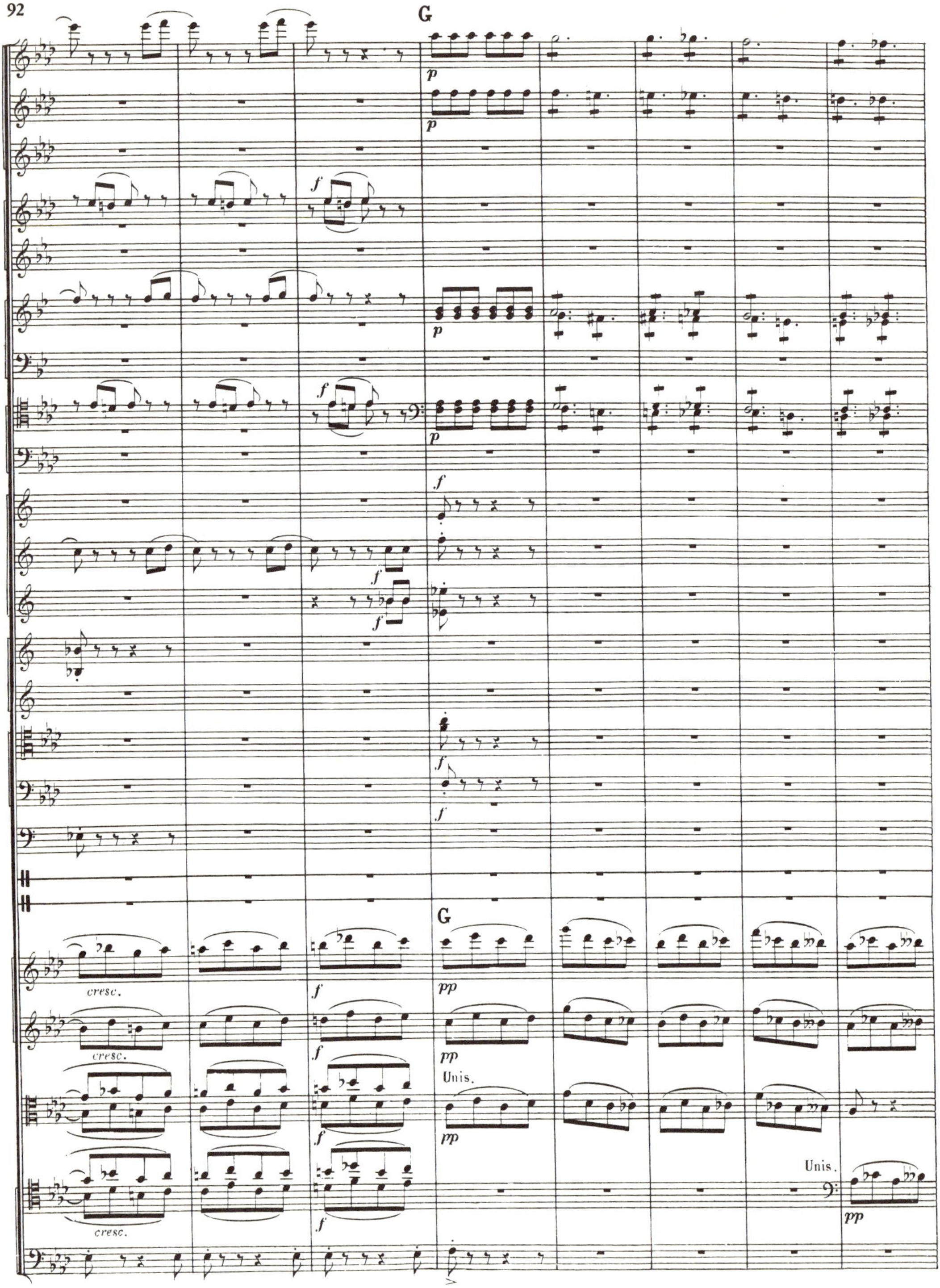
G
p
f
cresc.
pp
Unis.

poco a poco cresc.
poco a poco cresc.
p
poco a poco cresc.
poco a poco cresc.
poco a poco cresc.
p
p
p
poco a poco cresc.
poco a poco cresc.
poco a poco cresc.
poco a poco cresc.
pizz.
marcato
p poco a poco cresc.

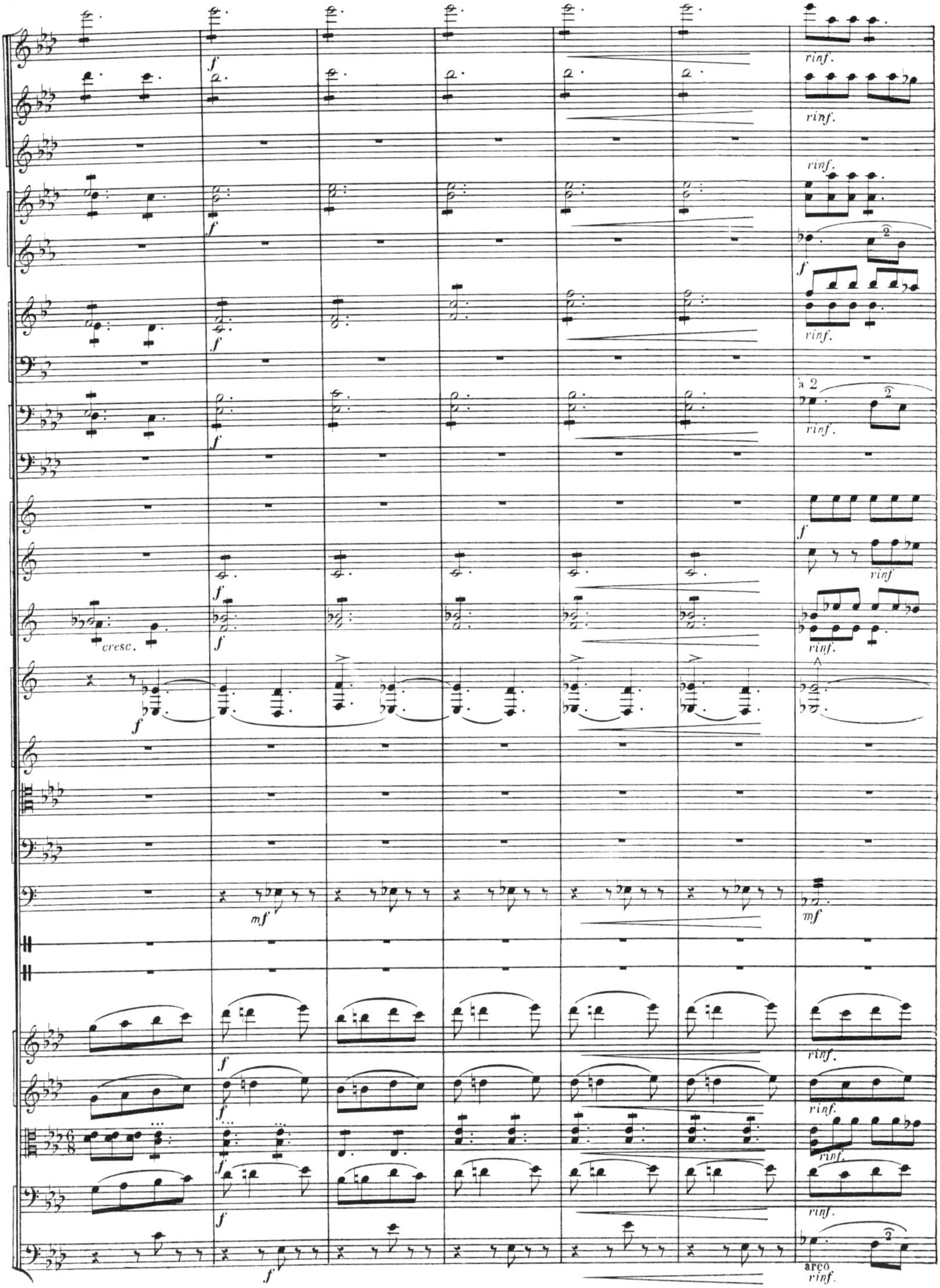
f
rinf.
cresc.
a 2
mf
arco

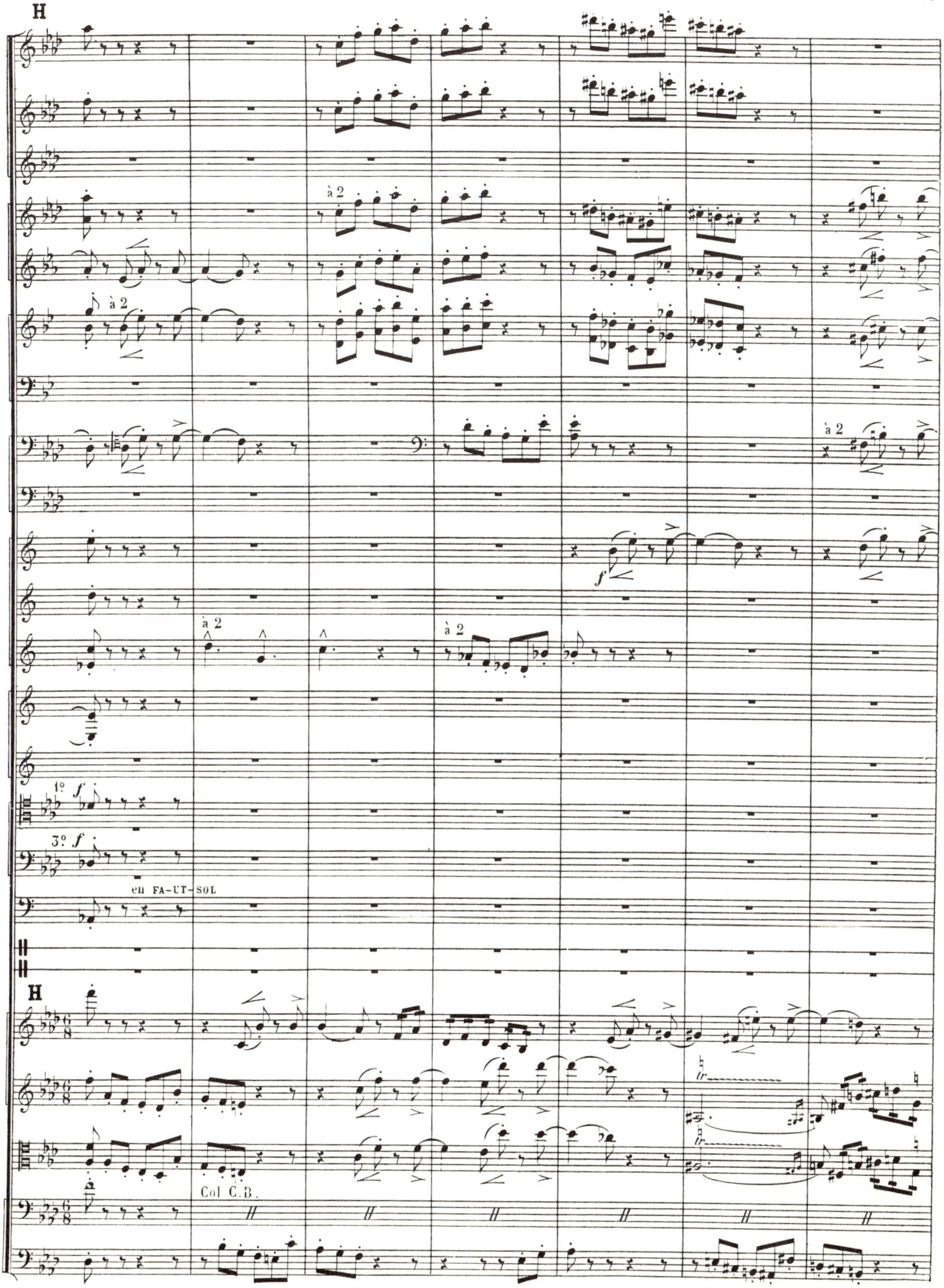
H
à 2
à 2
f
à 2
à 2
à 2
1º f
3º f
en FA-UT-SOL
H
Col C.B.
tr
tr

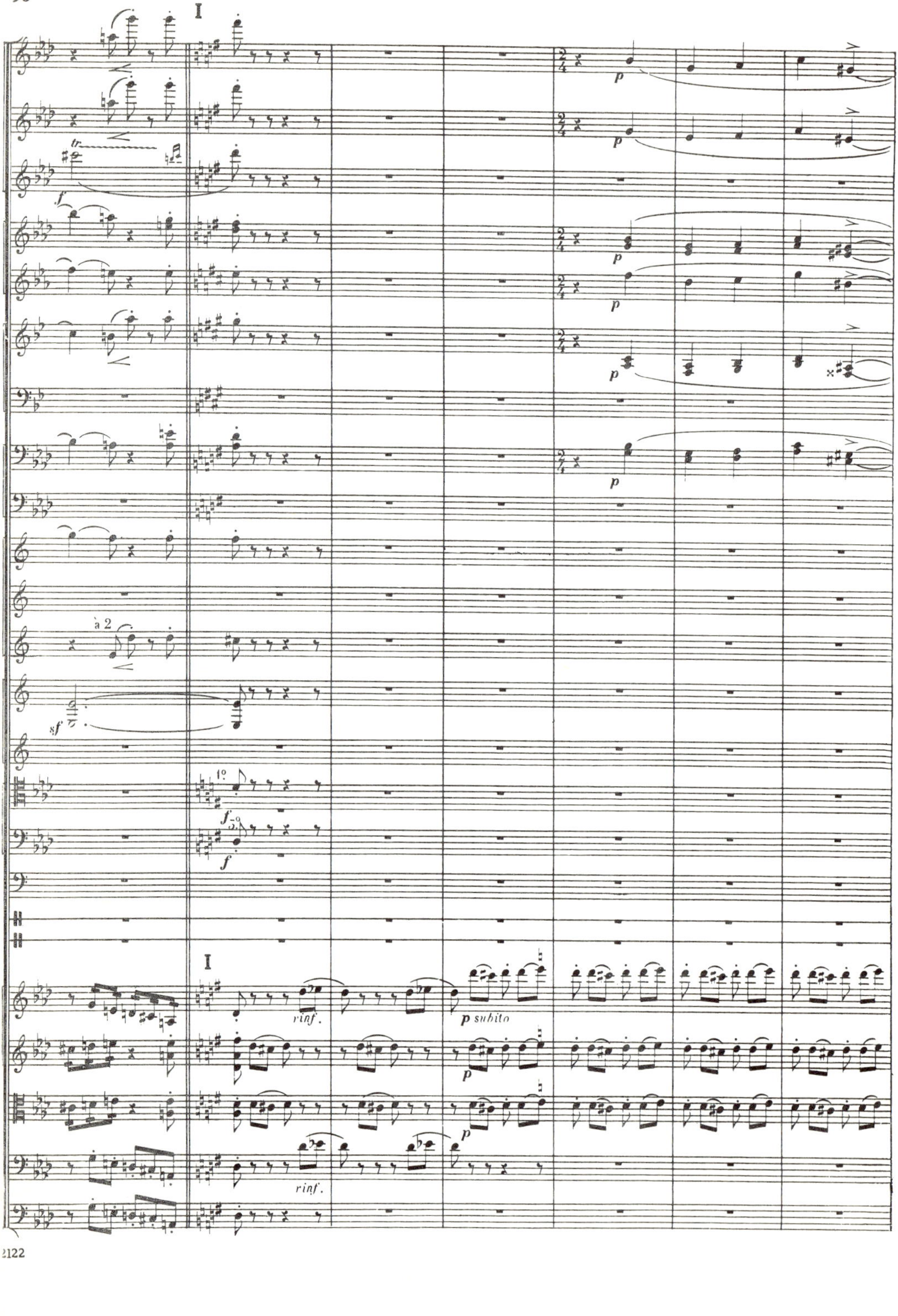
I
tr
f
à 2
sf
1º
2º
f
f
I
rinf.
p subito
p
p
rinf.
p
p
p
p
p
p

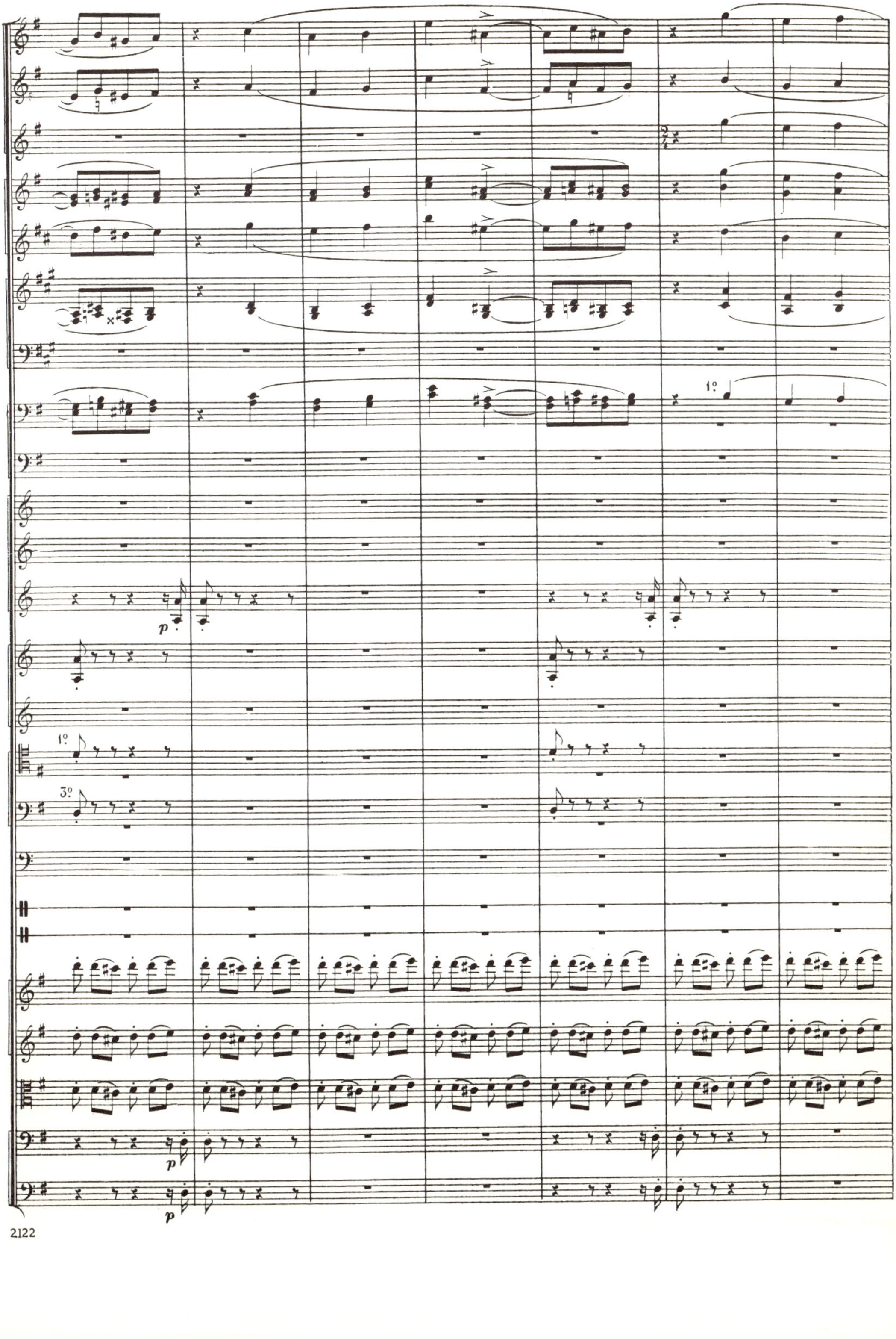
1º
1º
3º

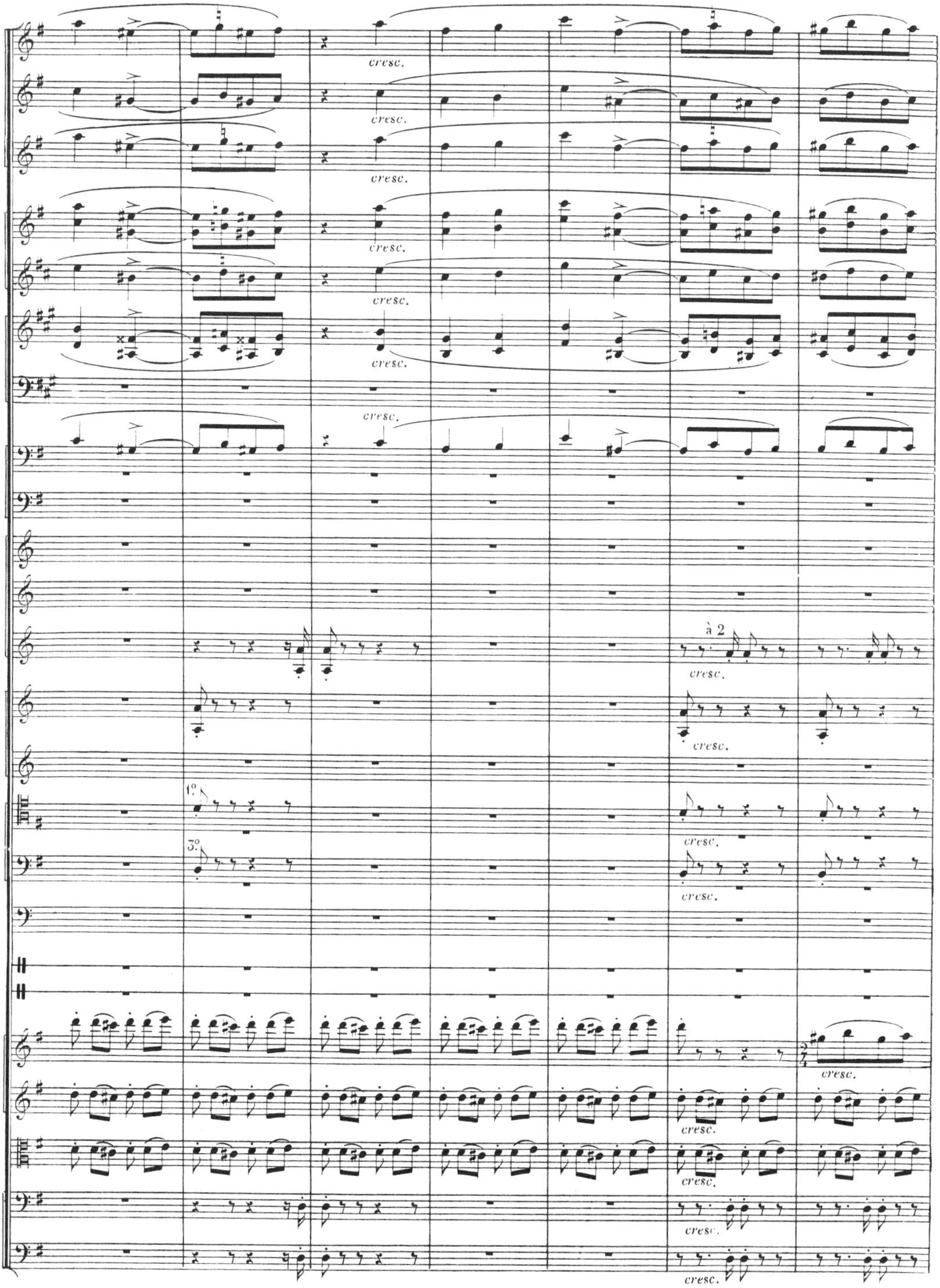
cresc.
à 2
1º.
3º.

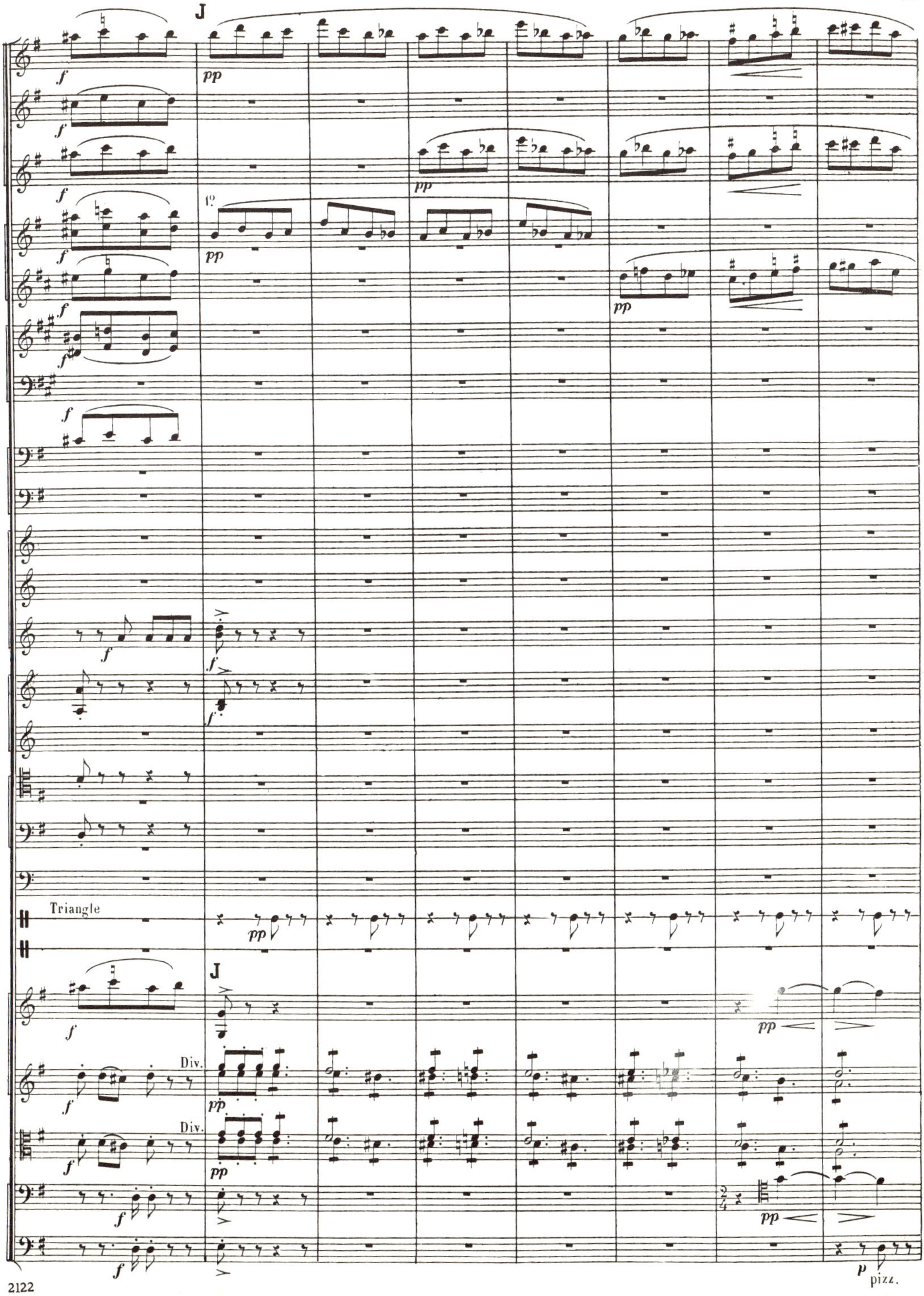
J
1º
Triangle
Div.
pizz.

K
cresc.
cresc.
cresc.
cresc.
à 2
p
1º
p
3º
p
K
cresc.
Unis
Unis.
pizz
cresc.
arco
cresc.
pizz
arco
cresc.

cresc.
à 2
p cresc.
cresc.
à 2
cresc.
cresc.
Piano
tr
pp
cresc.
arco
cresc.

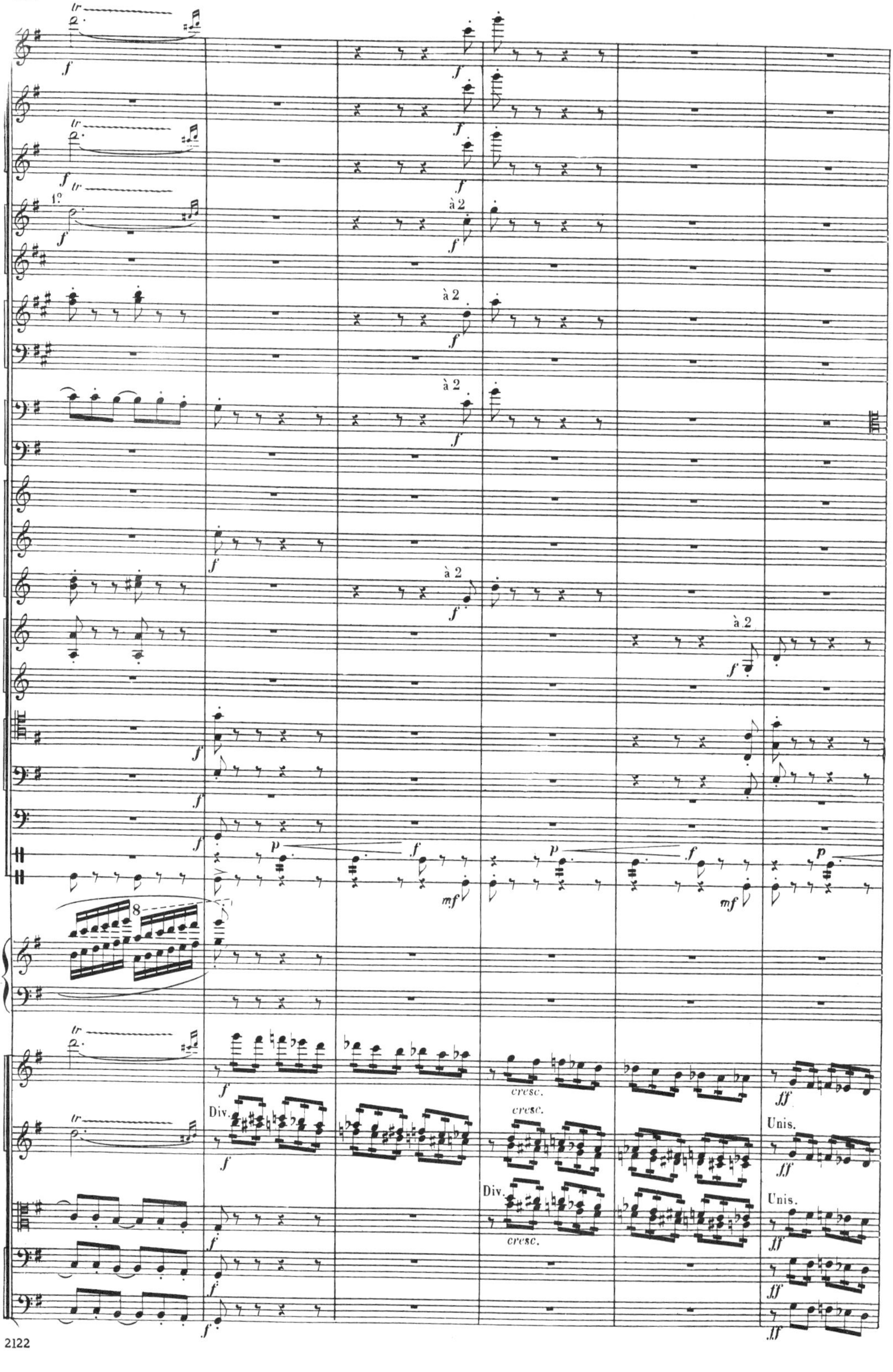
tr
f
1º
à 2
p
mf
8
Div.
cresc.
Unis.
ff

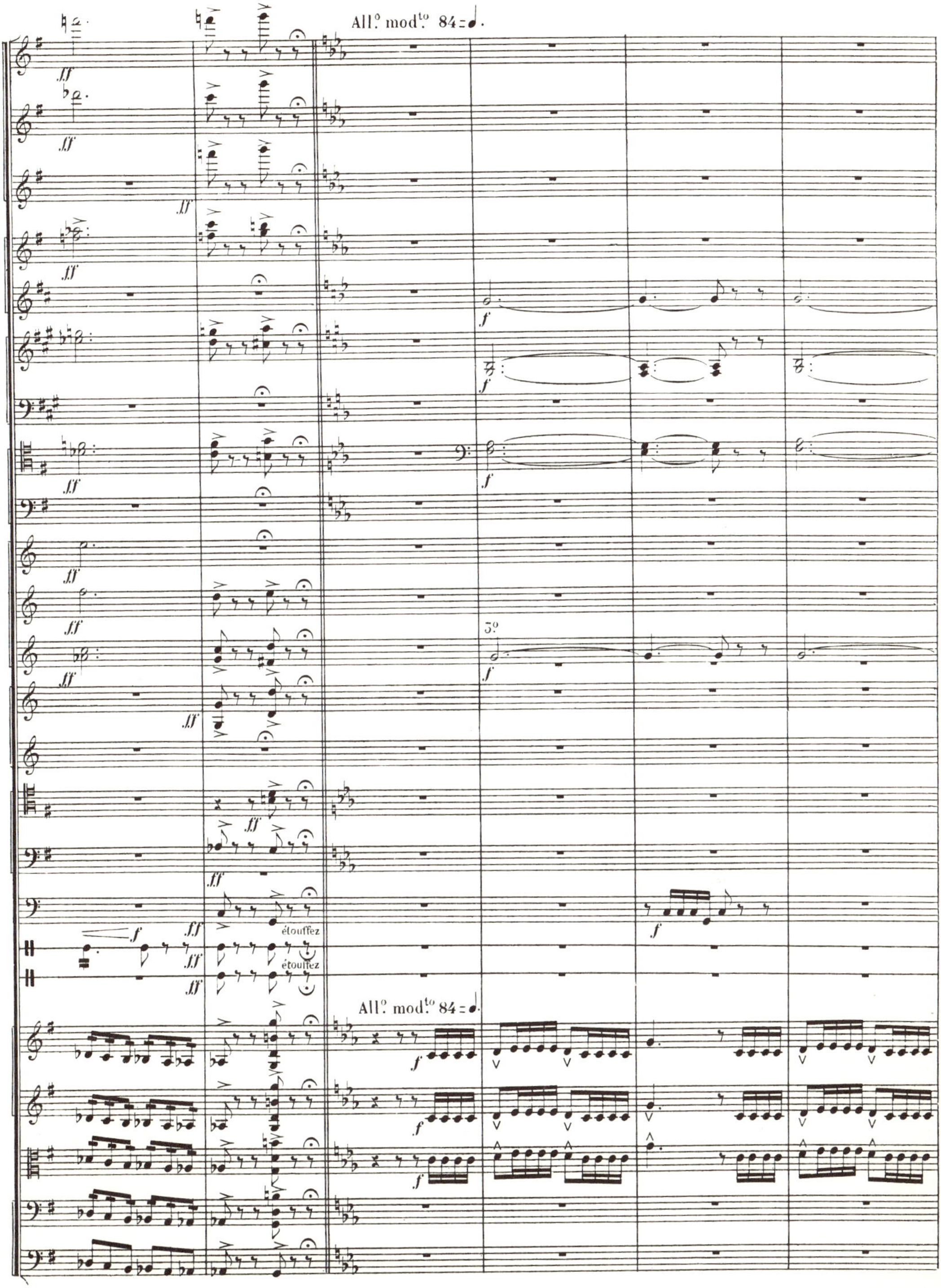
All.o mod.to 84 = ♩.
3o
étouffez
étouffez
All.o mod.to 84 = ♩.

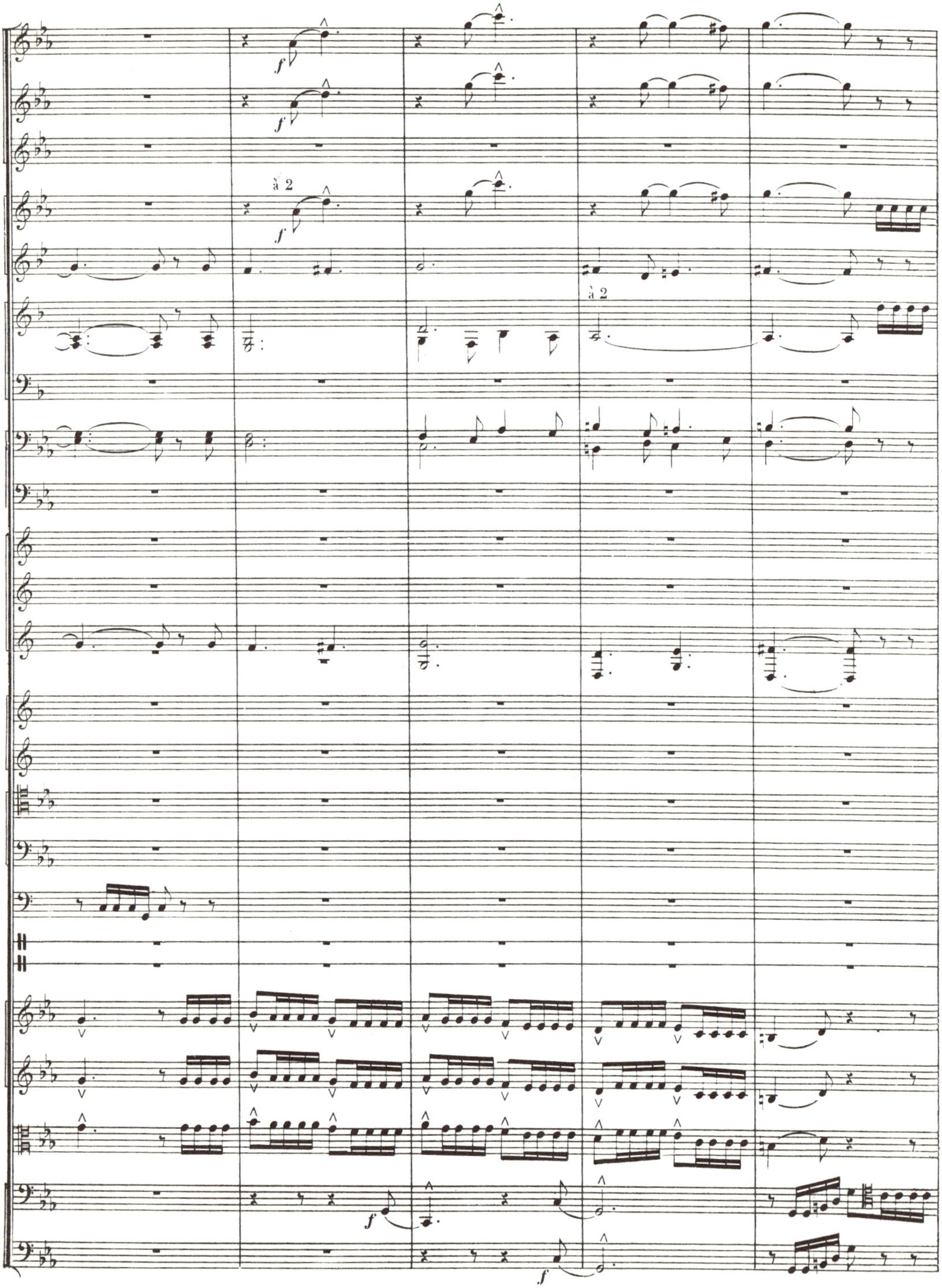
f
f
à 2
f
à 2
f
f

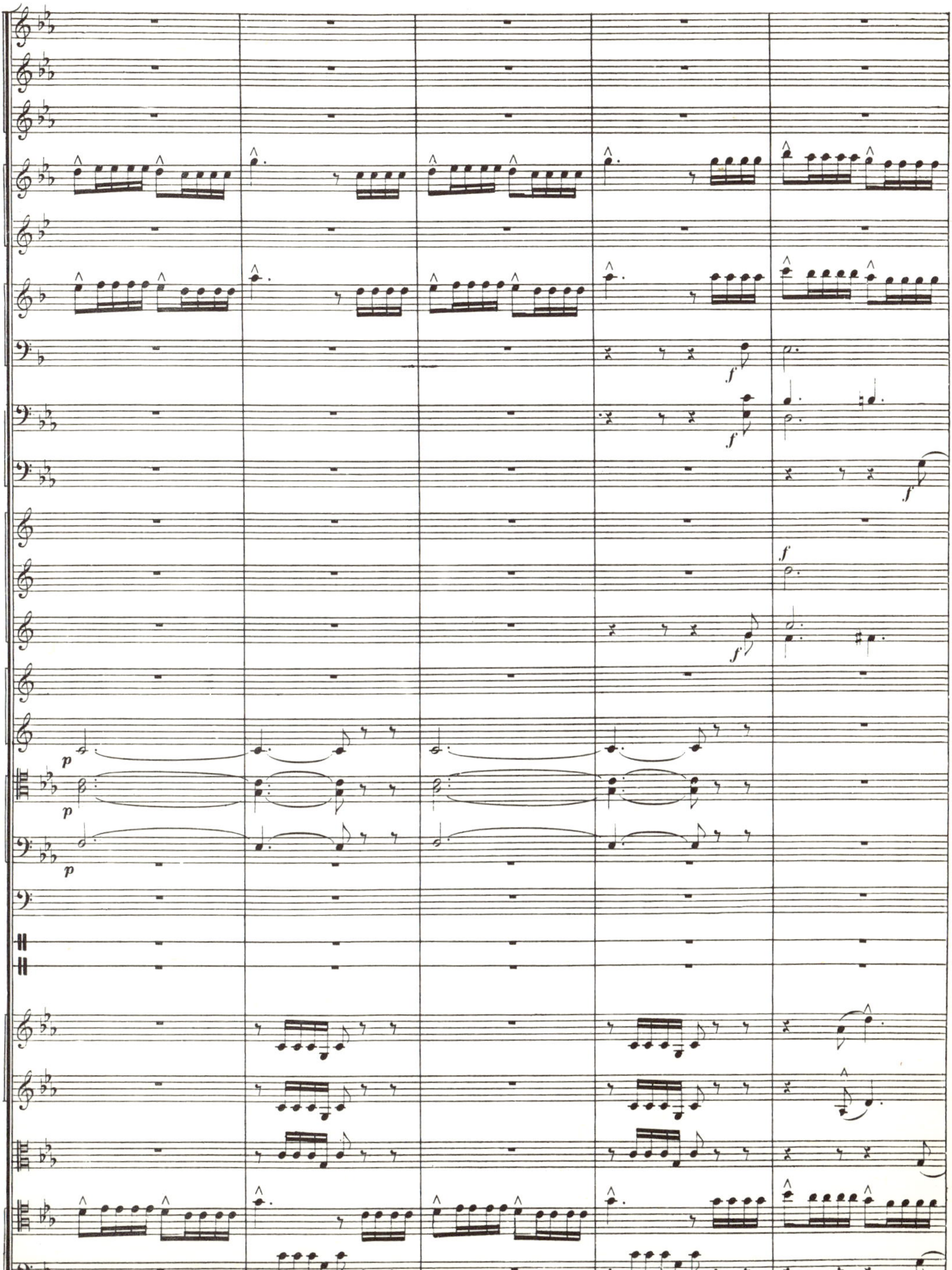

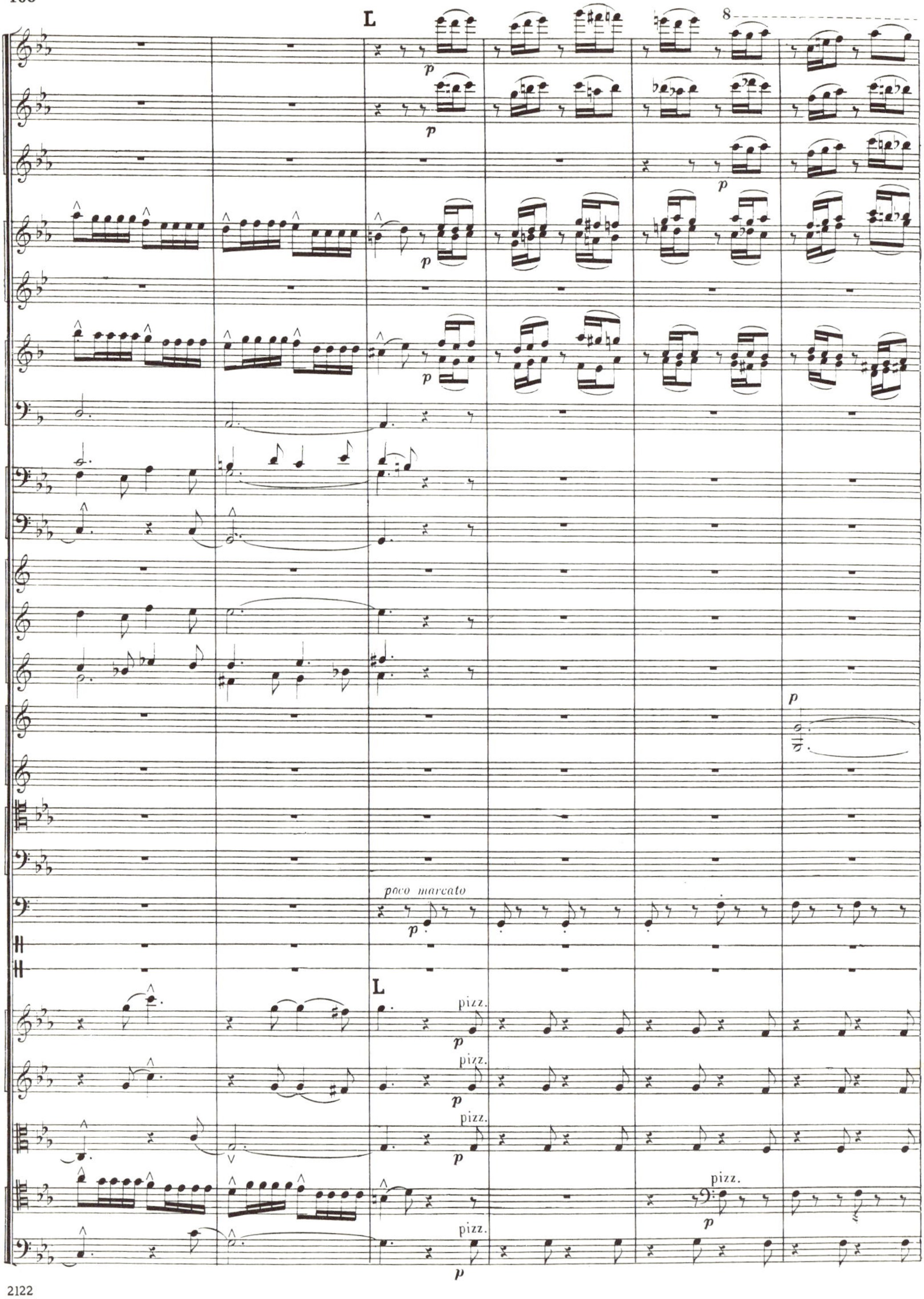
L
8
p
poco marcato
pizz.

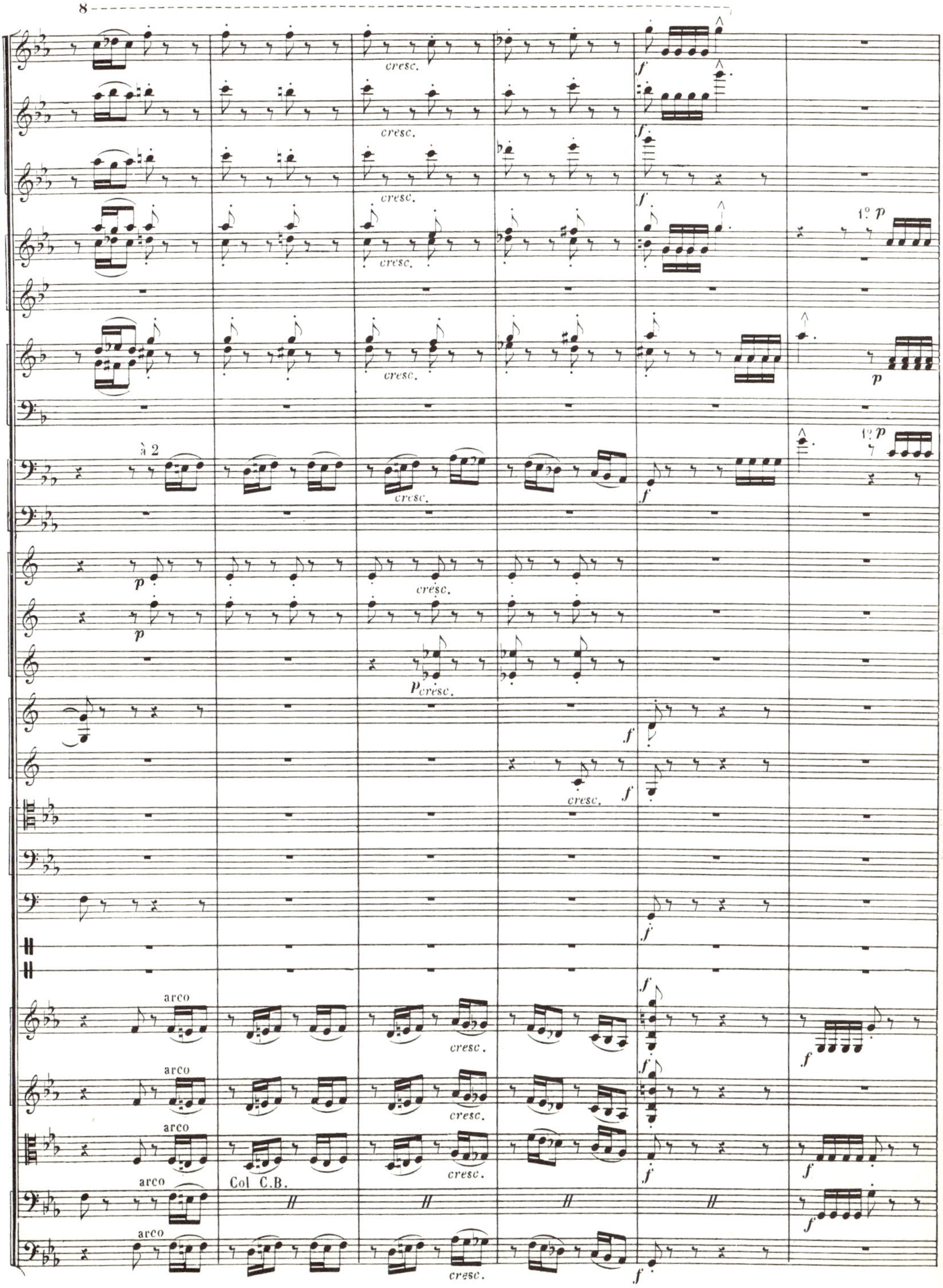
8
cresc.
f
1º p
p
à 2
arco
Col C.B.

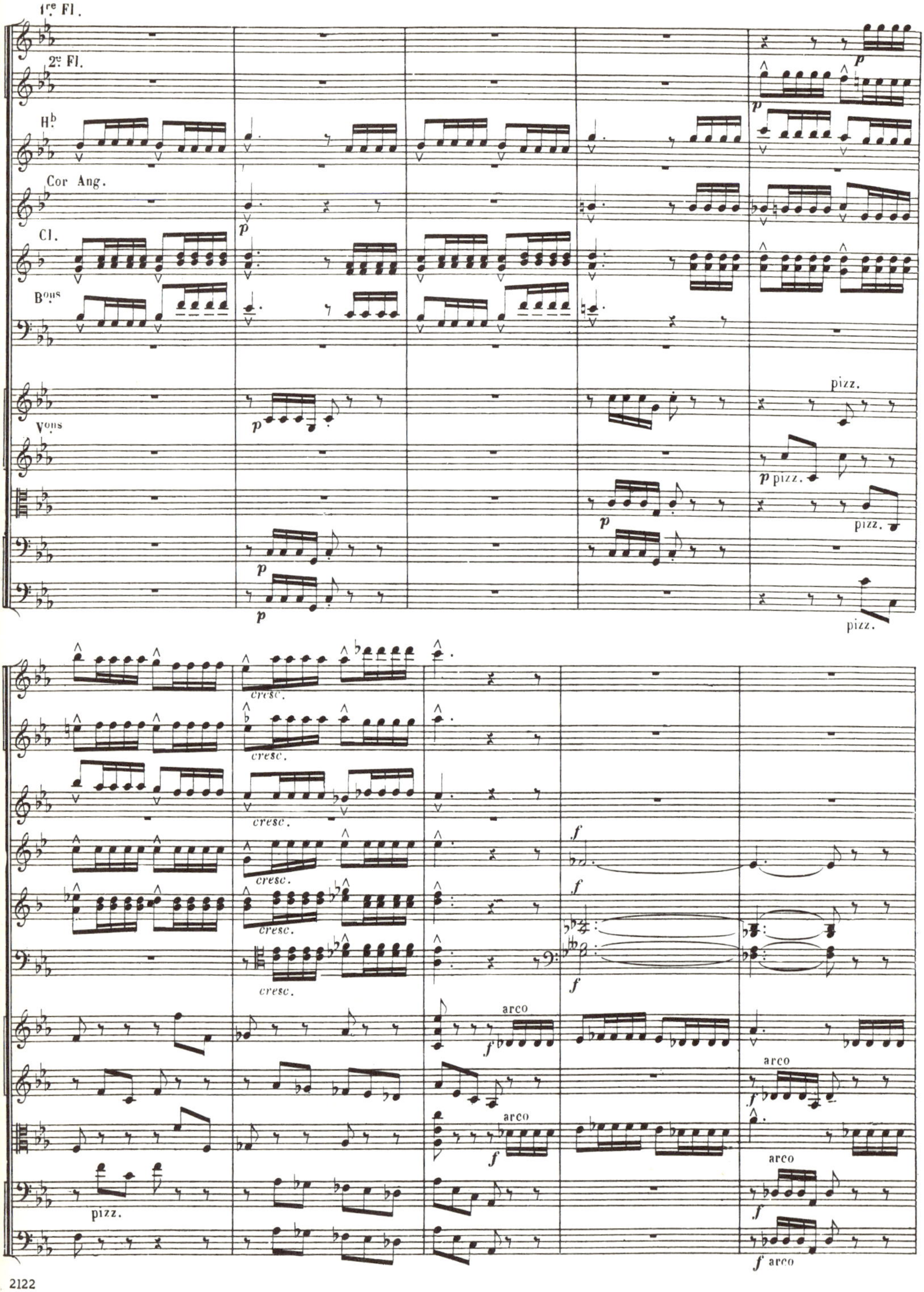
1re Fl.
2e Fl.
Hb
Cor Ang.
Cl.
Bons
Vons
p
pizz.
arco
cresc.
f

M
1re Fl.
2e Fl.
Petite Fl.
Hb.
à 2
Cor Ang.
Cl.
Cl. B.
Bons
Cors
3º
Tromp.
Tromb.
Timb.
Tr.
Cymb.
M

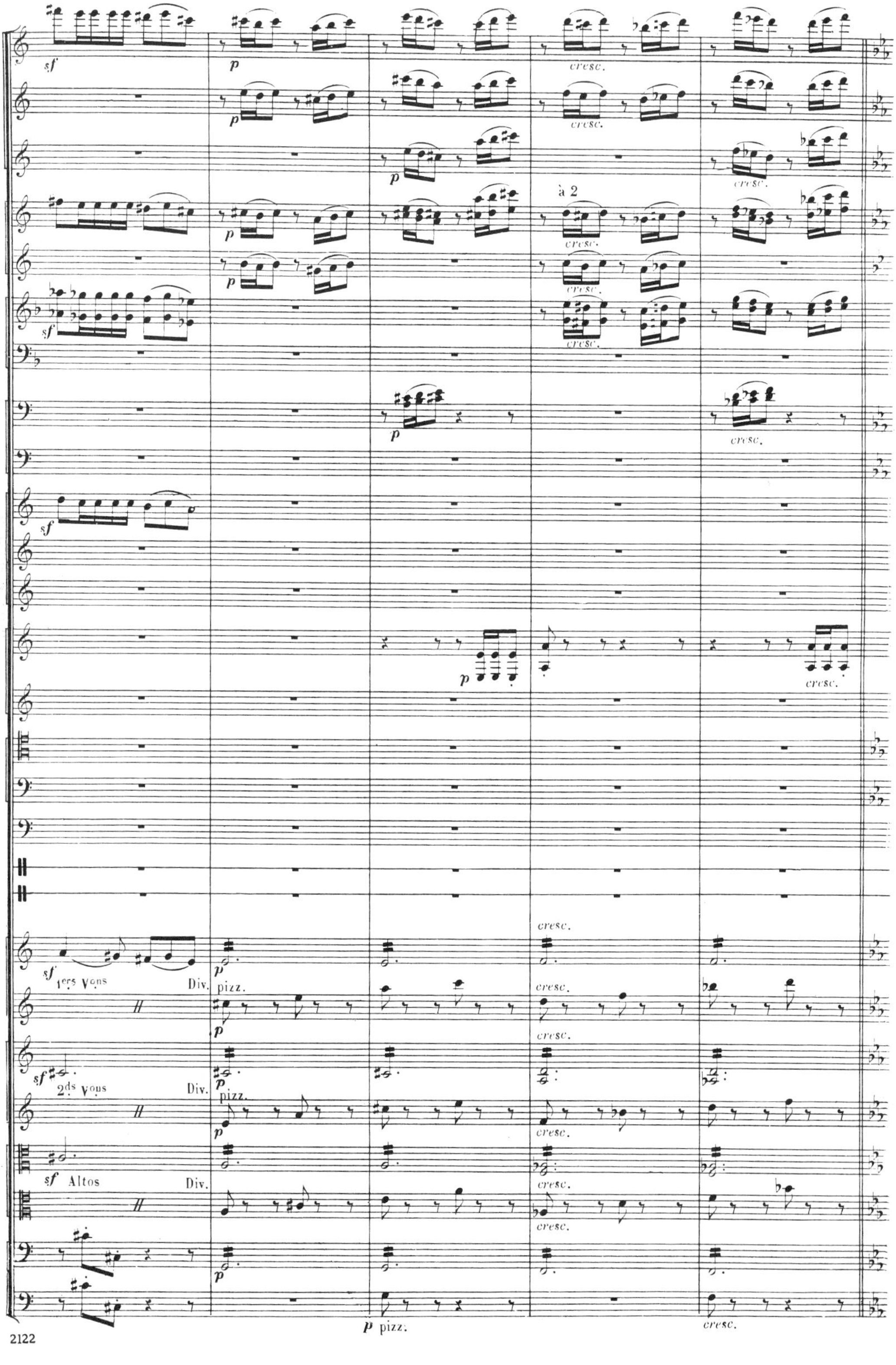
sf
p
cresc.
à 2
p
cresc.
1ers Vons
Div.
pizz.
2ds Vons
Altos
p pizz.

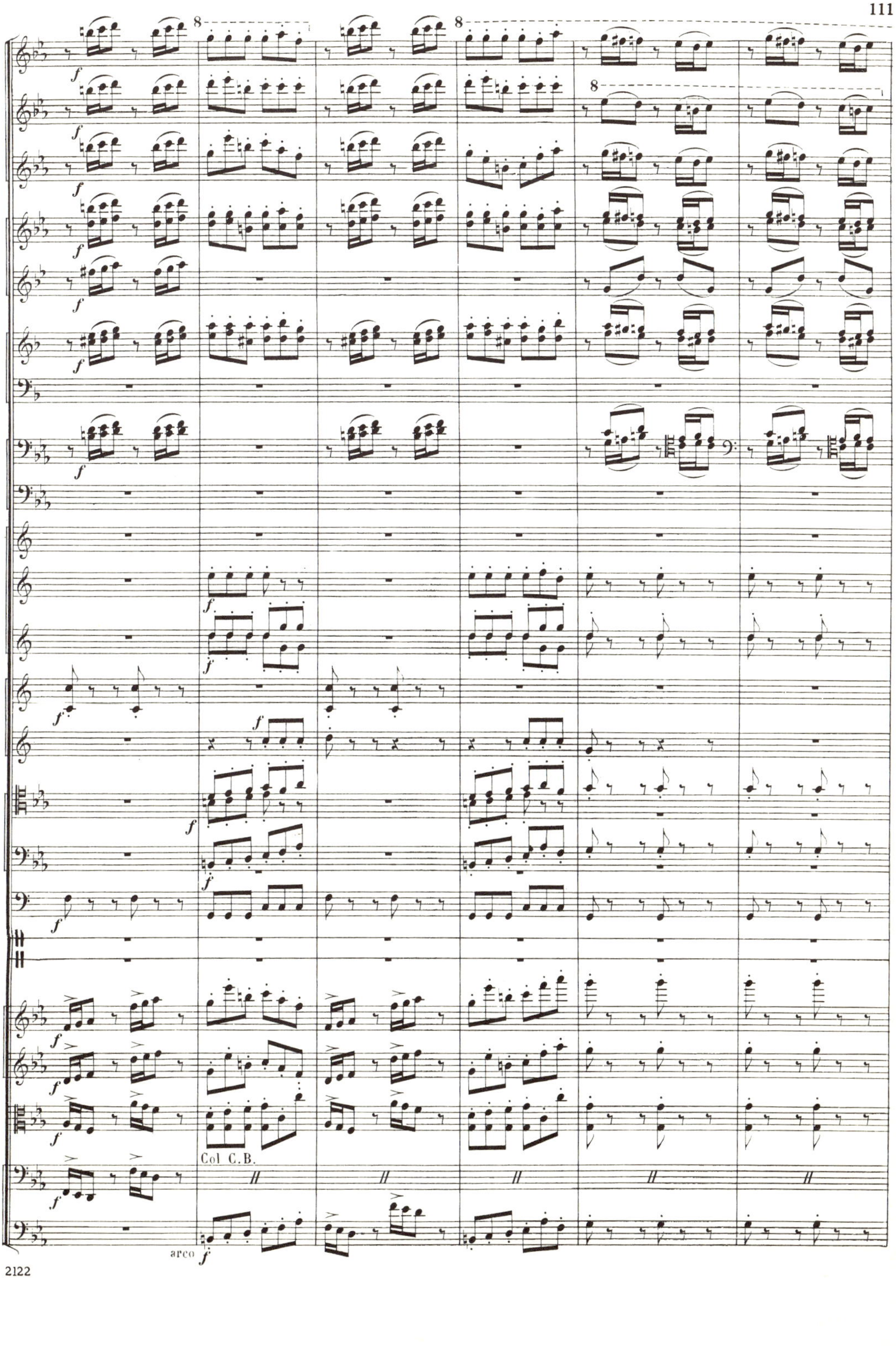
Col C.B.
arco

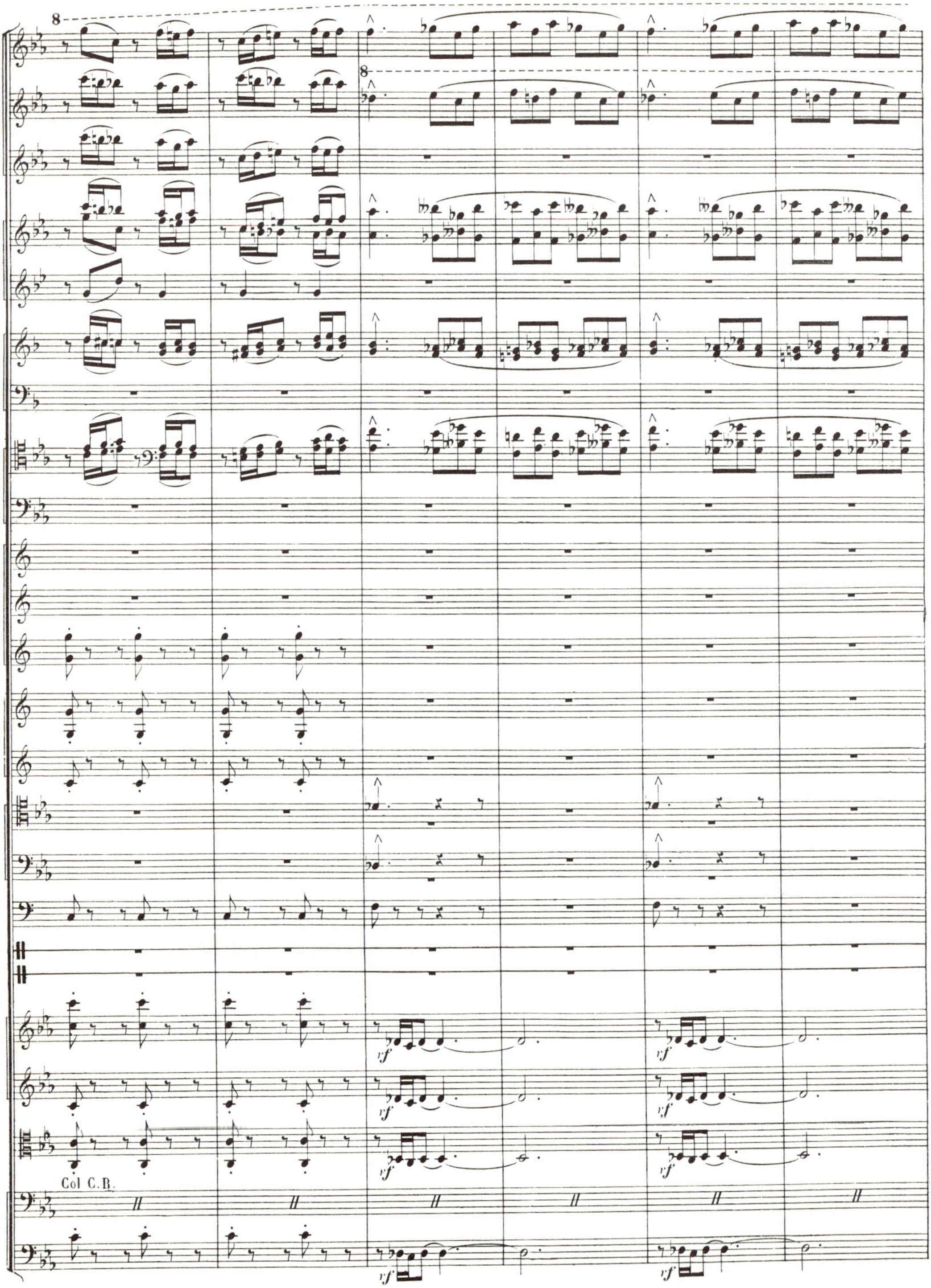
8
8
Col C.B.
rf
rf
rf
rf
rf
rf
rf
rf

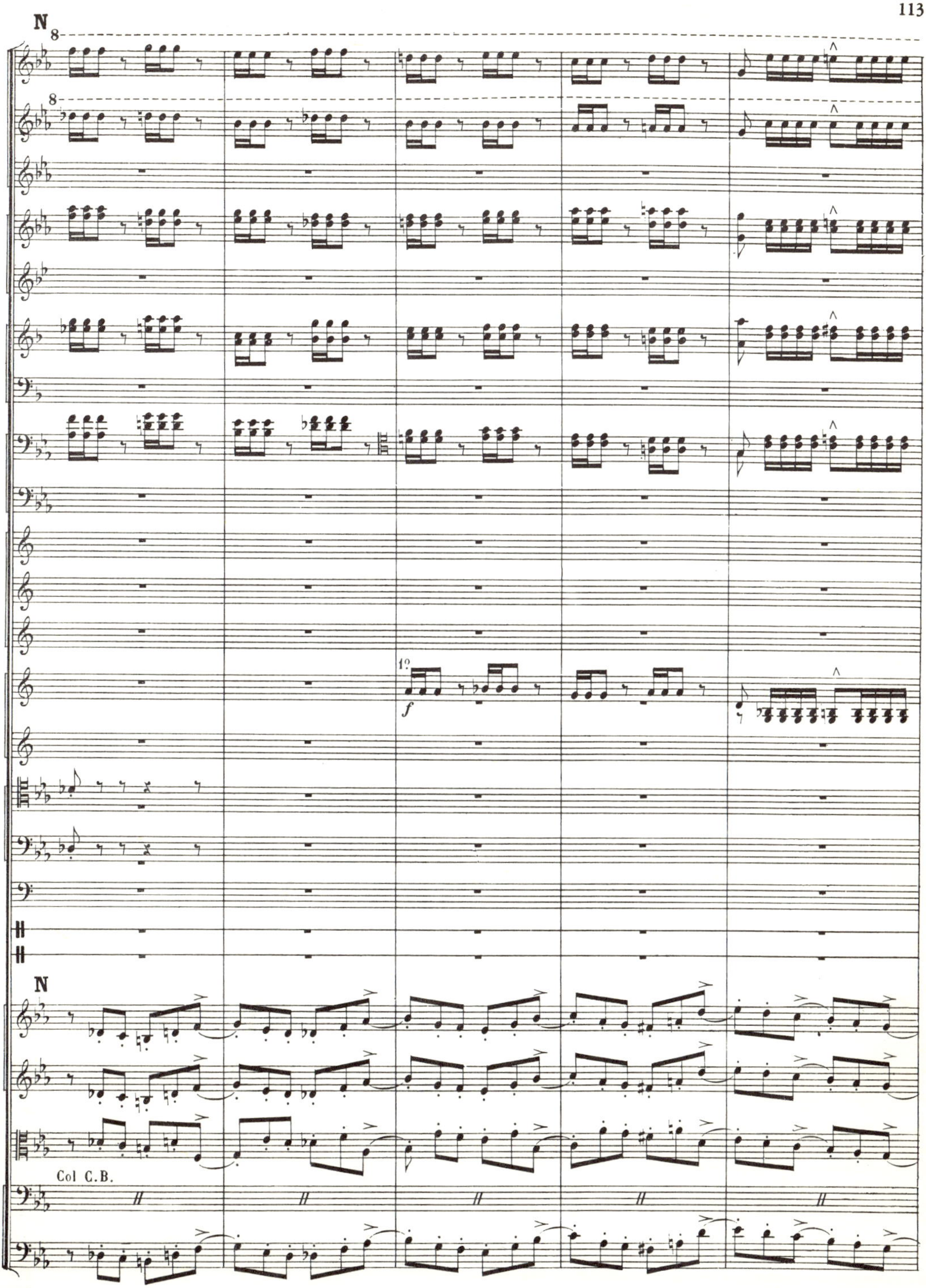
N
8
8
1º
f
N
Col C.B.

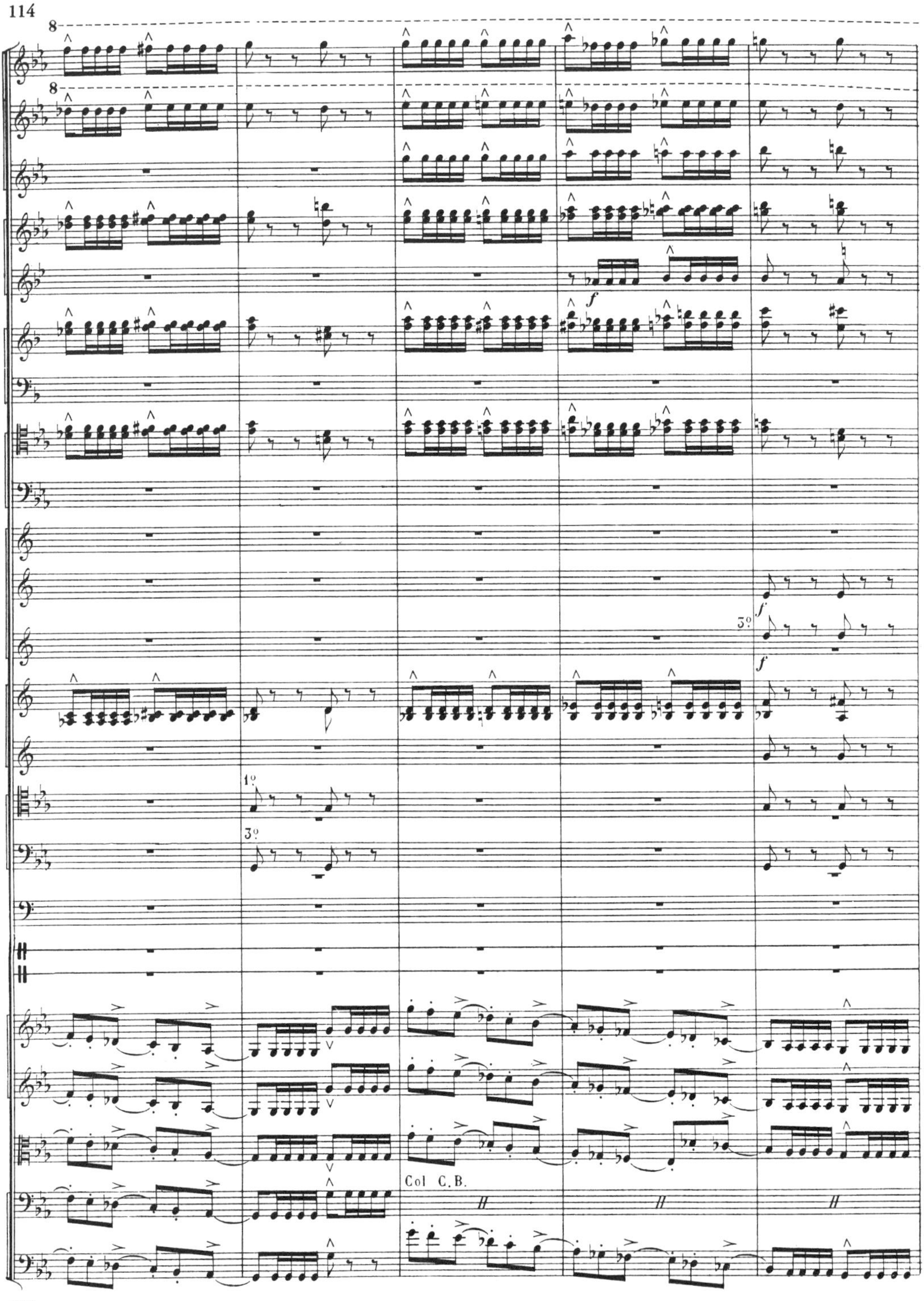
8
8
f
3º
f
1º
3º
Col C.B.

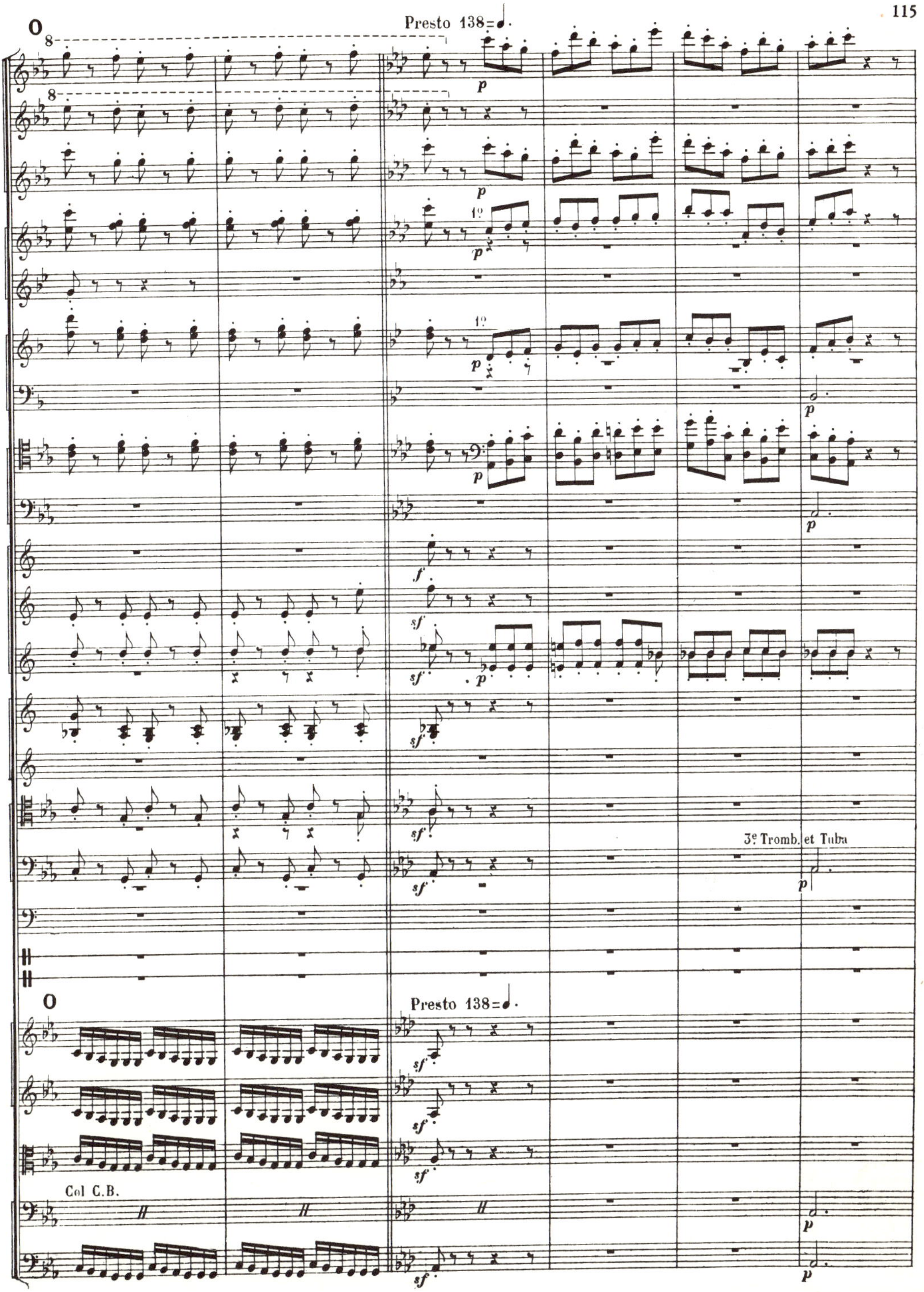
O
Presto 138=
1º
1º
3e Tromb. et Tuba
O
Presto 138=
Col C.B.

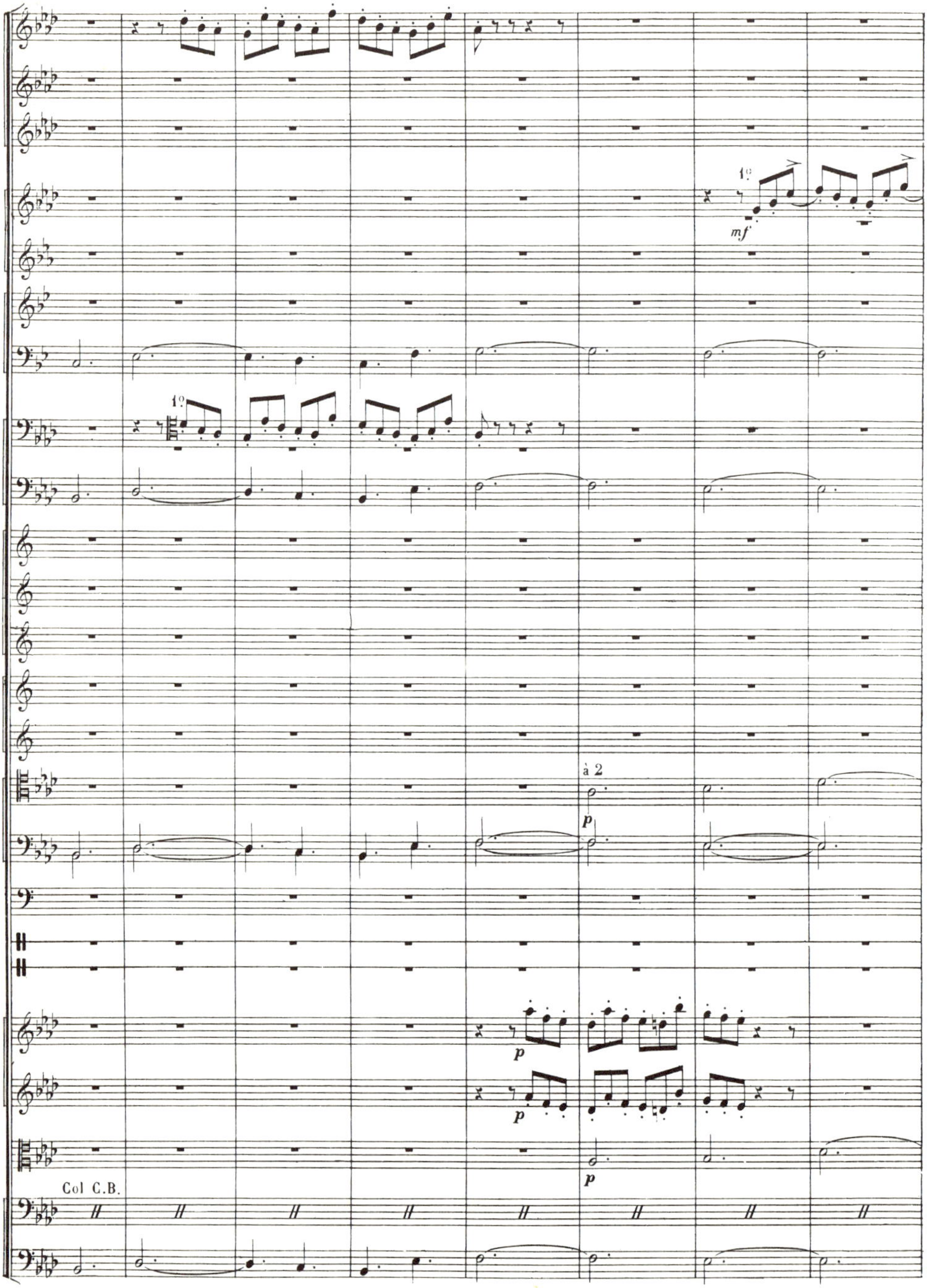
1º
mf
1º
à 2
p
p
p
p
Col C.B.

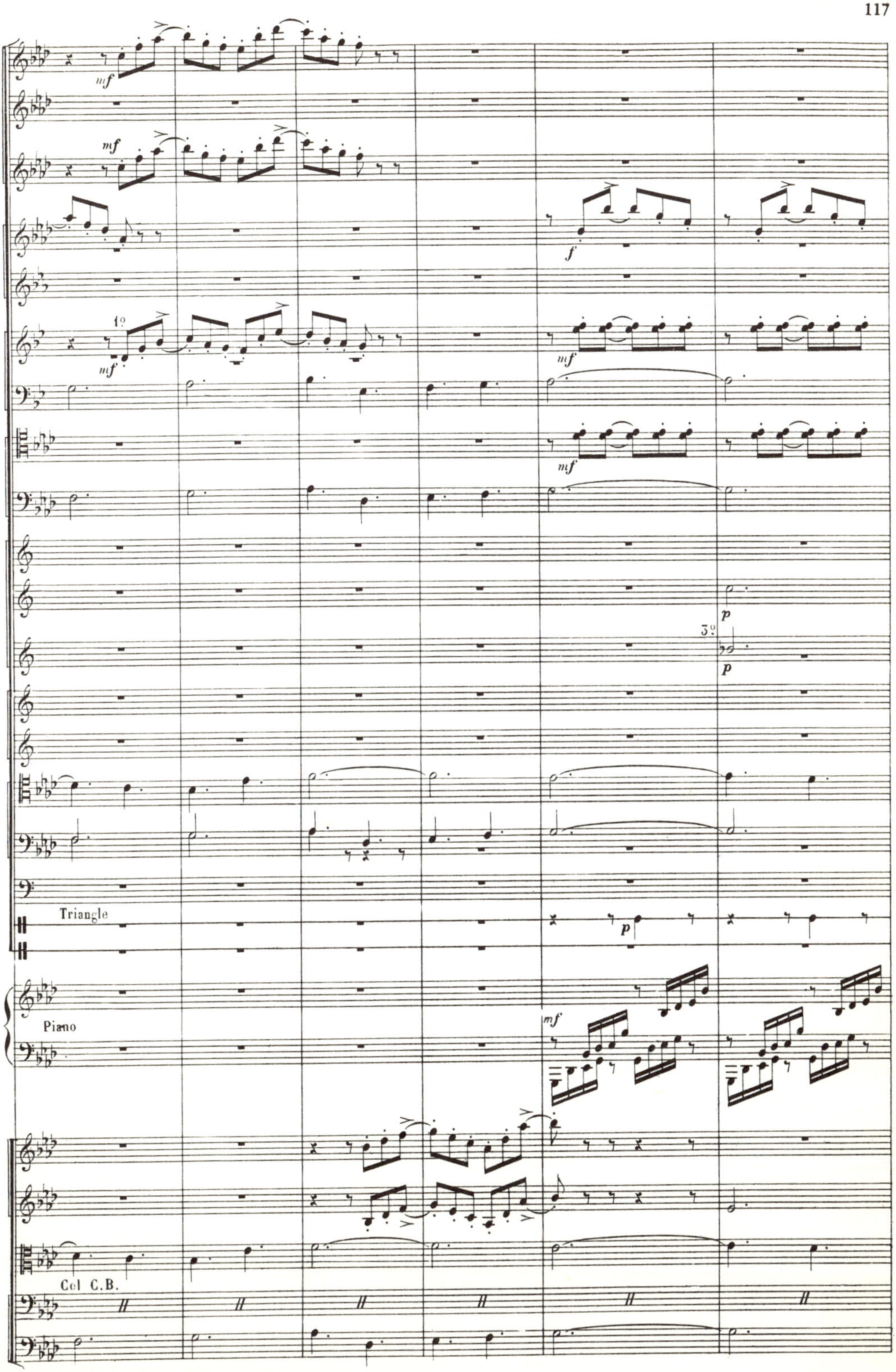
mf
f
1º
Triangle
3º
p
Piano
Col C.B.

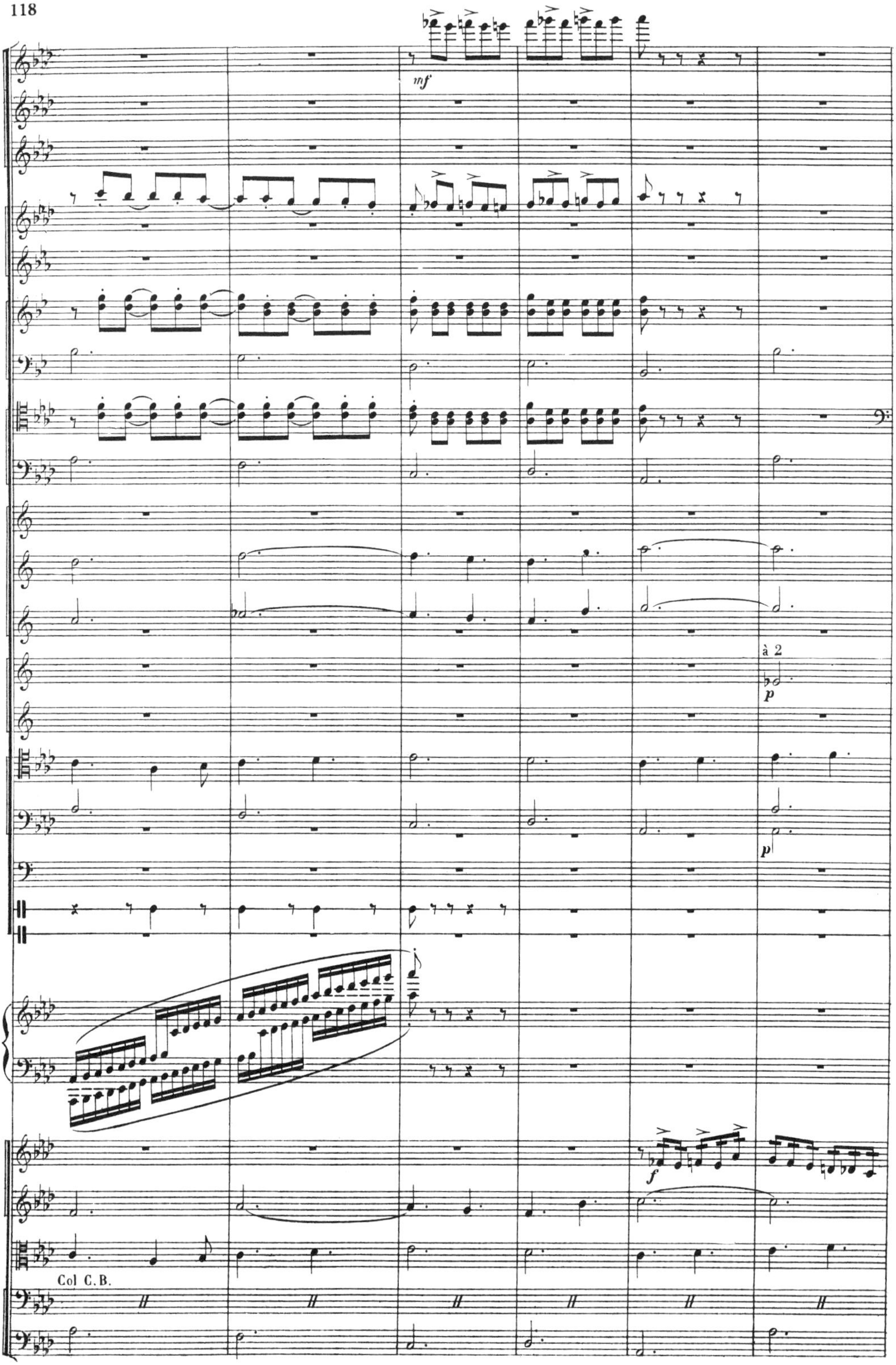
mf
à 2
p
p
f
Col C.B.

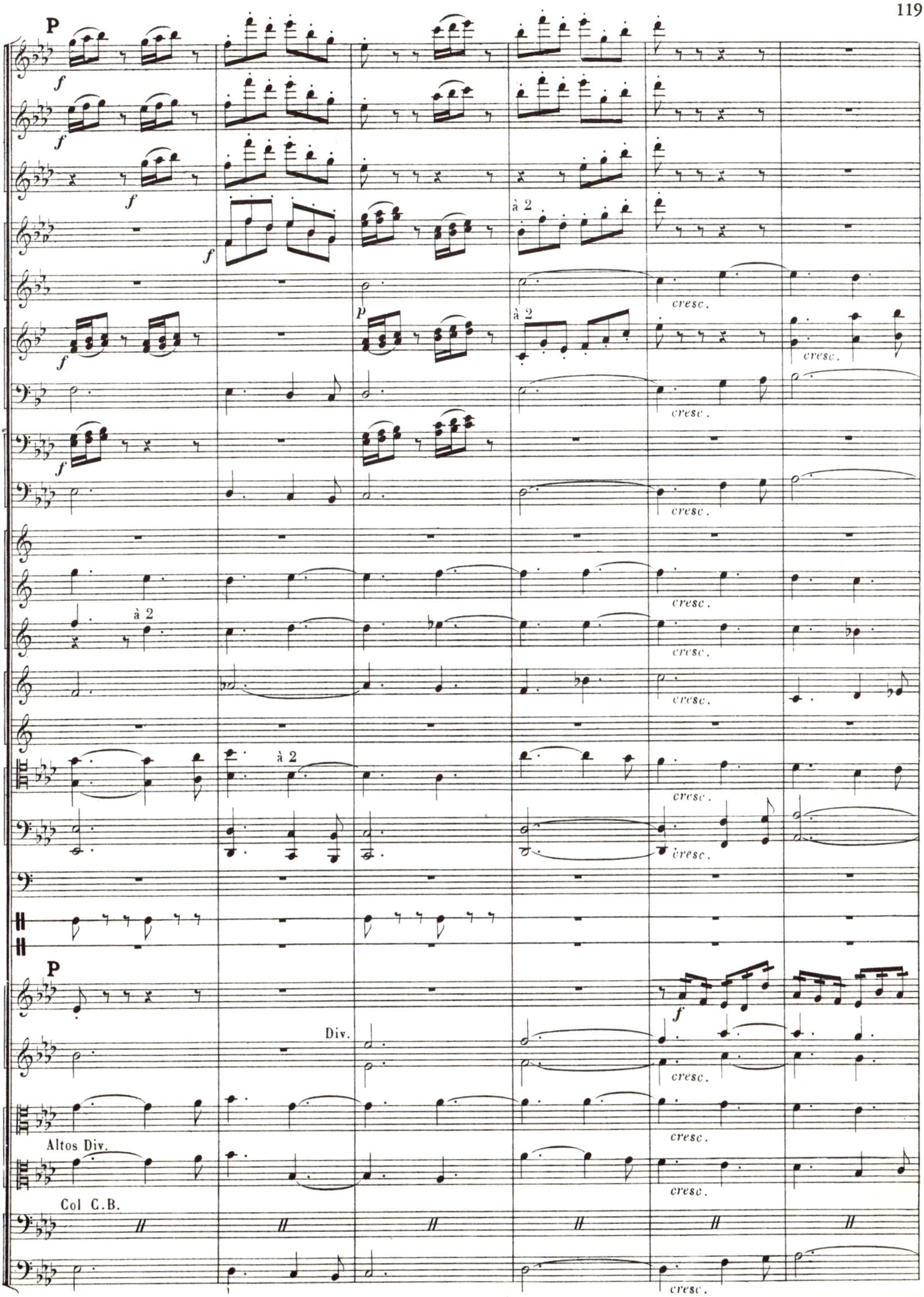
P
à 2
cresc.
Div.
Altos Div.
Col C.B.

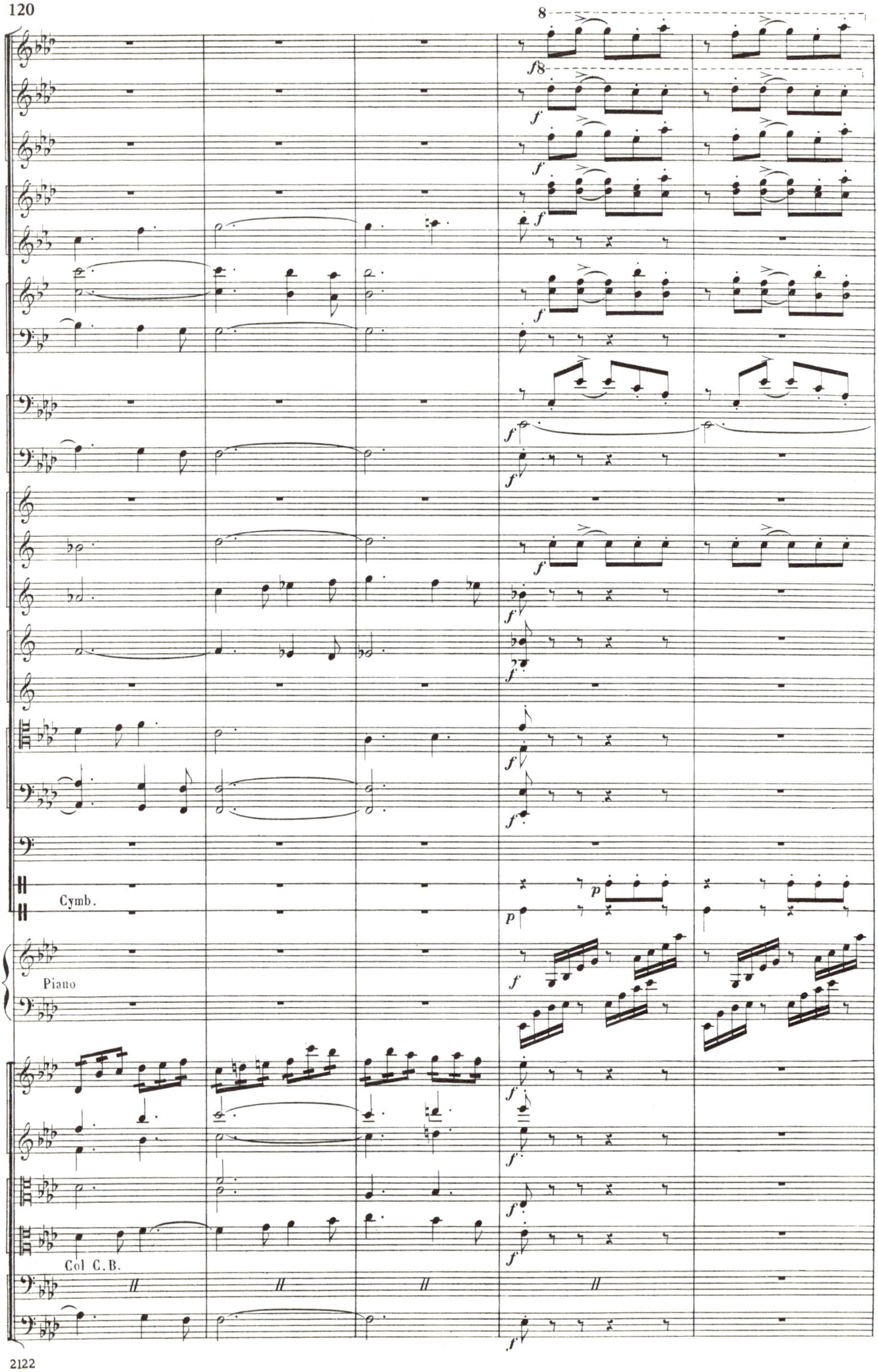
8
f8
Cymb.
Piano
Col C.B.

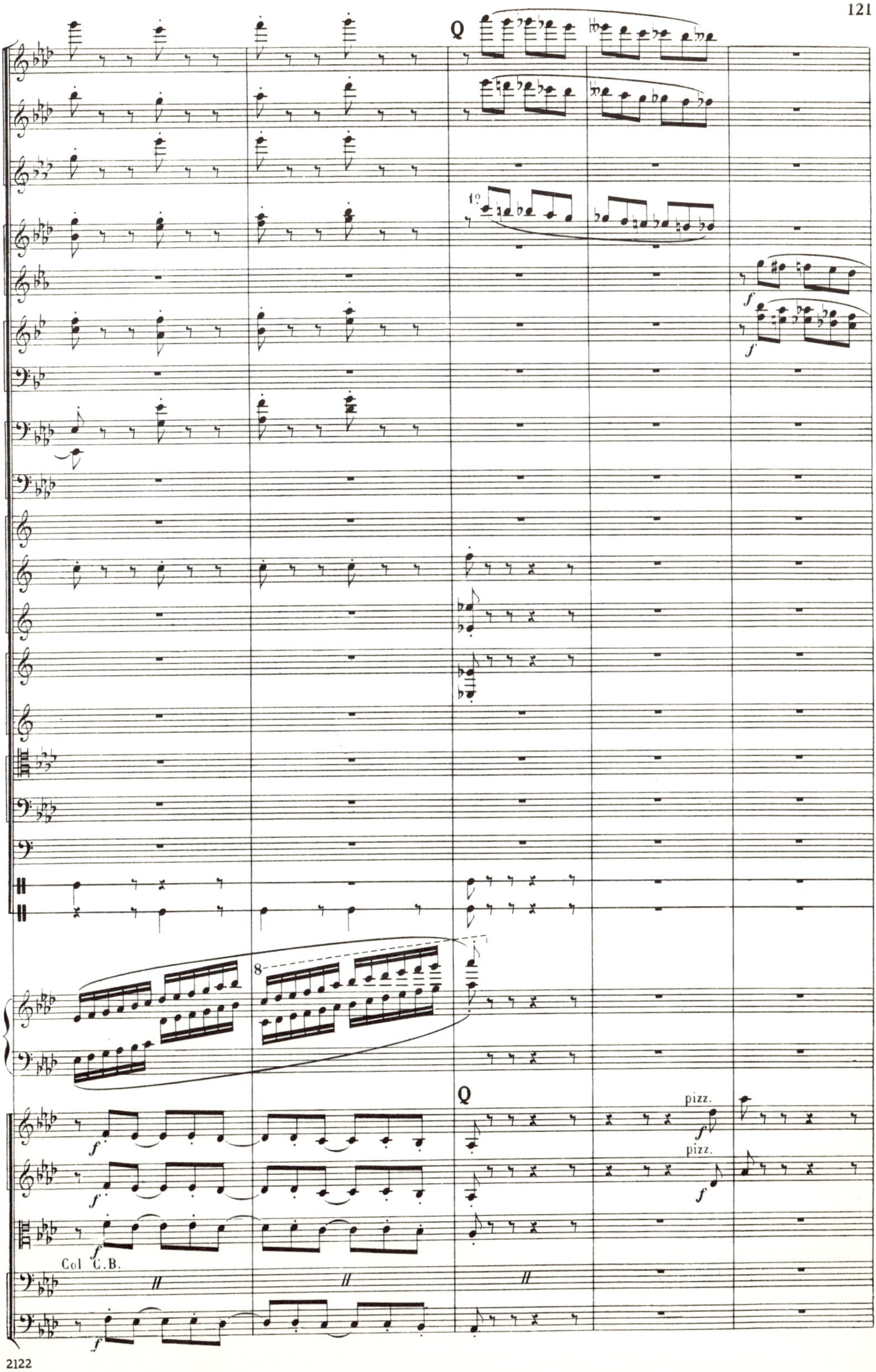
Q
1º
f
f
8
Q
pizz.
f
pizz.
f
f
f
f
Col C.B.
f

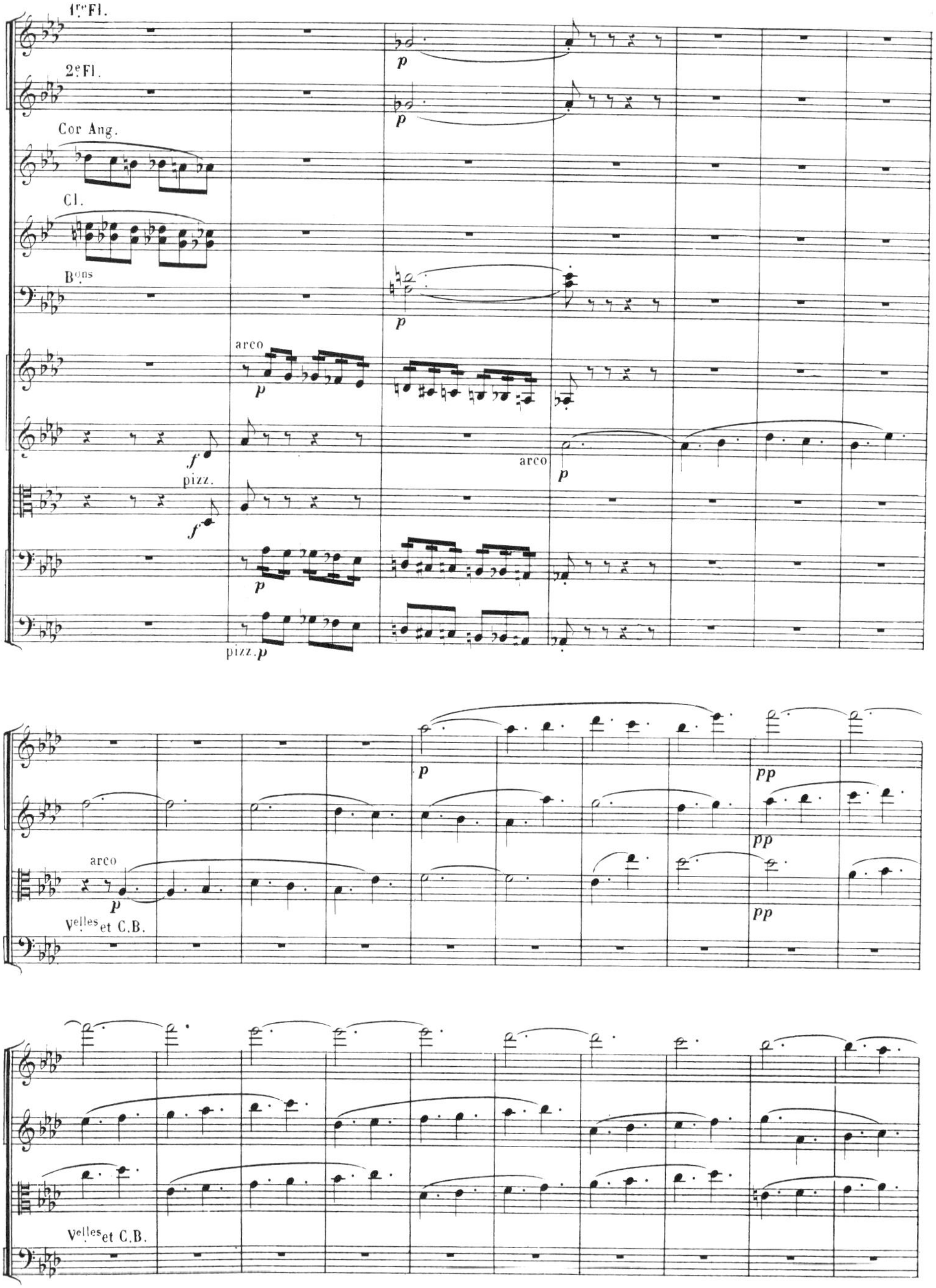
1re Fl.
2e Fl.
Cor Ang.
Cl.
Bons
p
arco
pizz.
f
pizz. p
Velles et C.B.
pp

cresc.
mf
dim.
Velles et C.B.
Hb.
R
1º
pp
Cors en FA
arco
Allo moderato 72 = ♩.
poco marcato
pizz.
dim.

1re Fl.
2e Fl.
Petite Fl.
Hb
Cor Ang.
Cl.
Cl. B.
Bon
C. Bon
Cors
Changer en UT
Changer en UT
Tromp.
Tromb.
Timb.
Triangle
Cymb.
(Triangle Tacet)
Orgue
Maestoso 96=
à 2
ppp
pp
f
pizz.
arco
Col C.B.

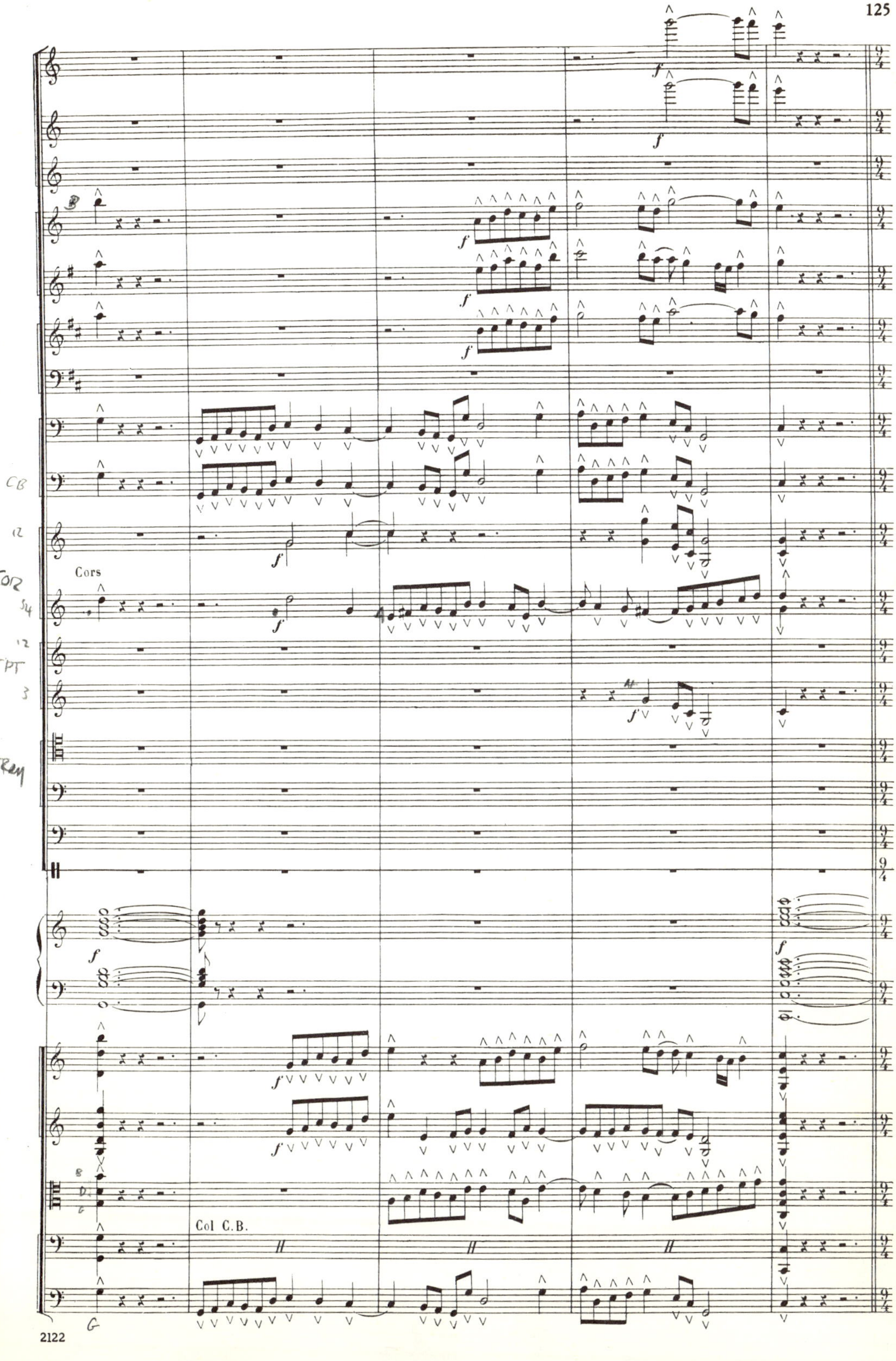
Cors
Col C.B.

S

PIANO A 4 MAINS

8 - - - - - - - - - - - - -

S

Div.
Div.
Div.
Div.

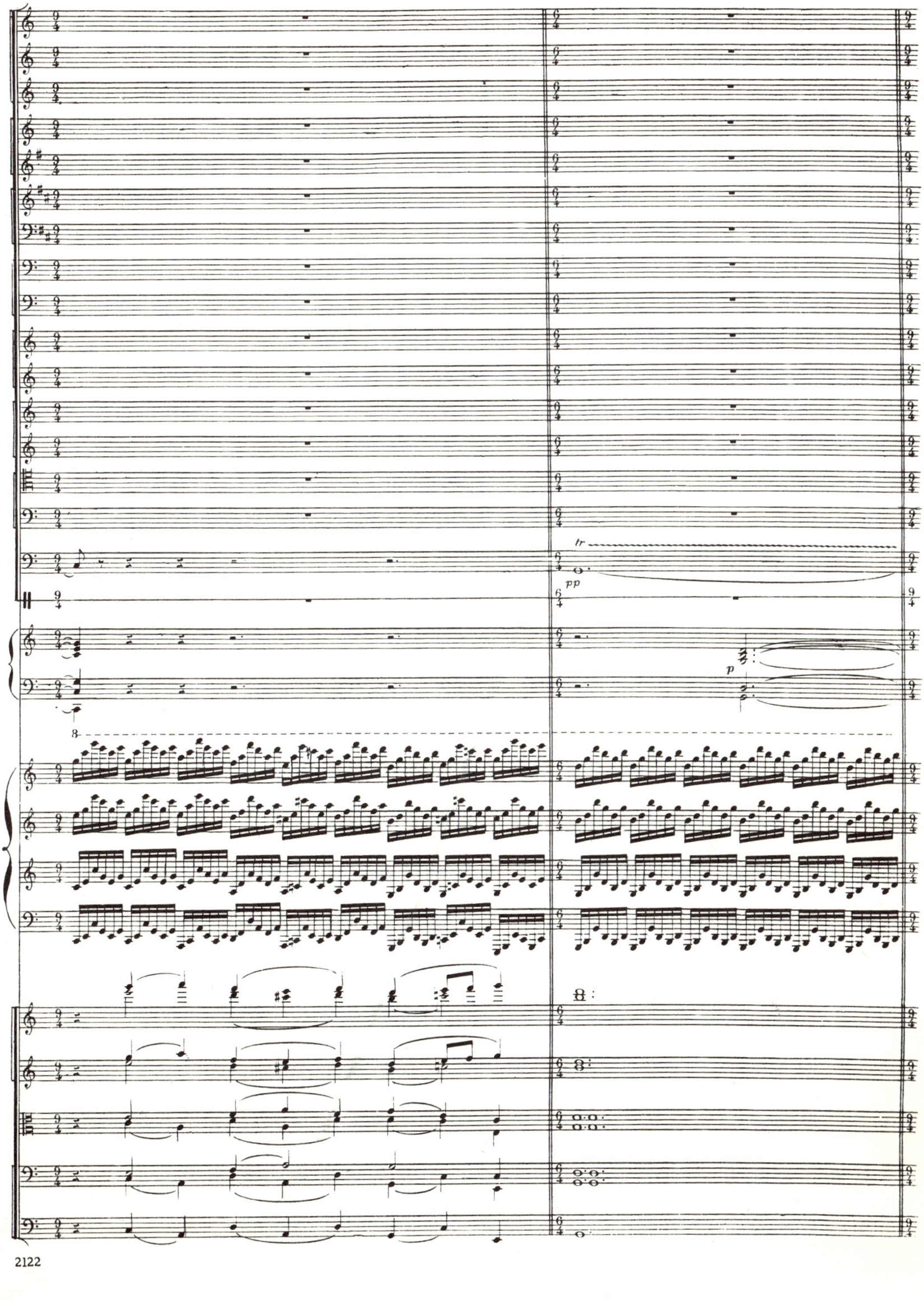
tr
pp
p
8

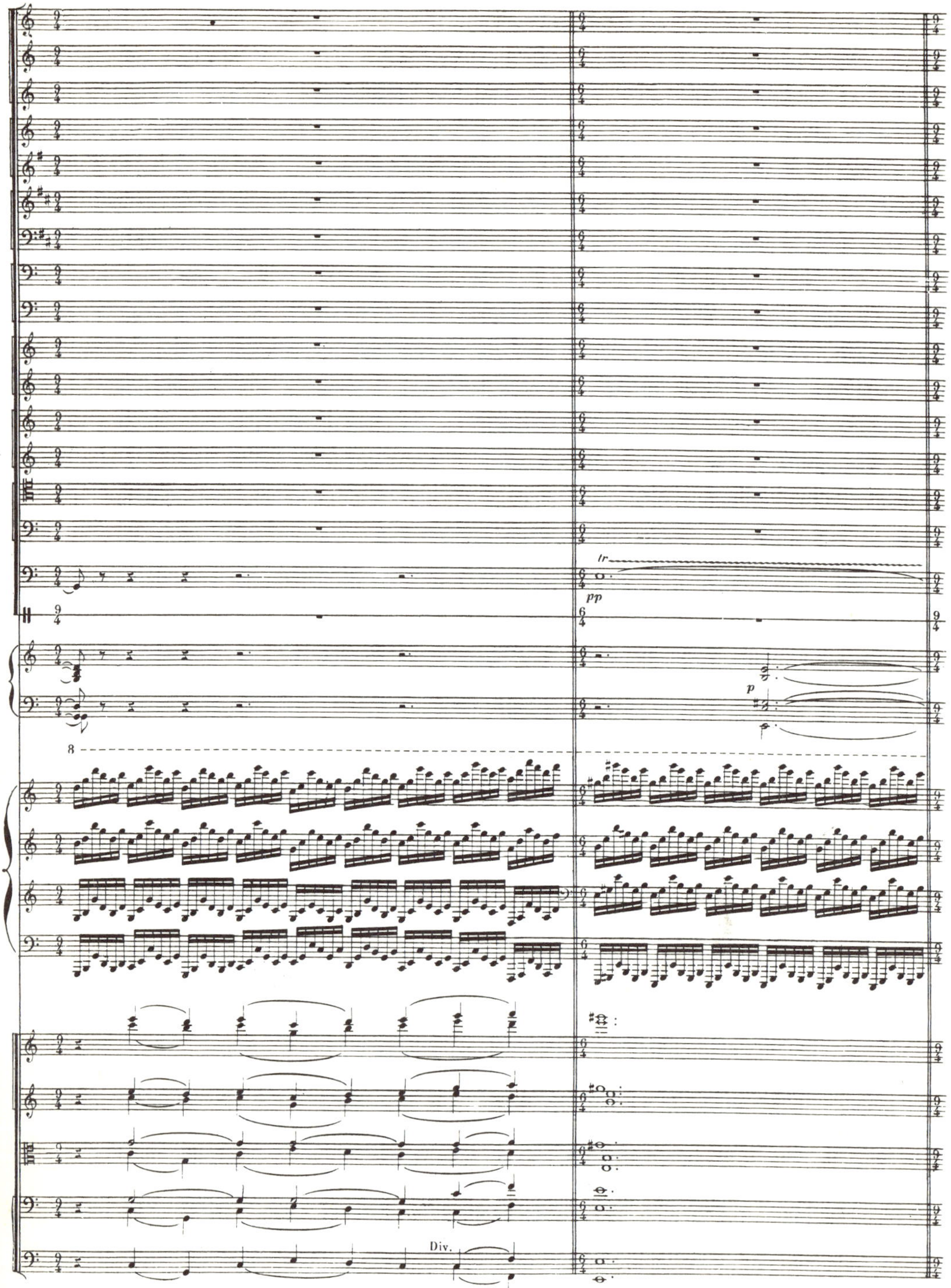
tr
pp
p
8
Div.

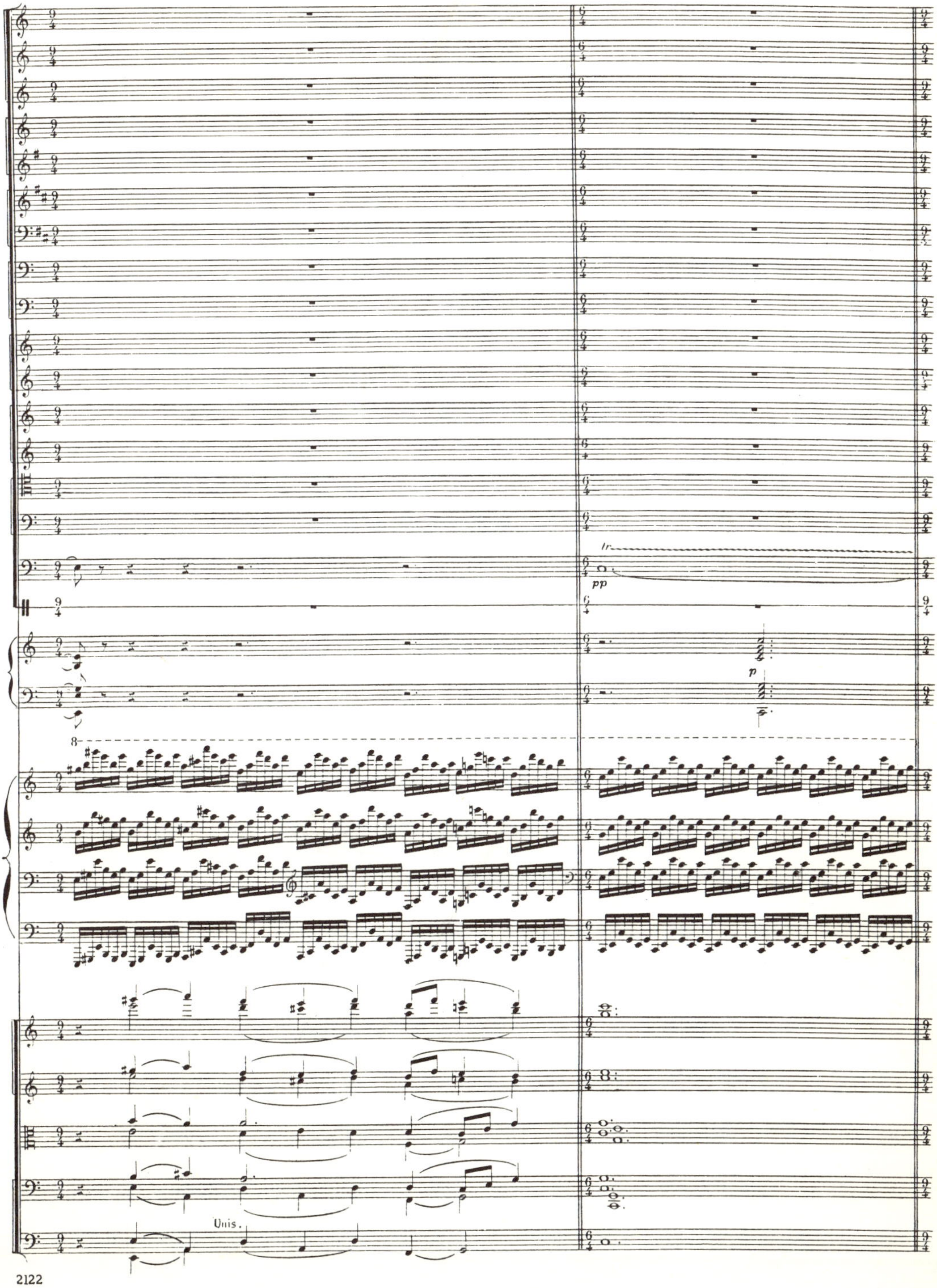
tr
pp
p
8
Unis.

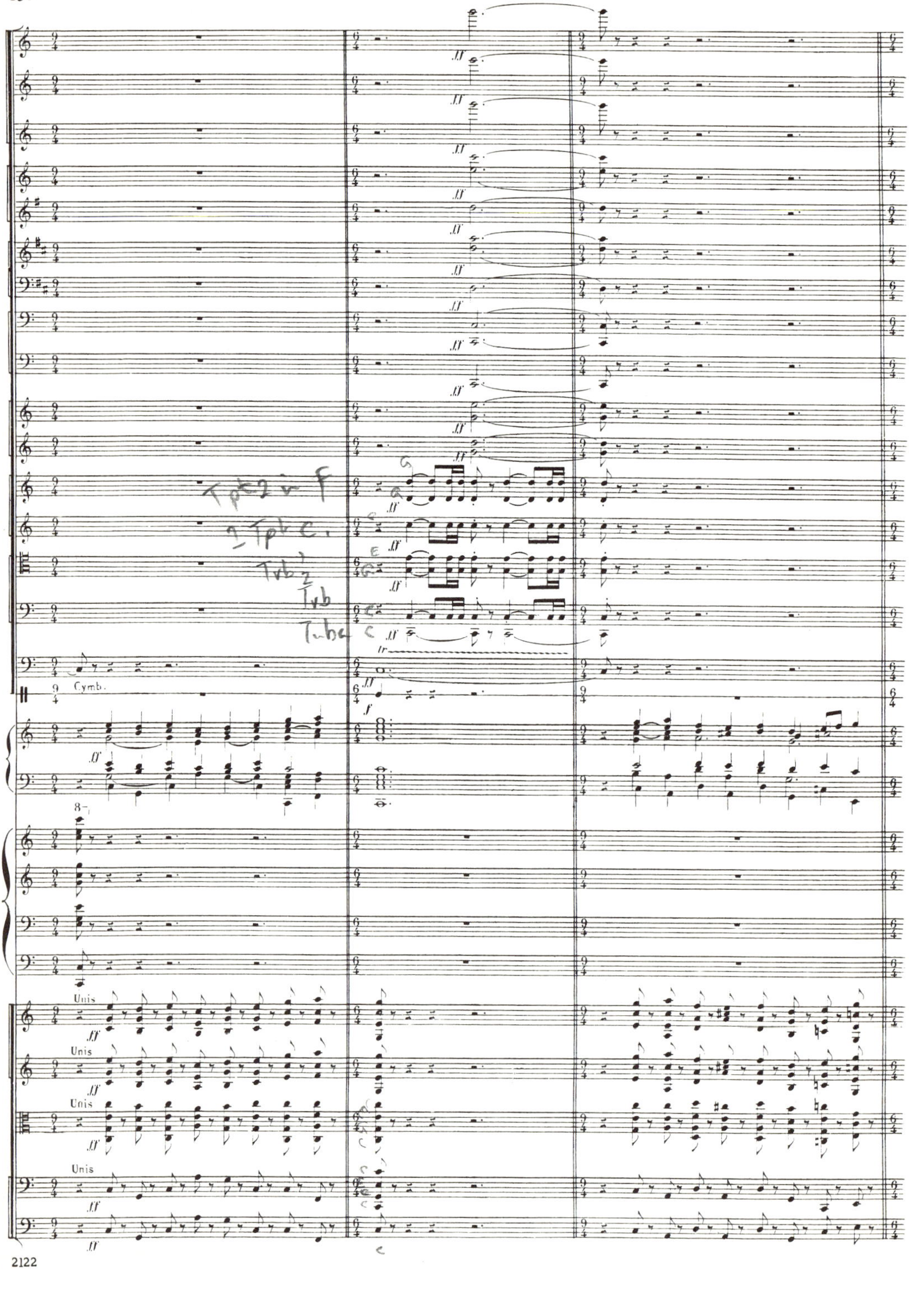
Tpt 2 in F
2 Tpt C
Trb 1 2
Trb
Tuba C
Cymb.
Unis
Unis
Unis
Unis

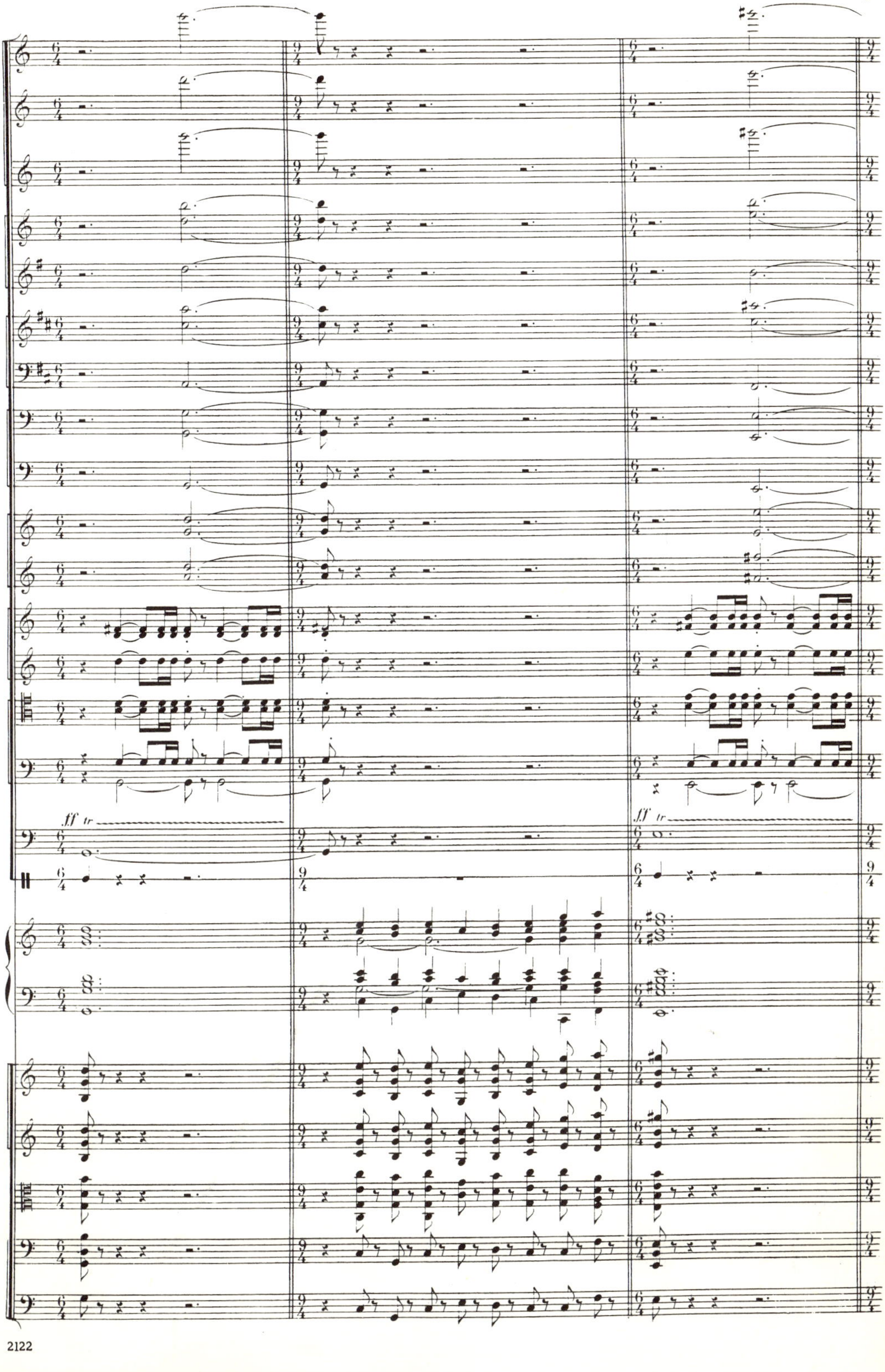
ff tr
ff tr

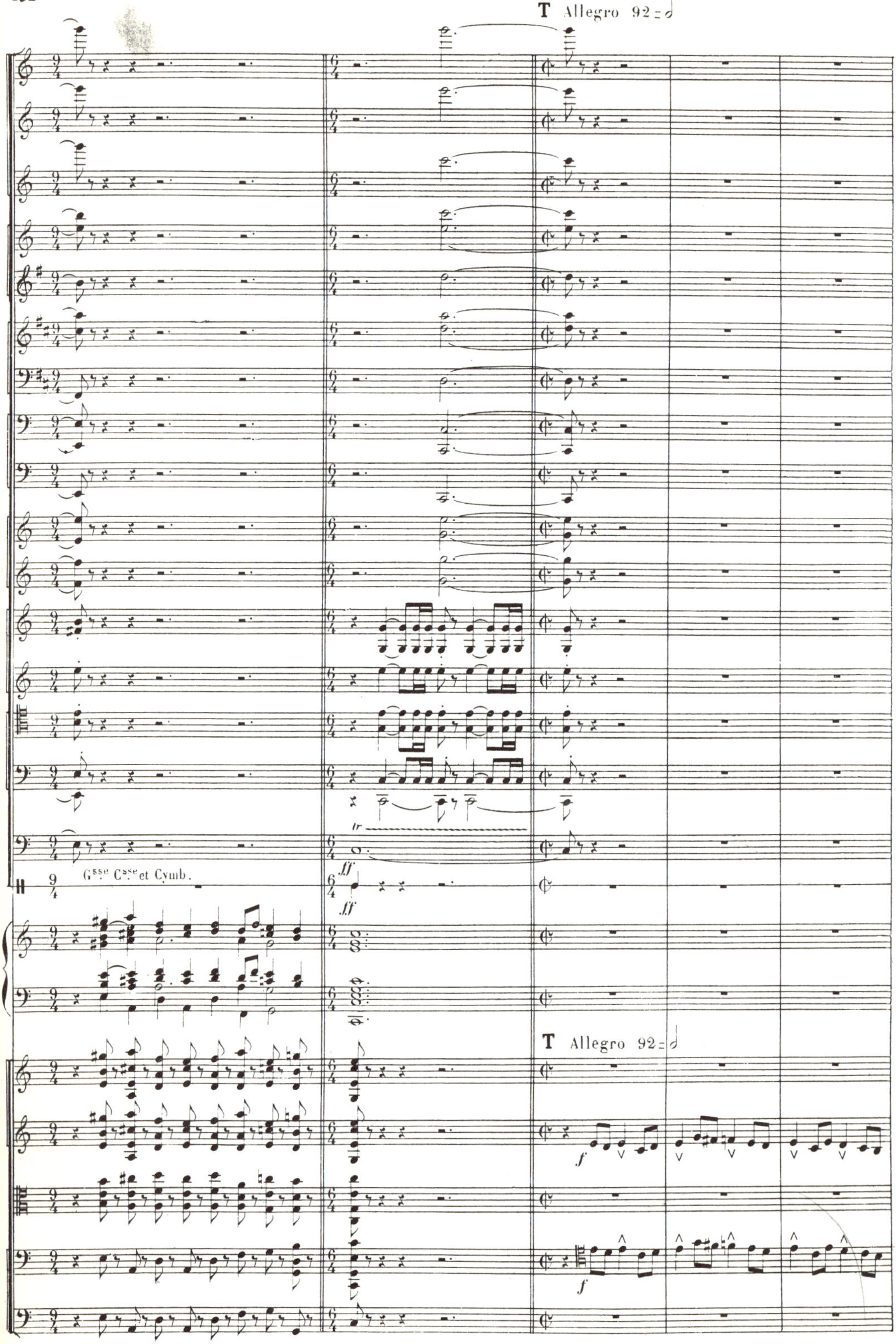
T Allegro 92 = 𝅗𝅥
Gsse Csse et Cymb.
ff
ff
tr
T Allegro 92 = 𝅗𝅥
f
f

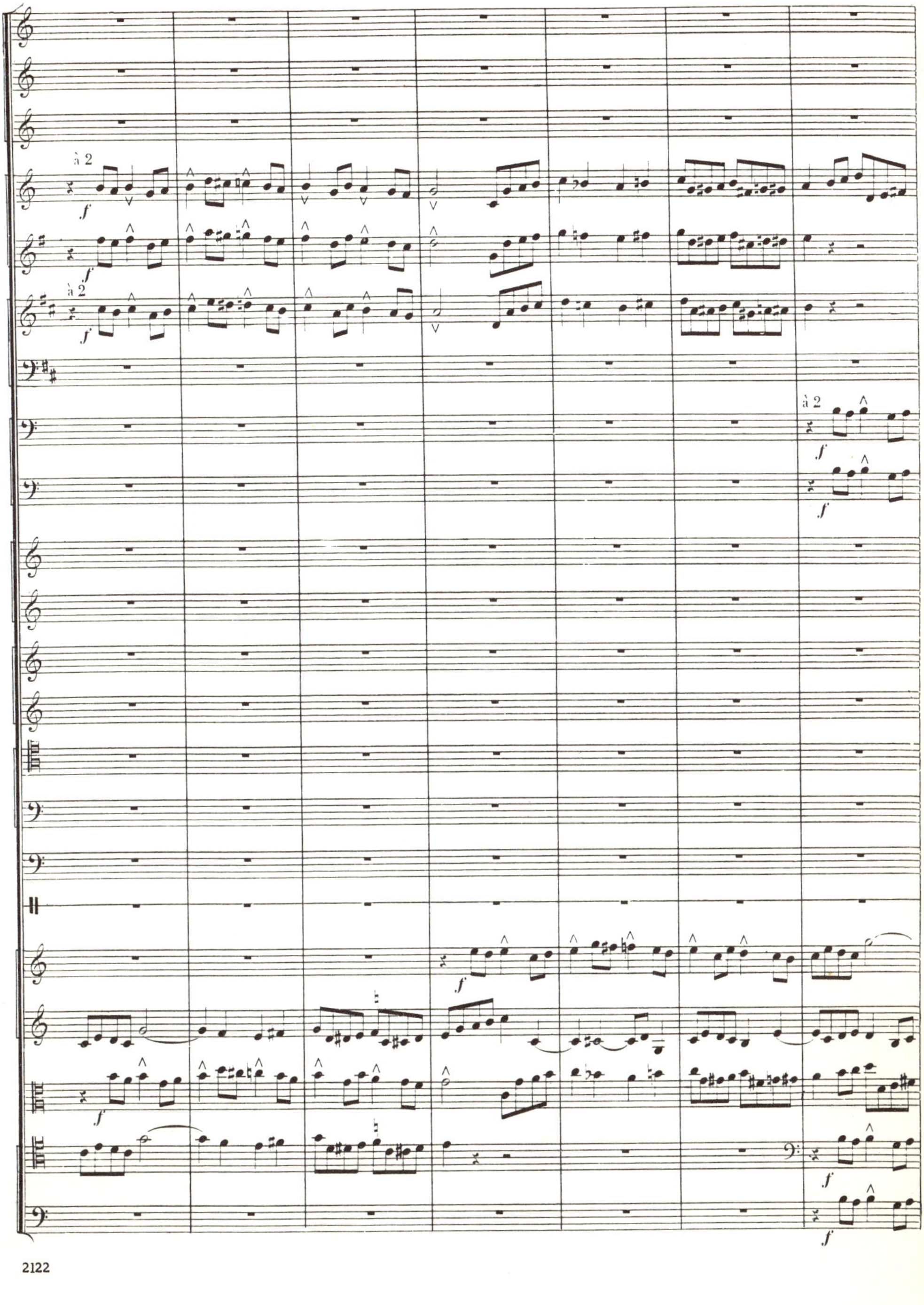
à 2
f
à 2
f
à 2
f
f
f
f

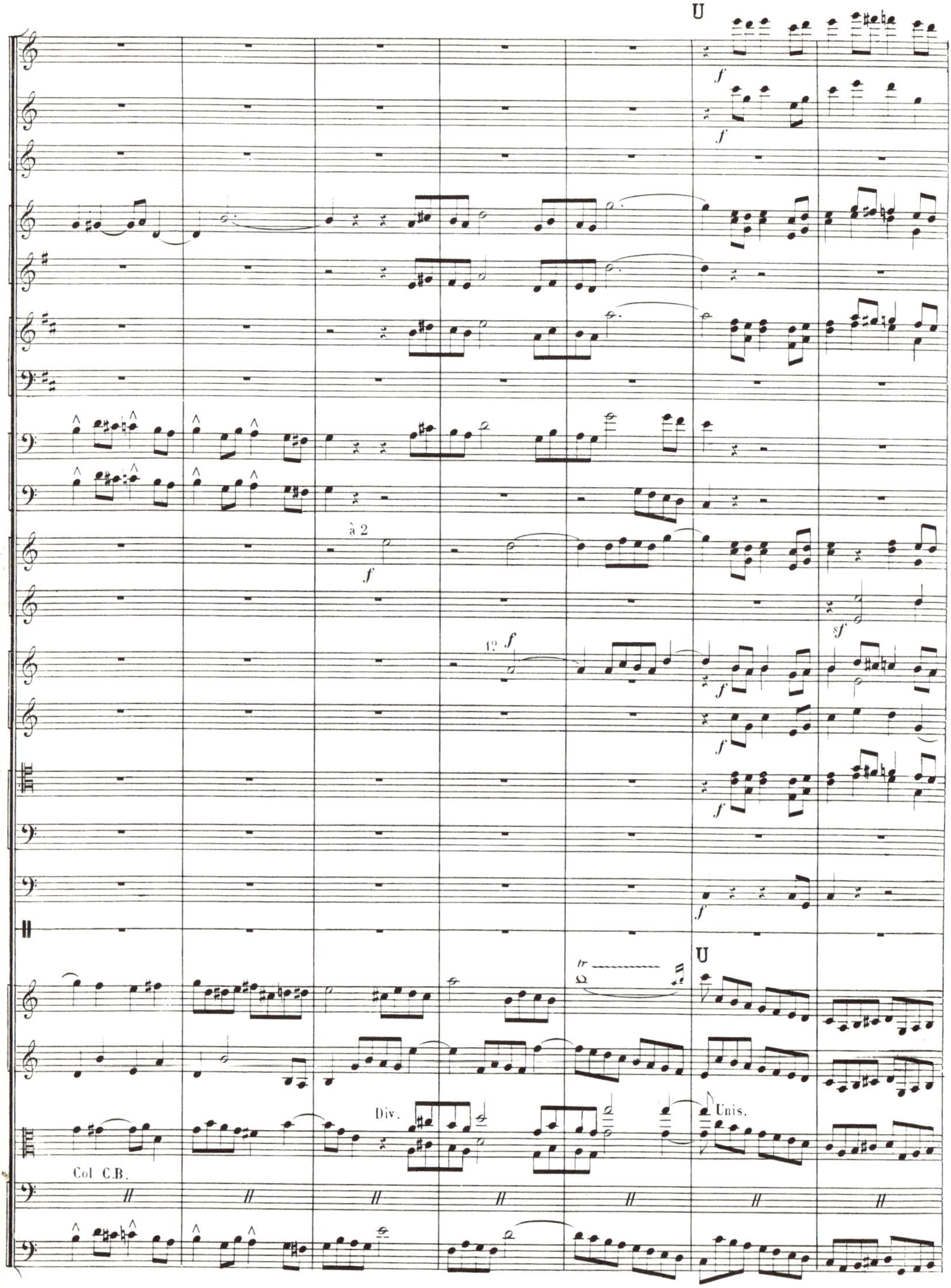
U
f
à 2
1?
sf
tr
Div.
Unis.
Col C.B.

f
f
à 2
à 2
3e Tromb.
f
Orgue
p
f
sempre f
sempre f
sempre f
pizz.
Col C.B.
sempre f
pizz.
sempre f

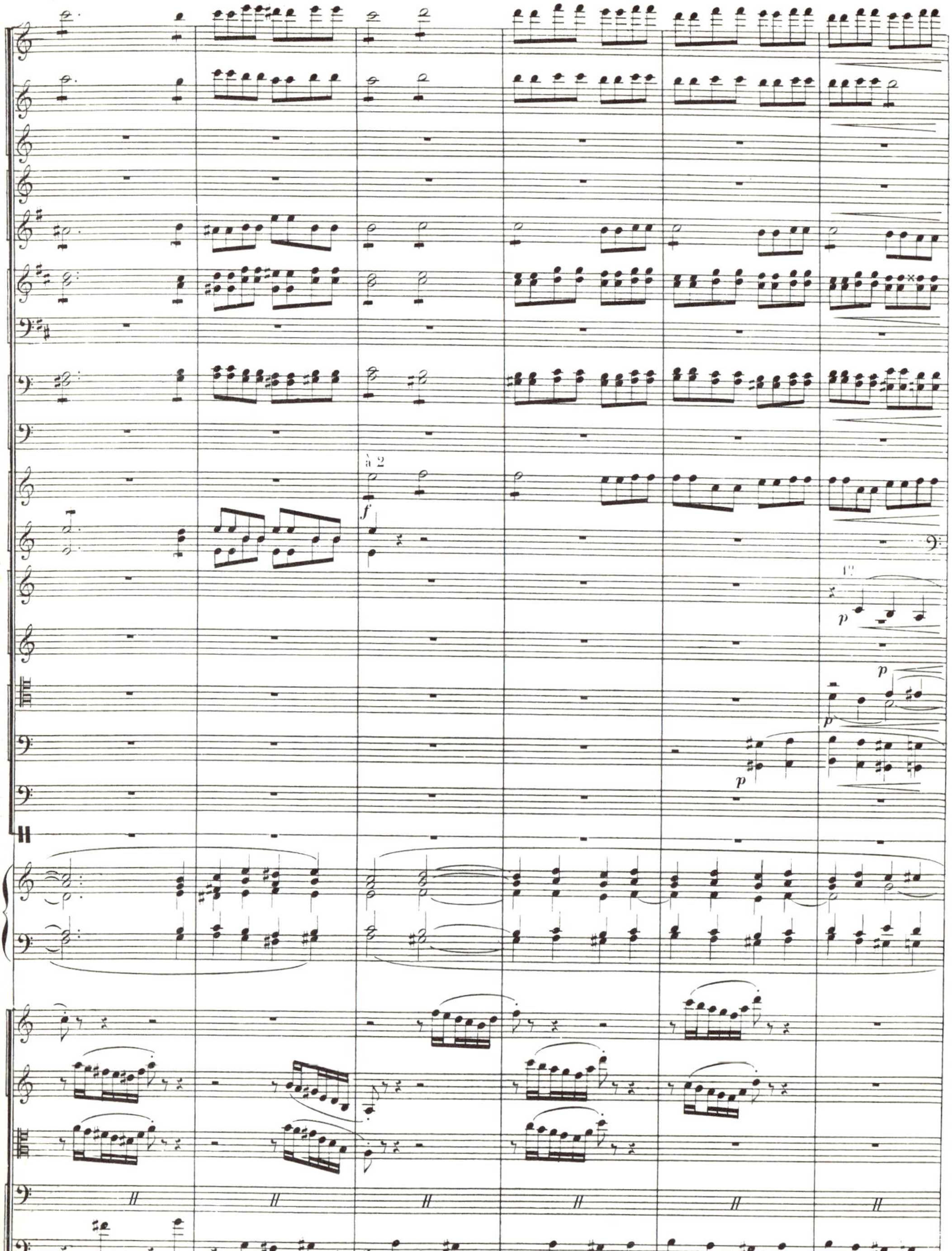
à 2
f
1º
p
p
p
p

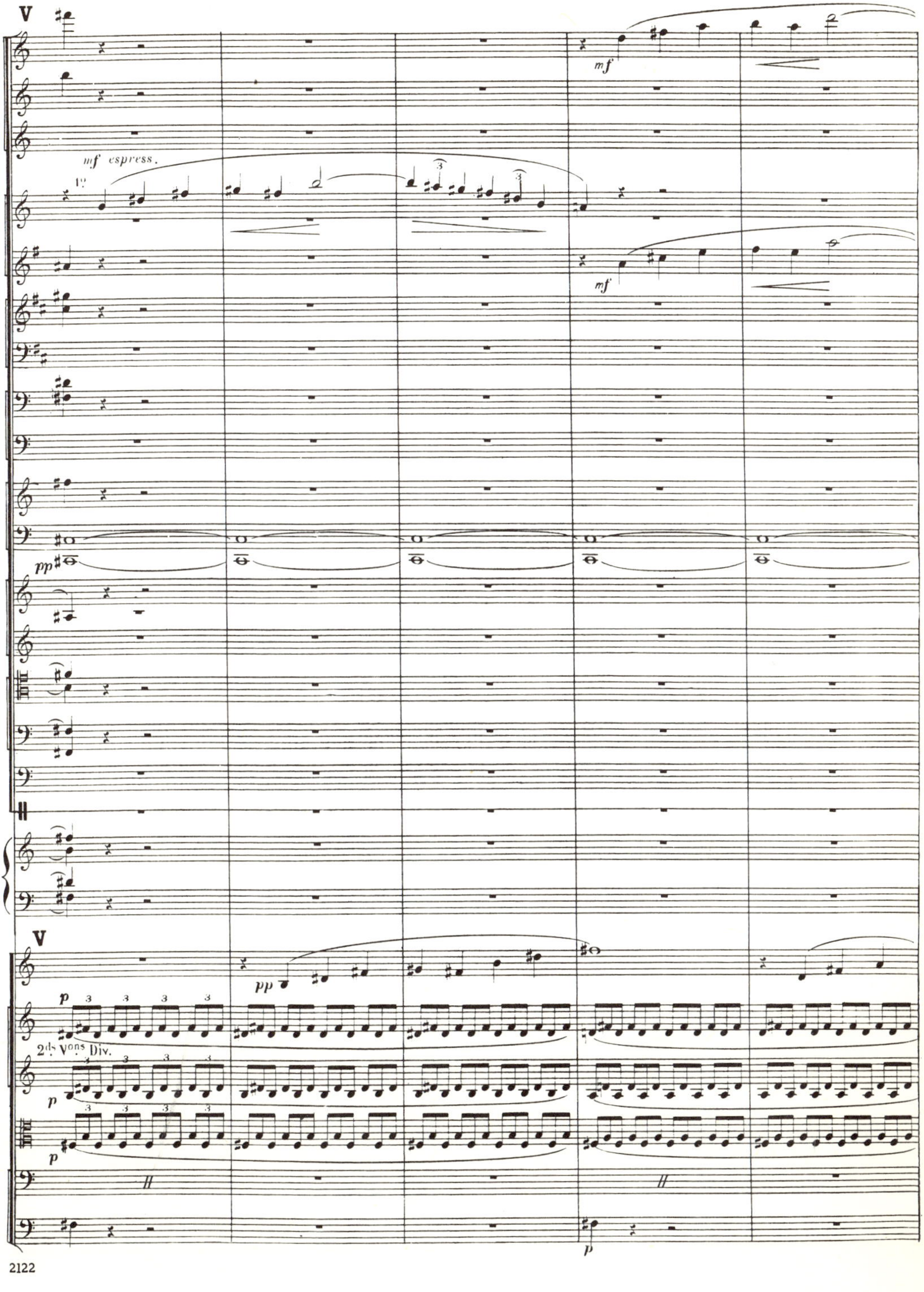
V
mf espress.
1º
mf
mf
pp
V
pp
p
2ds Vons Div.
p
p
p

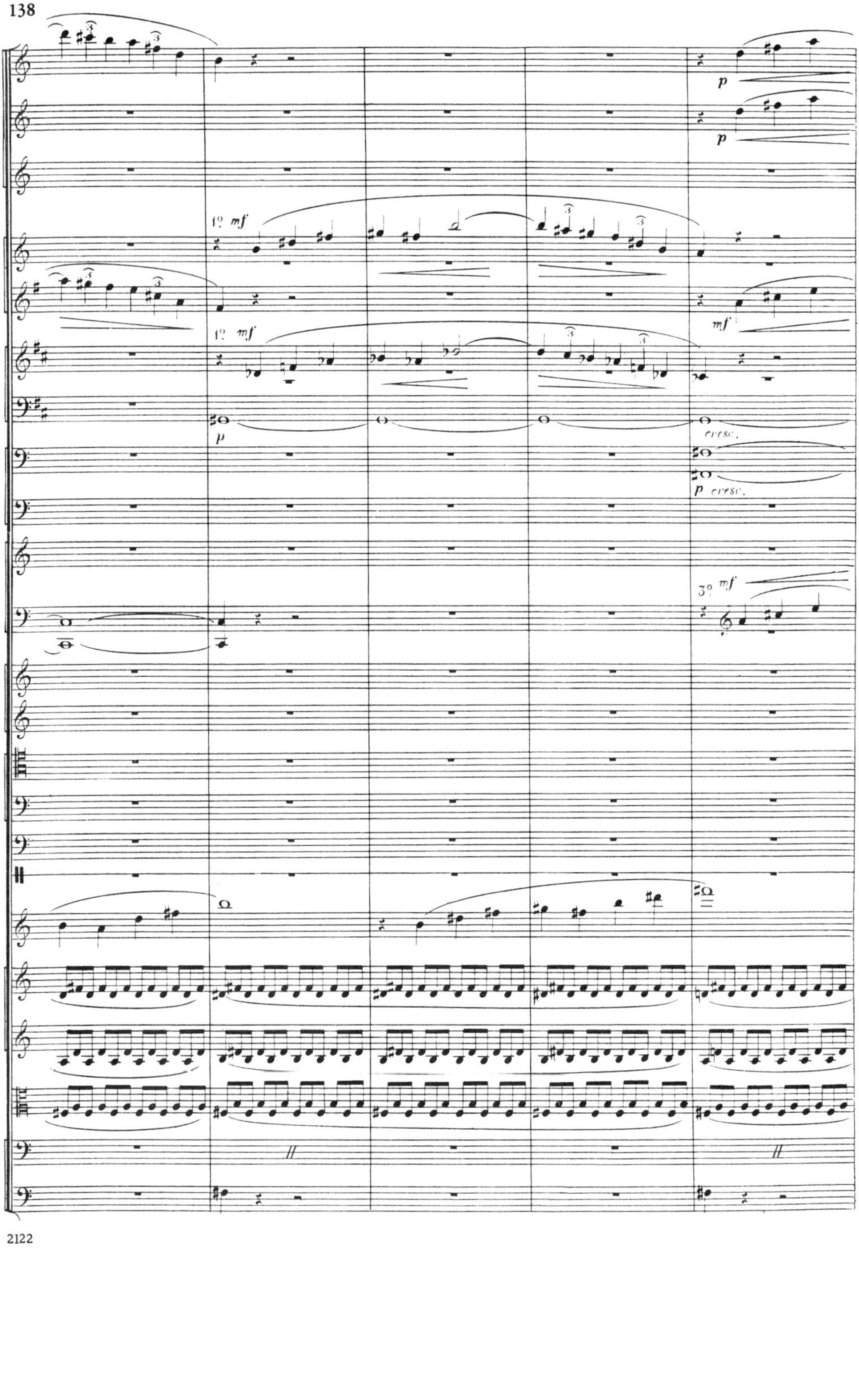
p
p
1º mf
mf
1º mf
p
cresc.
p cresc.
3º mf

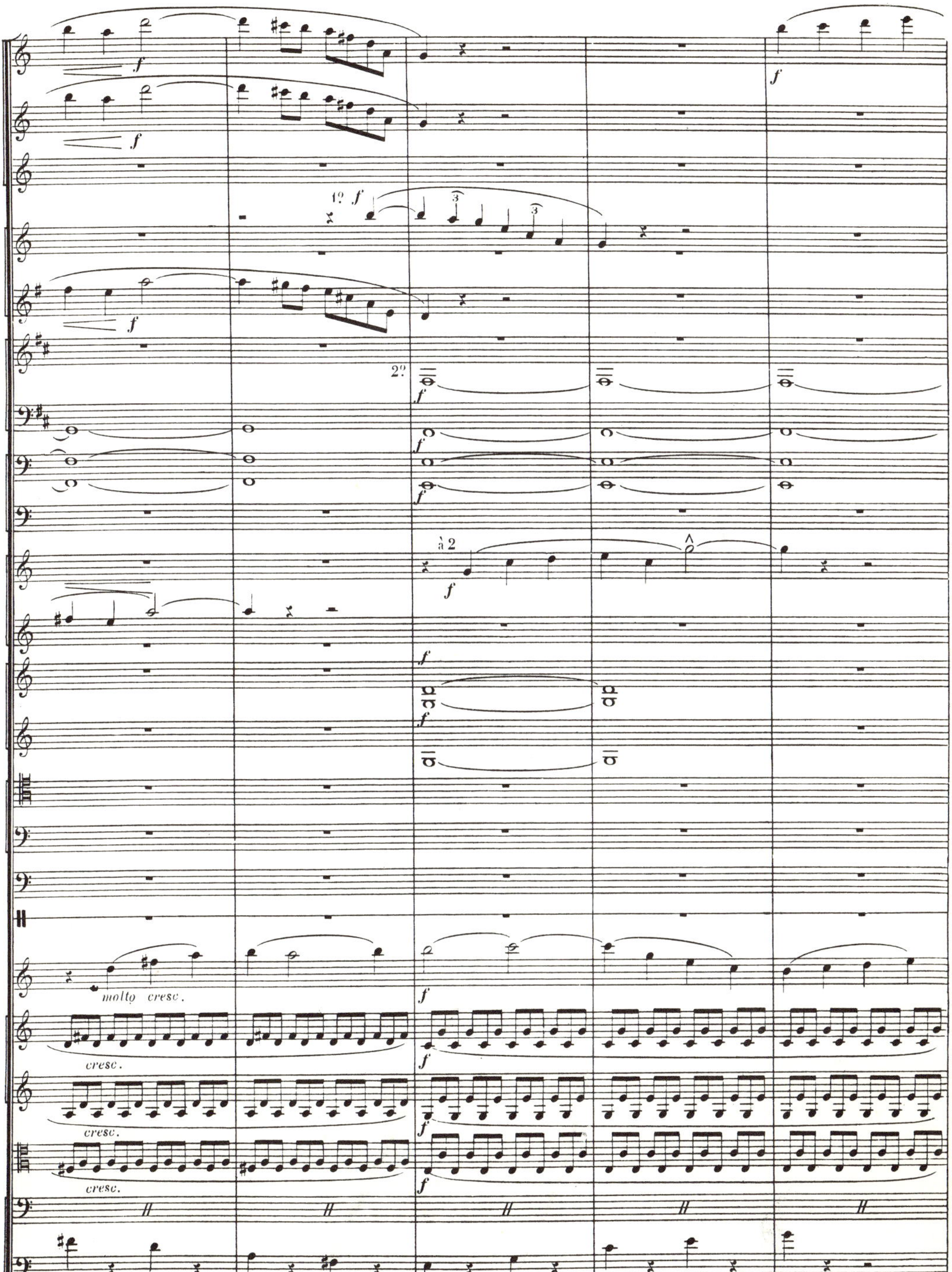

1º
2º
à 2
molto cresc.
cresc.

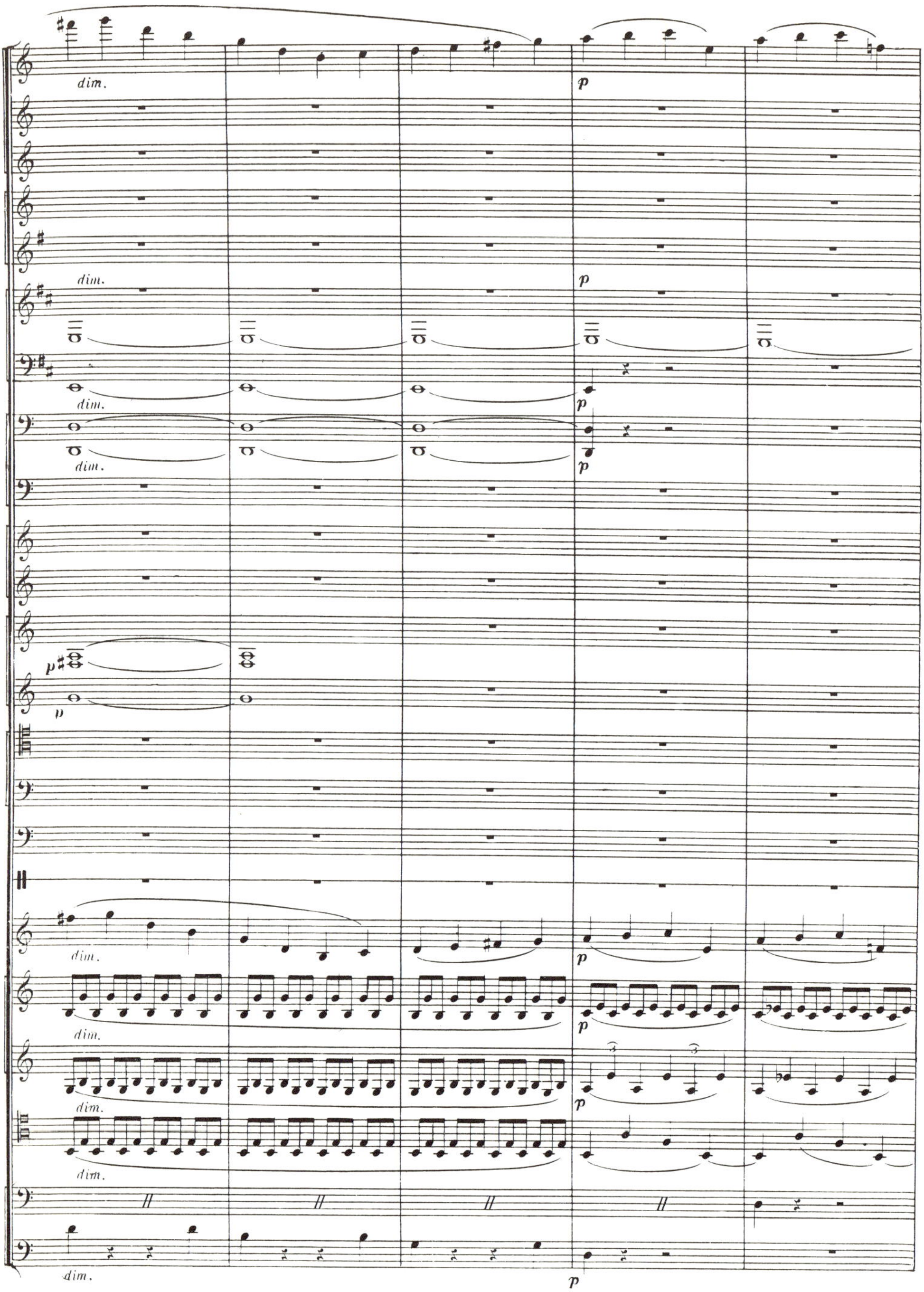
dim.
p
dim.
p
dim.
dim.
p
p
dim.
p
dim.
p
dim.
p
dim.
dim.
p

X
dim.
1º
p
dim.
2º
pp
1º
p
3º
pp
sons bouchés
pp
ppp
Ped.
X
dim.
dim.
pp
dim.
pp
dim.
pp
dim. Velles Div.
pp
pp
pp

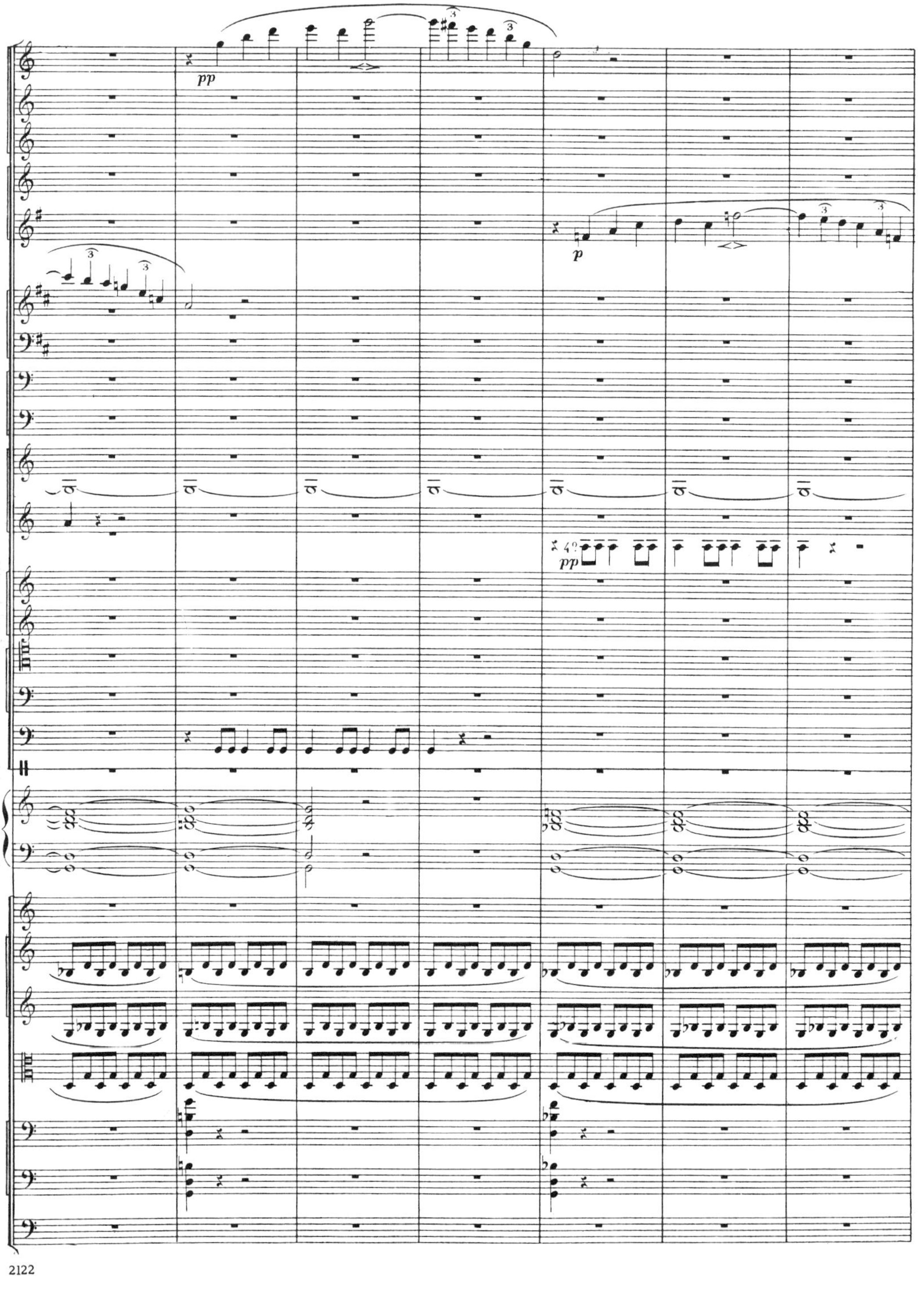
pp
p
pp

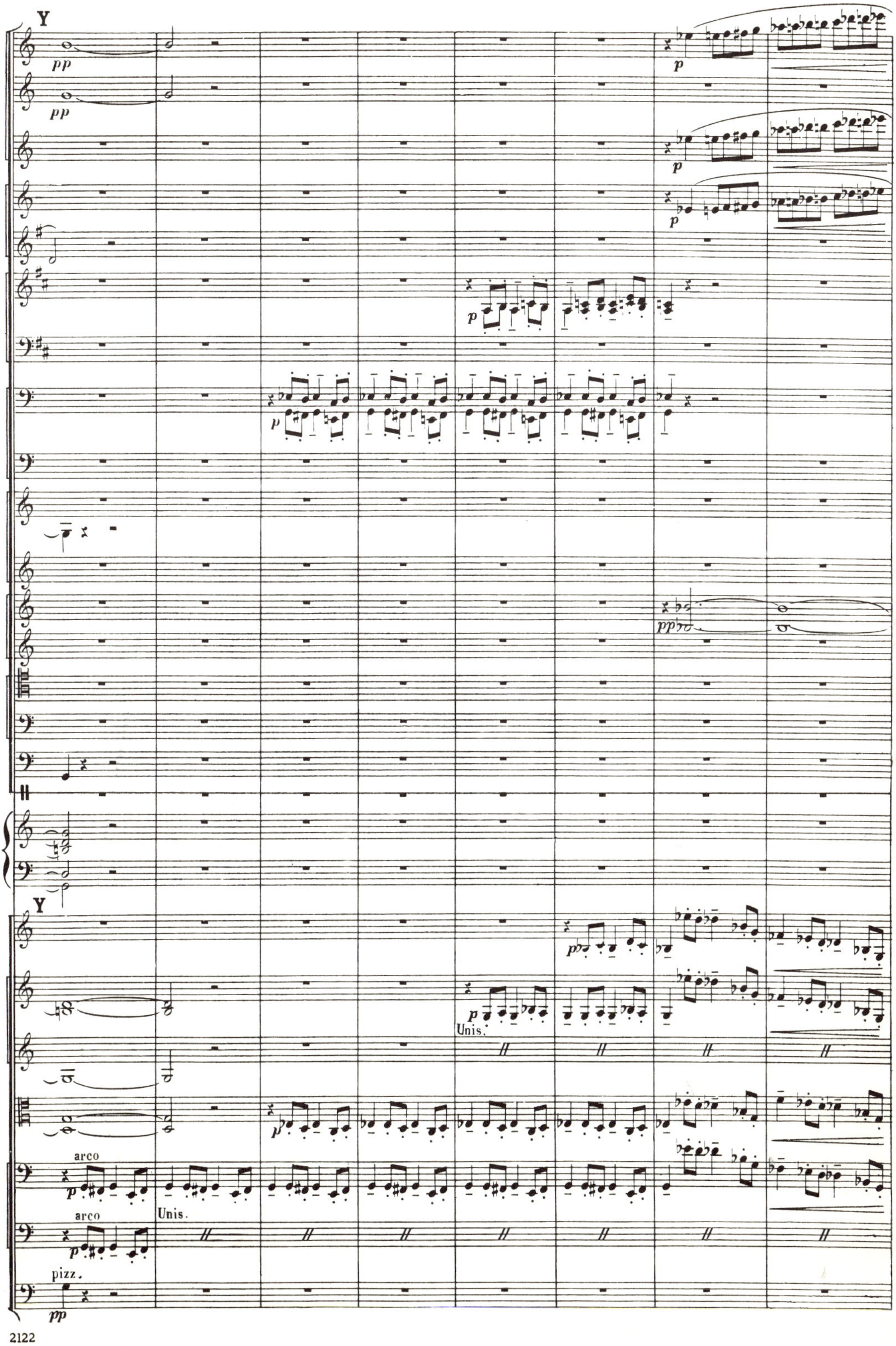
Y
pp
pp
p
p
p
p
p
pp
Y
p
p
Unis.
arco
p
Unis.
arco
p
pizz.
pp

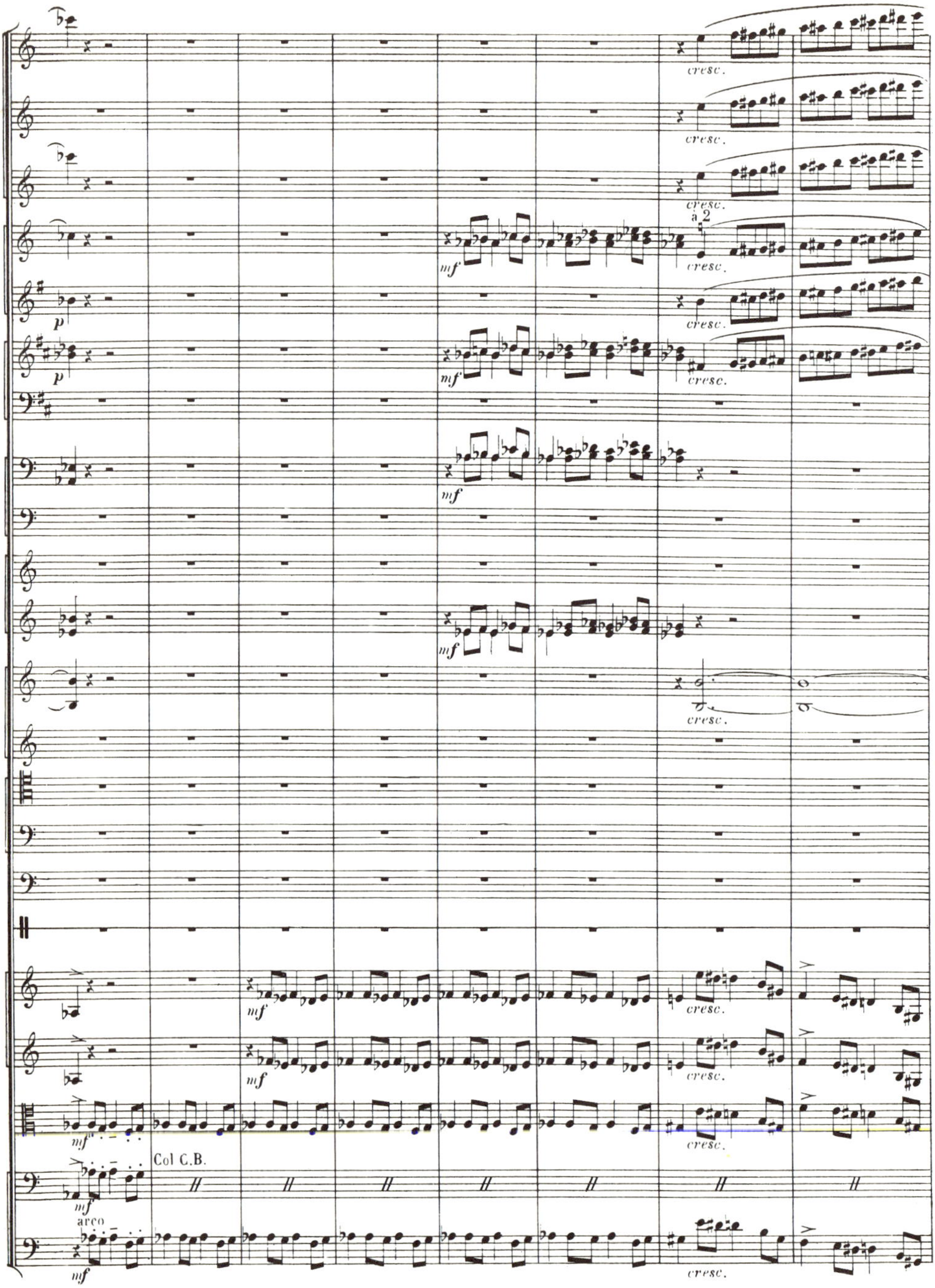
cresc.
a 2
mf
p
Col C.B.
arco

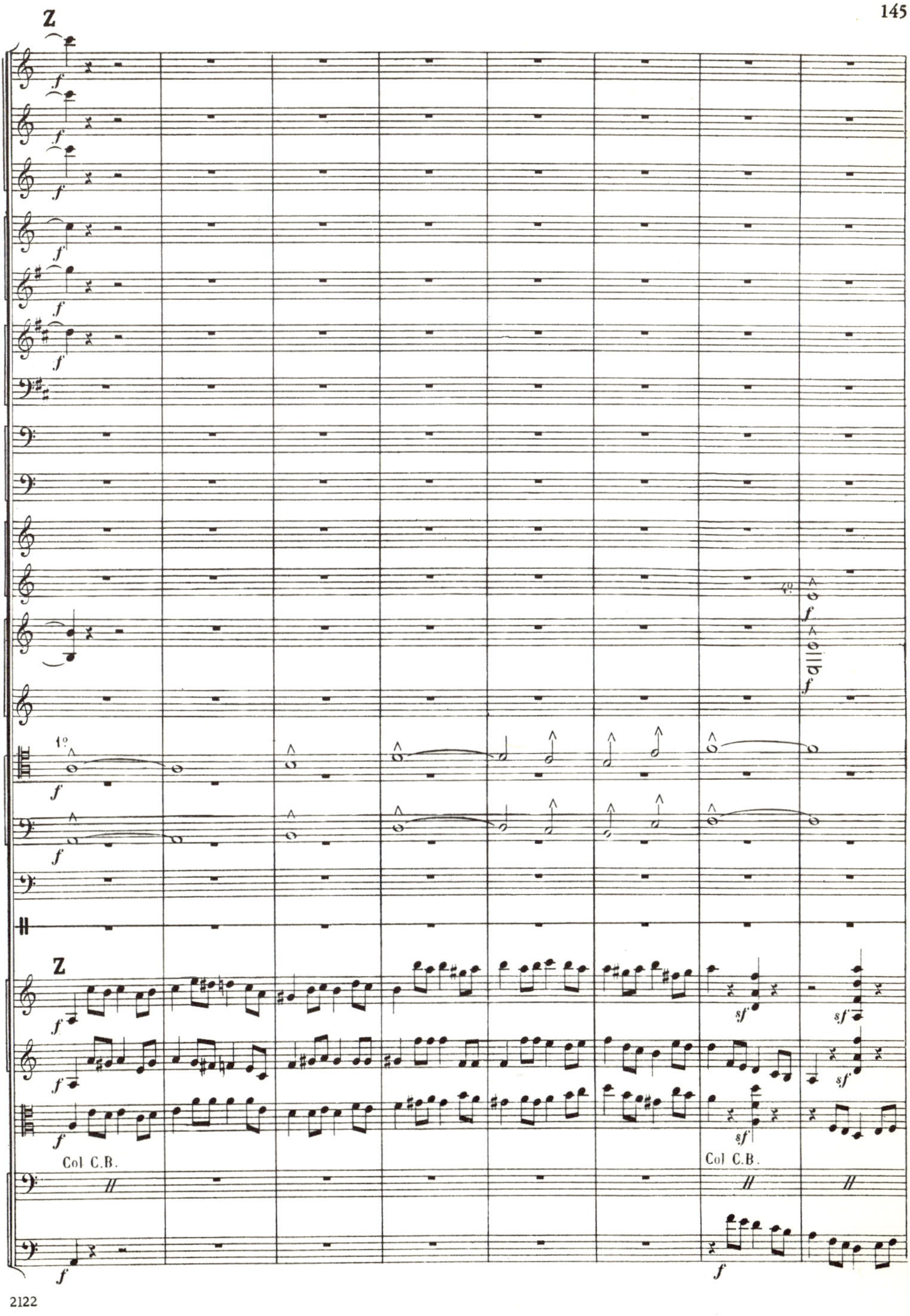
Z
1º
4º
Z
Col C.B.
Col C.B.

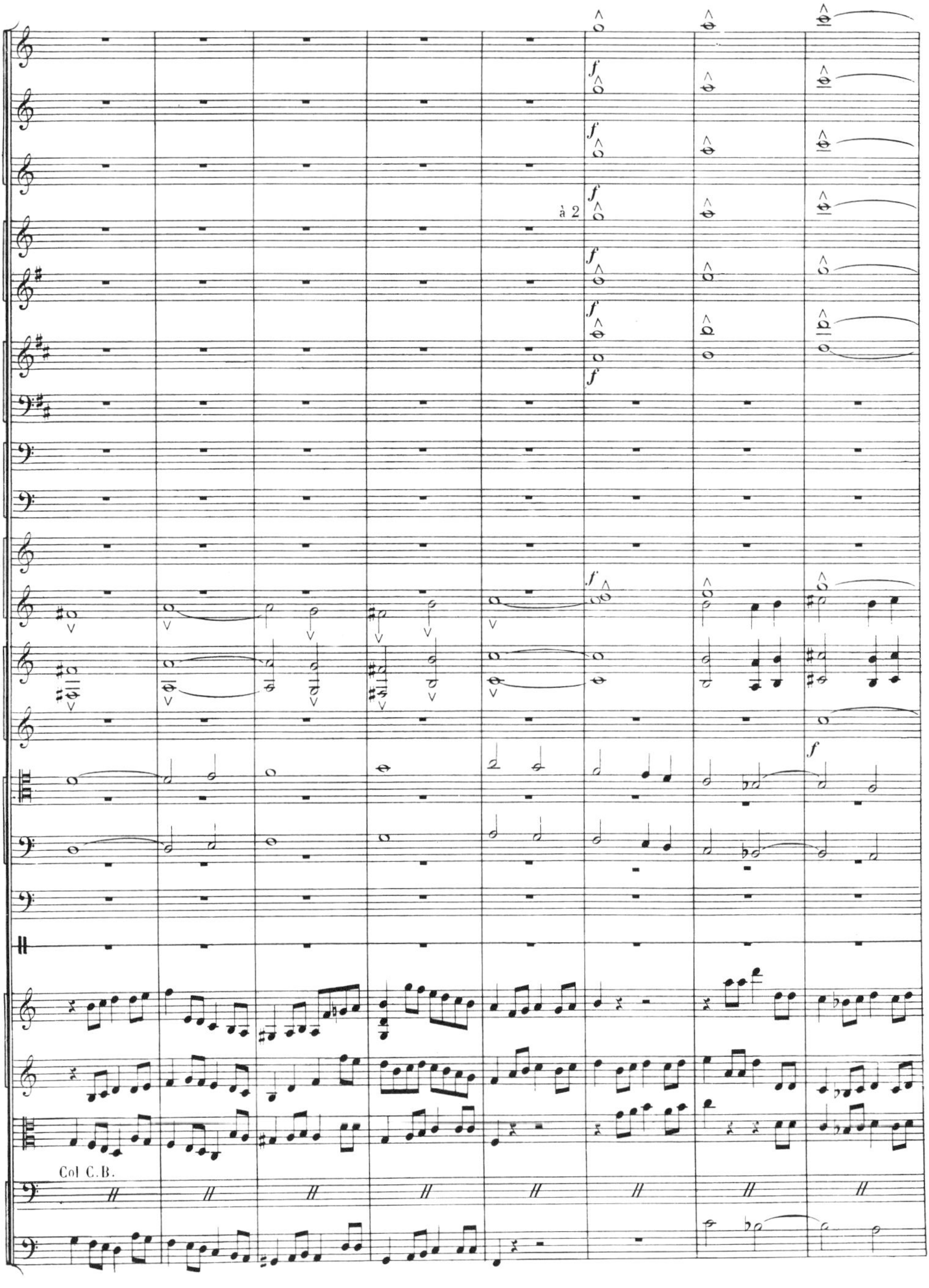
à 2
f
Col C.B.

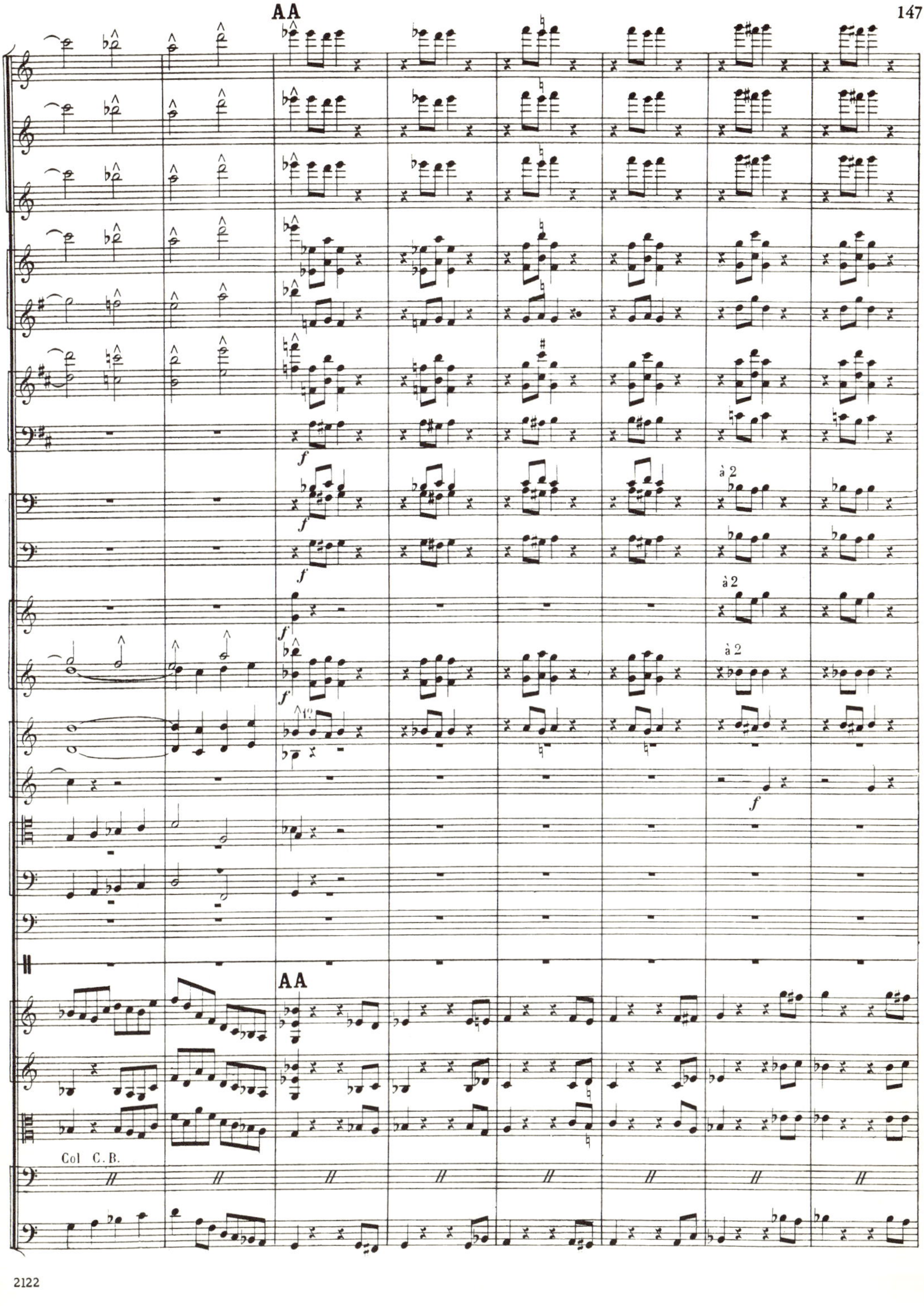
AA
f
à 2
1º
Col C.B.
AA

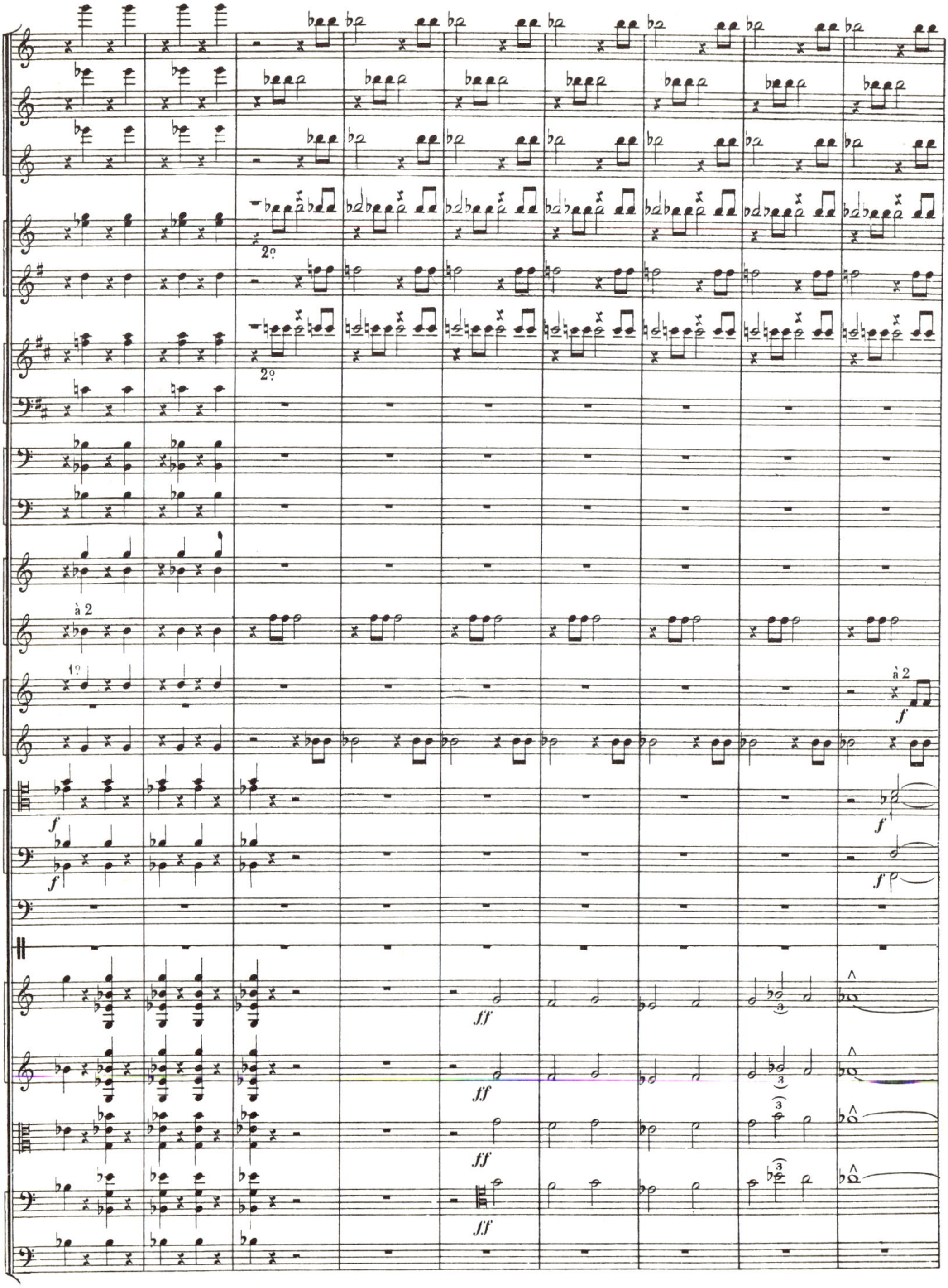
2º
2º
à 2
1º
à 2
f
f
f
f
f
ff
ff
ff
ff
3
3
3

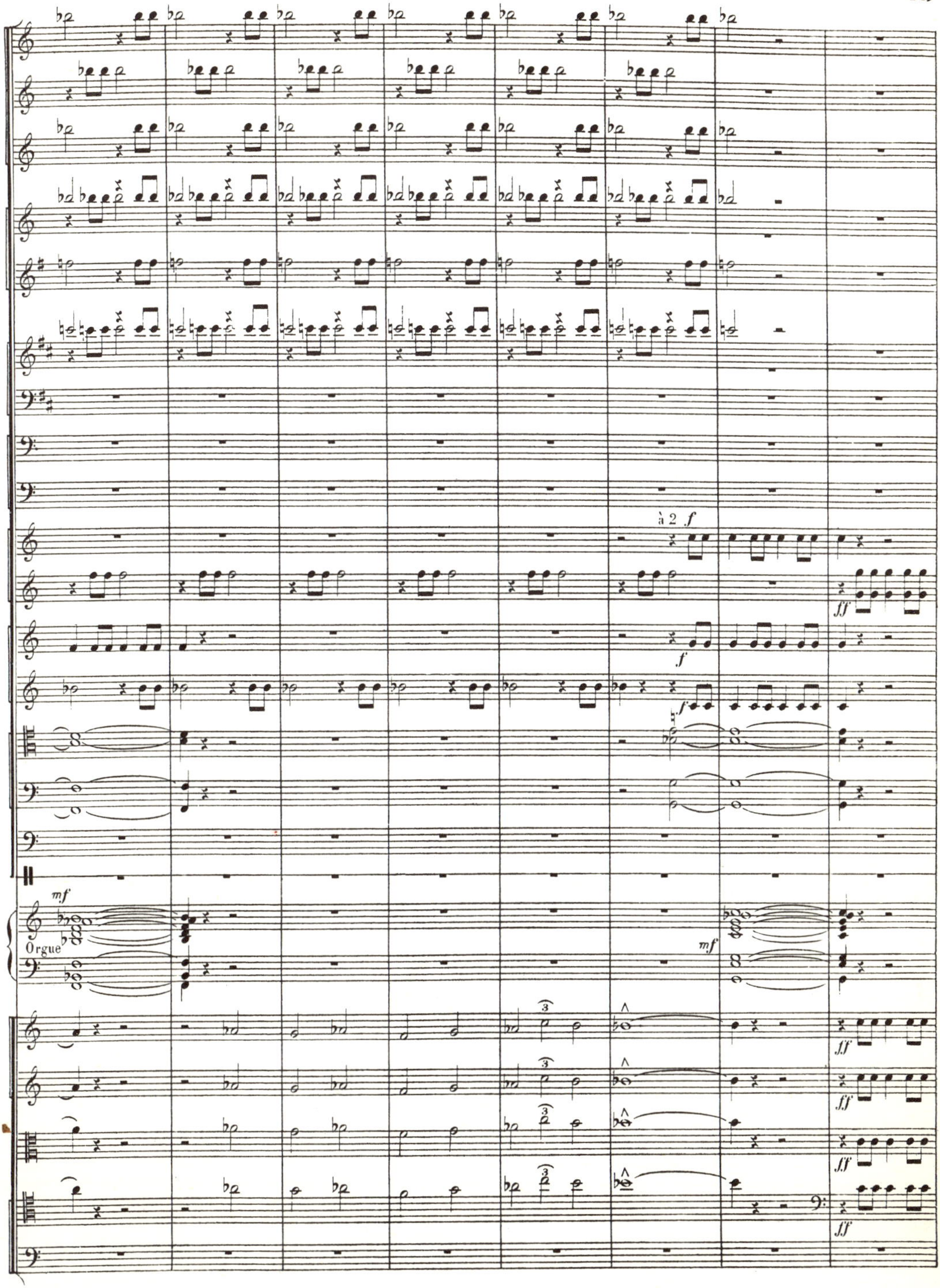
à 2 f
f
ff
mf
Orgue
mf
ff
ff
ff
ff

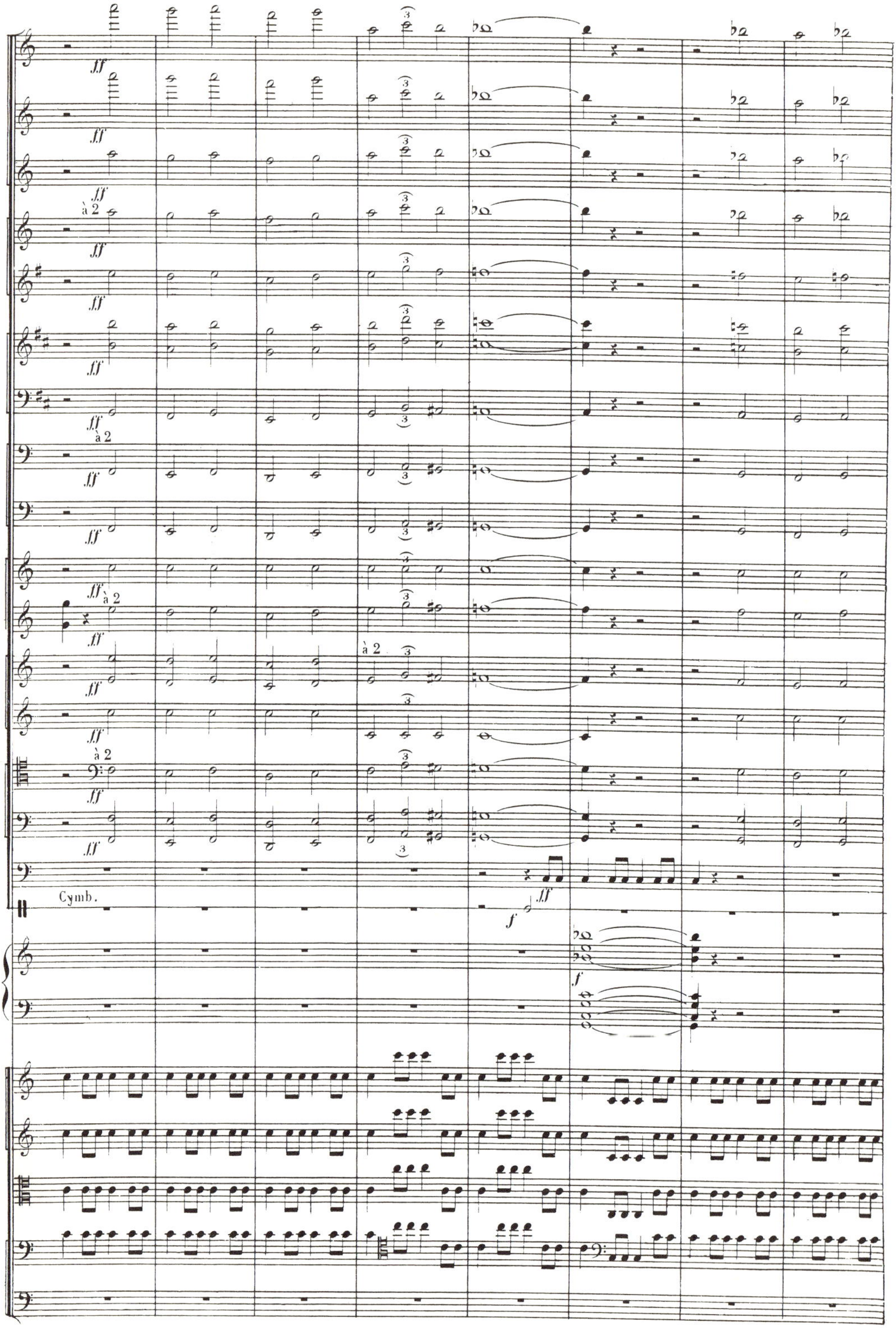

ff
à 2
Cymb.
f
3

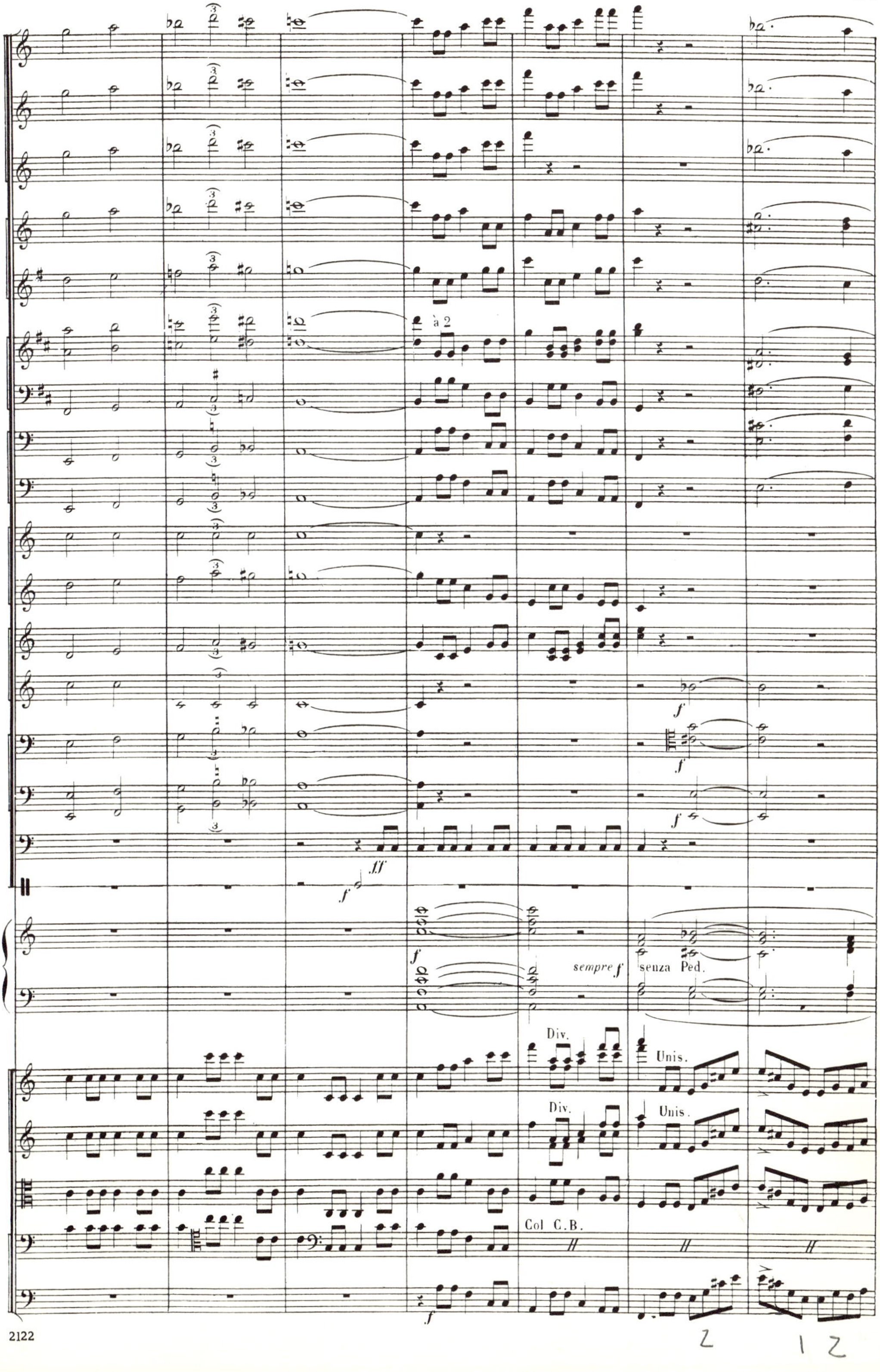
à 2
ff
sempre f
senza Ped.
Div.
Unis.
Div.
Unis.
Col C.B.

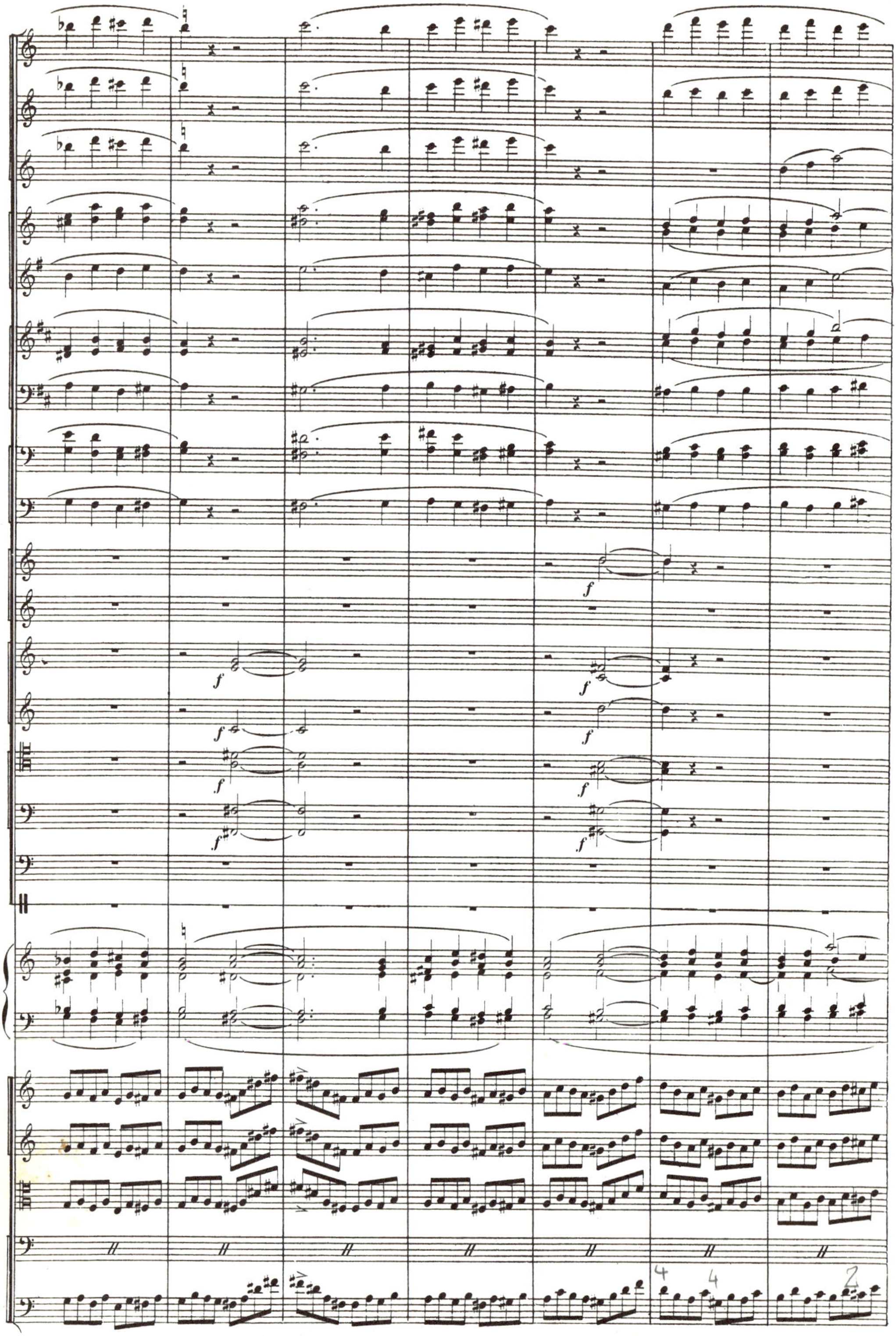

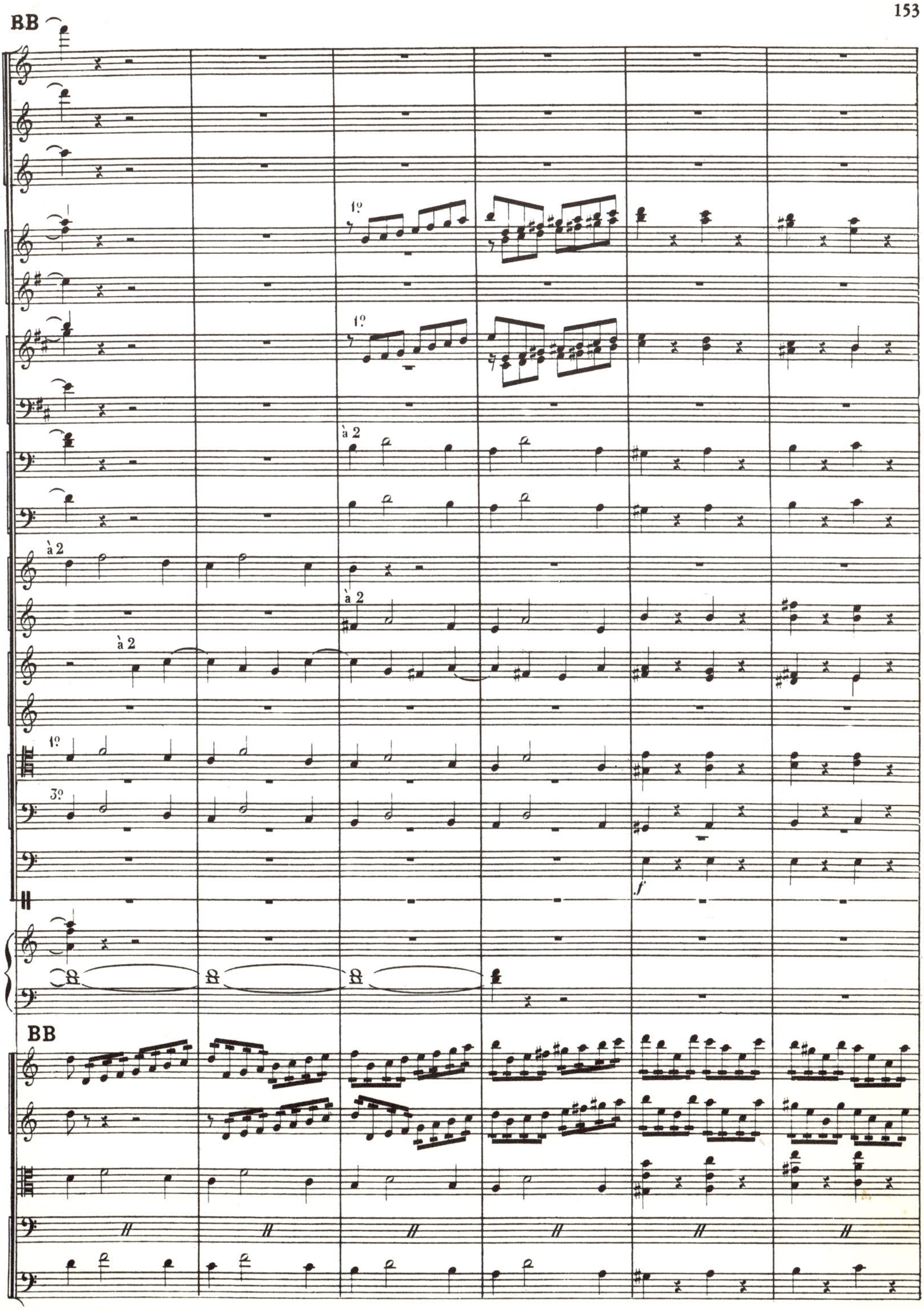
BB
1º
1º
à 2
à 2
à 2
à 2
1º
3º
f
BB

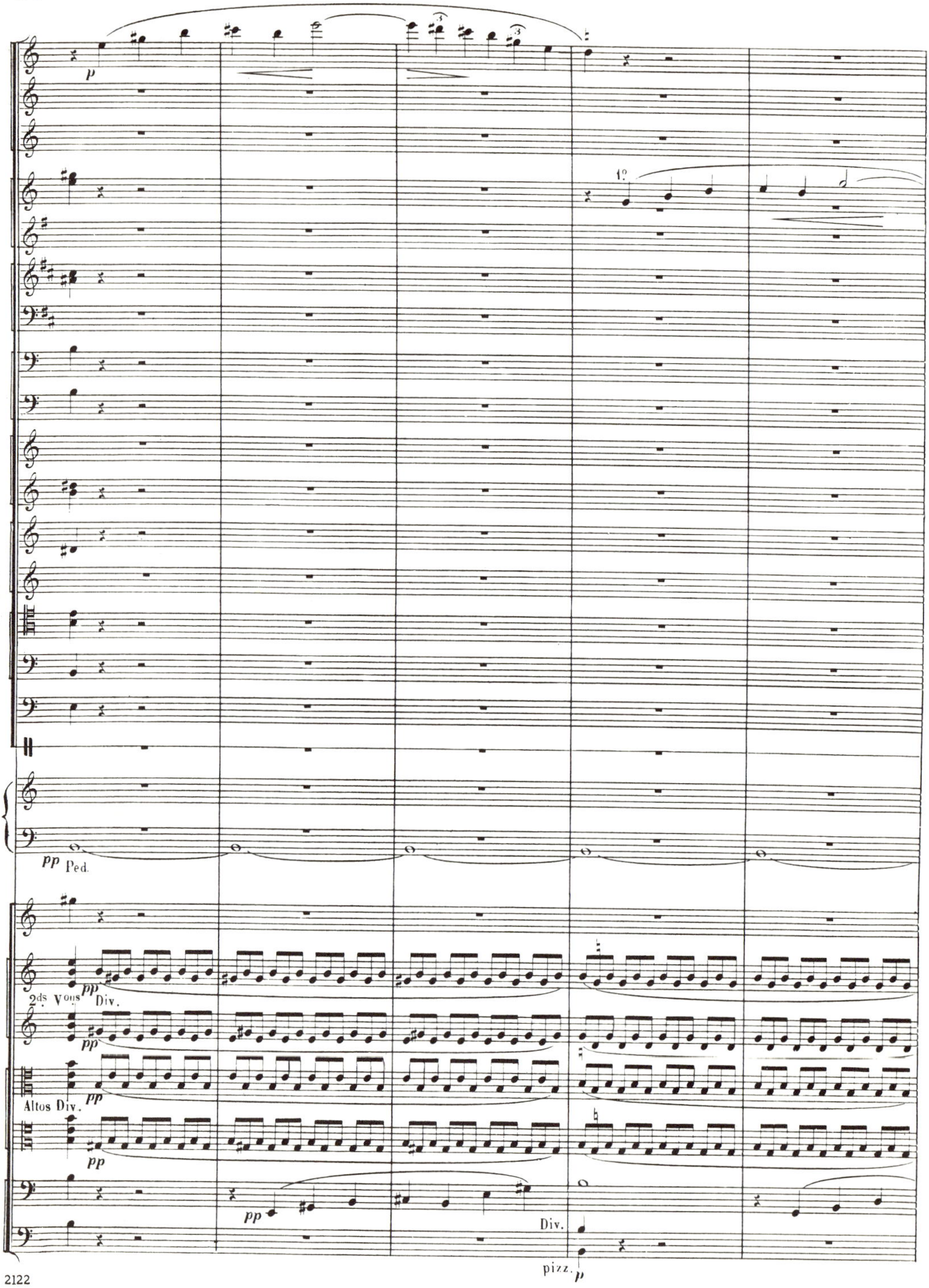
p
1º
pp
Ped.
2ds Vons
Div.
pp
pp
Altos Div.
pp
pp
pp
Div.
pizz.
p

cresc.
3
3
1º p
cresc.
p
cresc.
p
p
cresc.
pp
3
3
cresc.
cresc.
cresc.
cresc.

dim.
mf
mf
dim.
mf
mf
4º
f
p
p
1º
p
p
tr
p
cresc.
mf
p
mf
mf
mf
mf
cresc.
mf
Unis.
p
cresc
mf
dim.

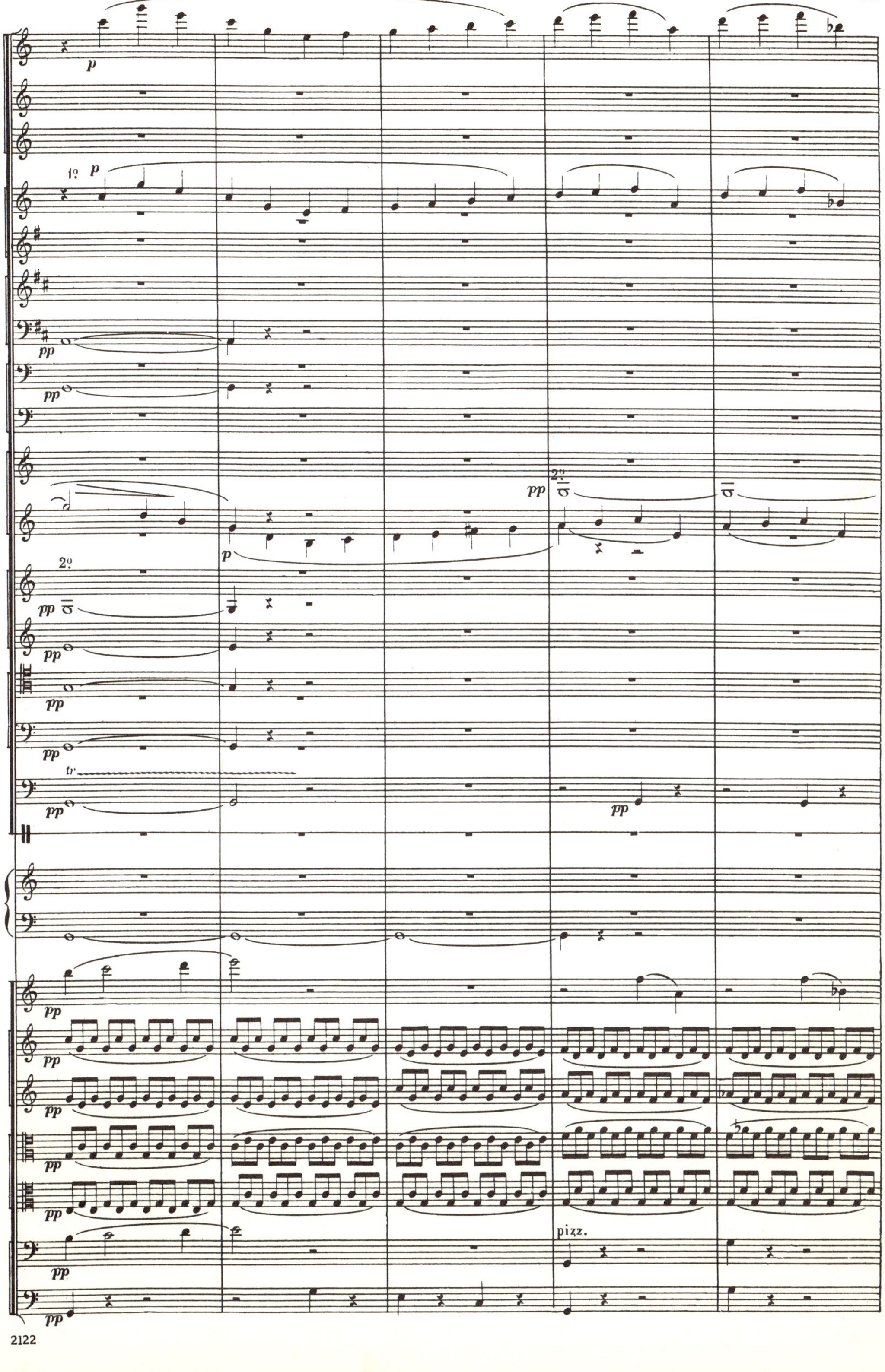
p
1º
p
pp
pp
2º
pp
p
2º
pp
pp
pp
pp
tr
pp
pp
pp
pp
pp
pp
pp
pizz.
pp
pp

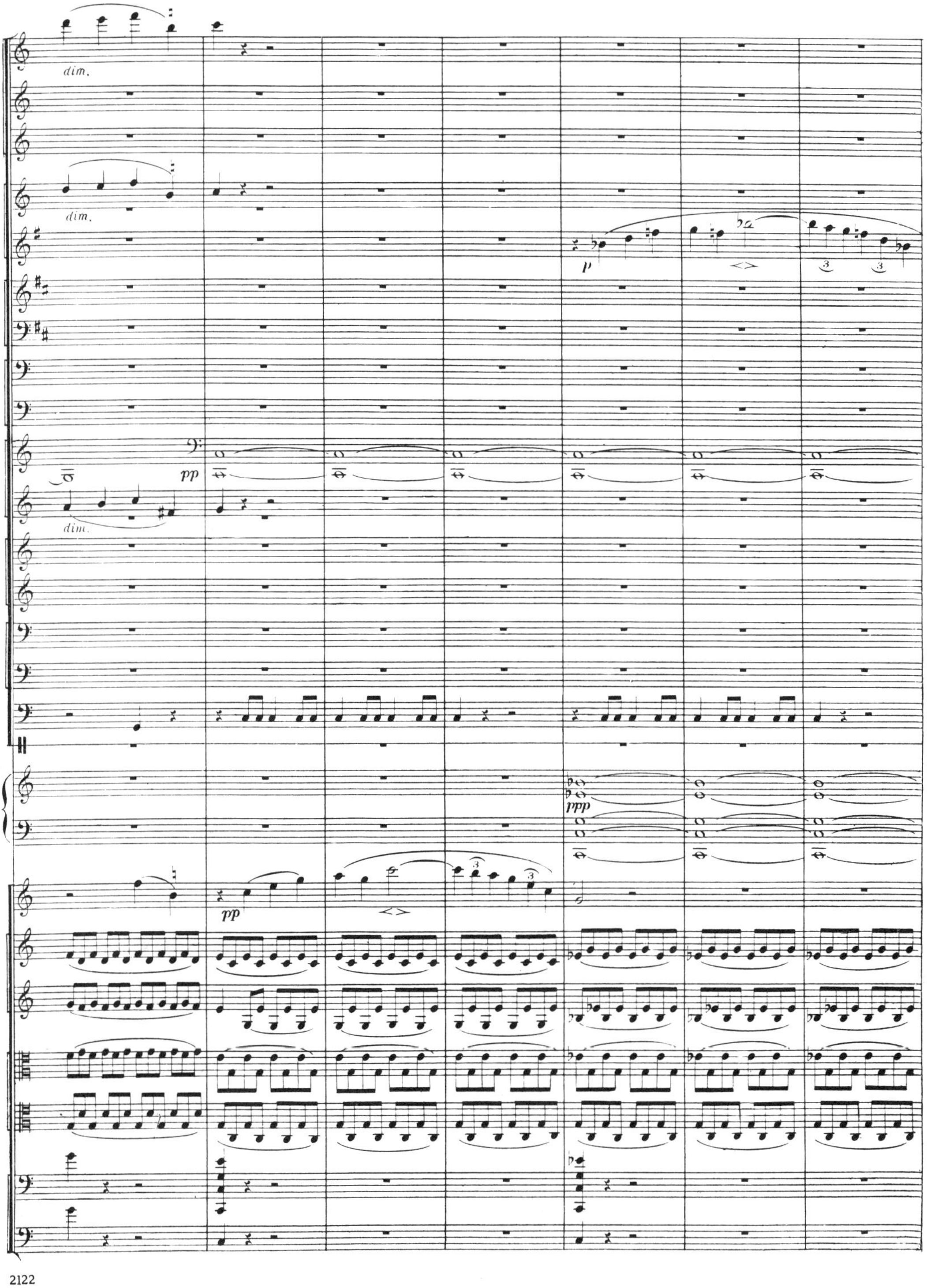
dim.
dim.
p
pp
dim.
ppp
pp

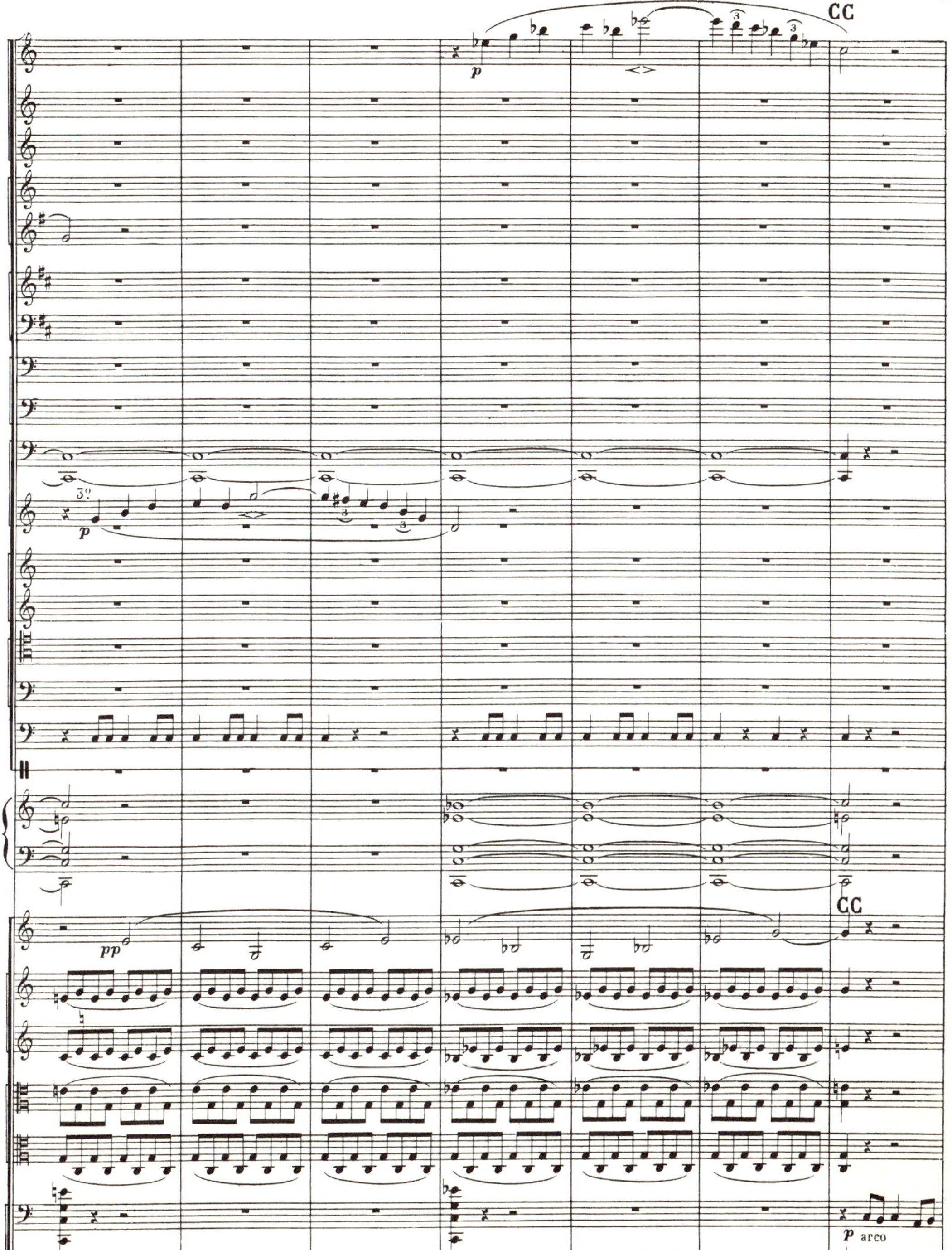

2122

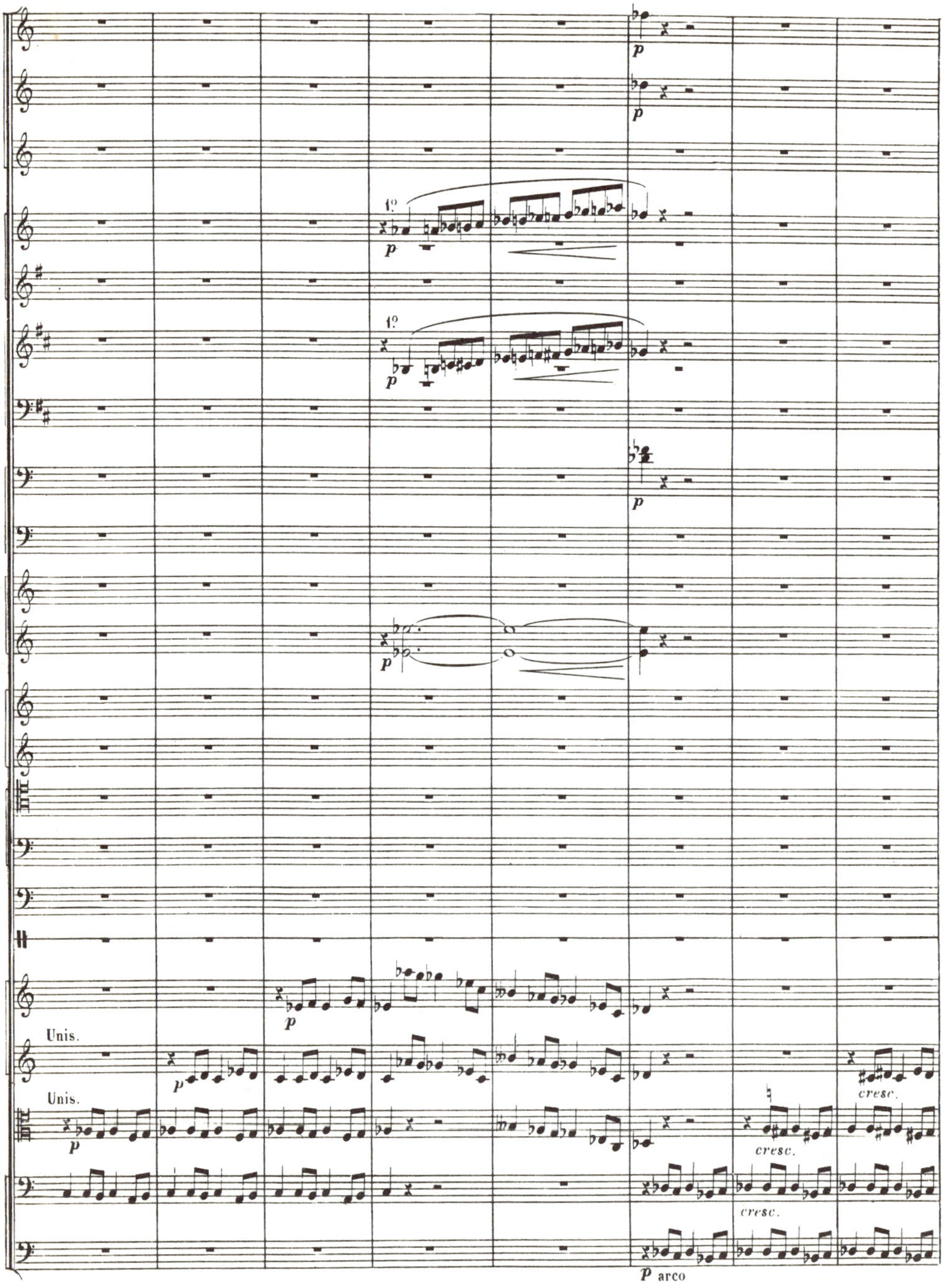
1º
p
1º
p
p
p
p
p
Unis.
p
cresc.
Unis.
p
cresc.
cresc.
p arco

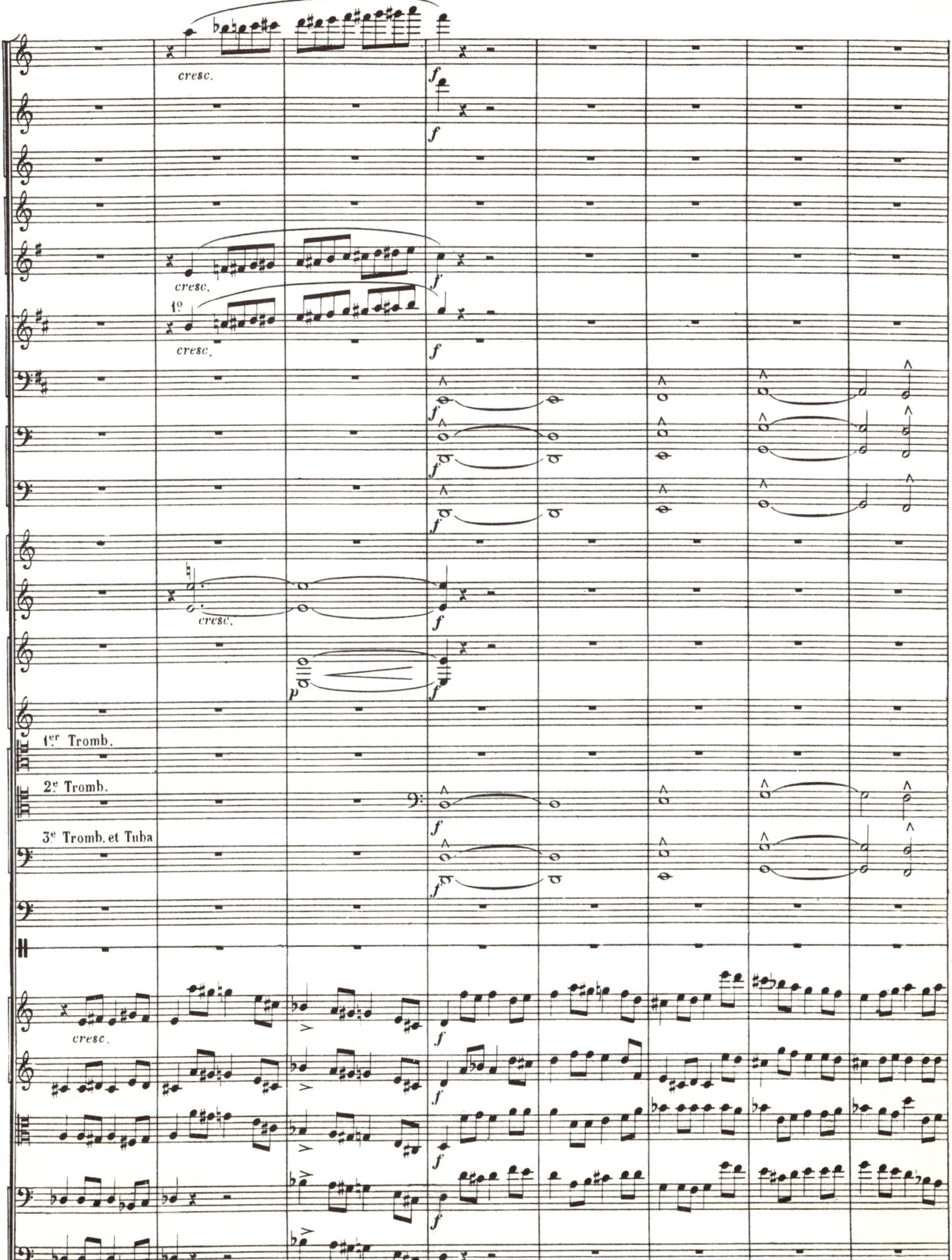
cresc.
f
1º
1er Tromb.
2e Tromb.
3e Tromb. et Tuba
p

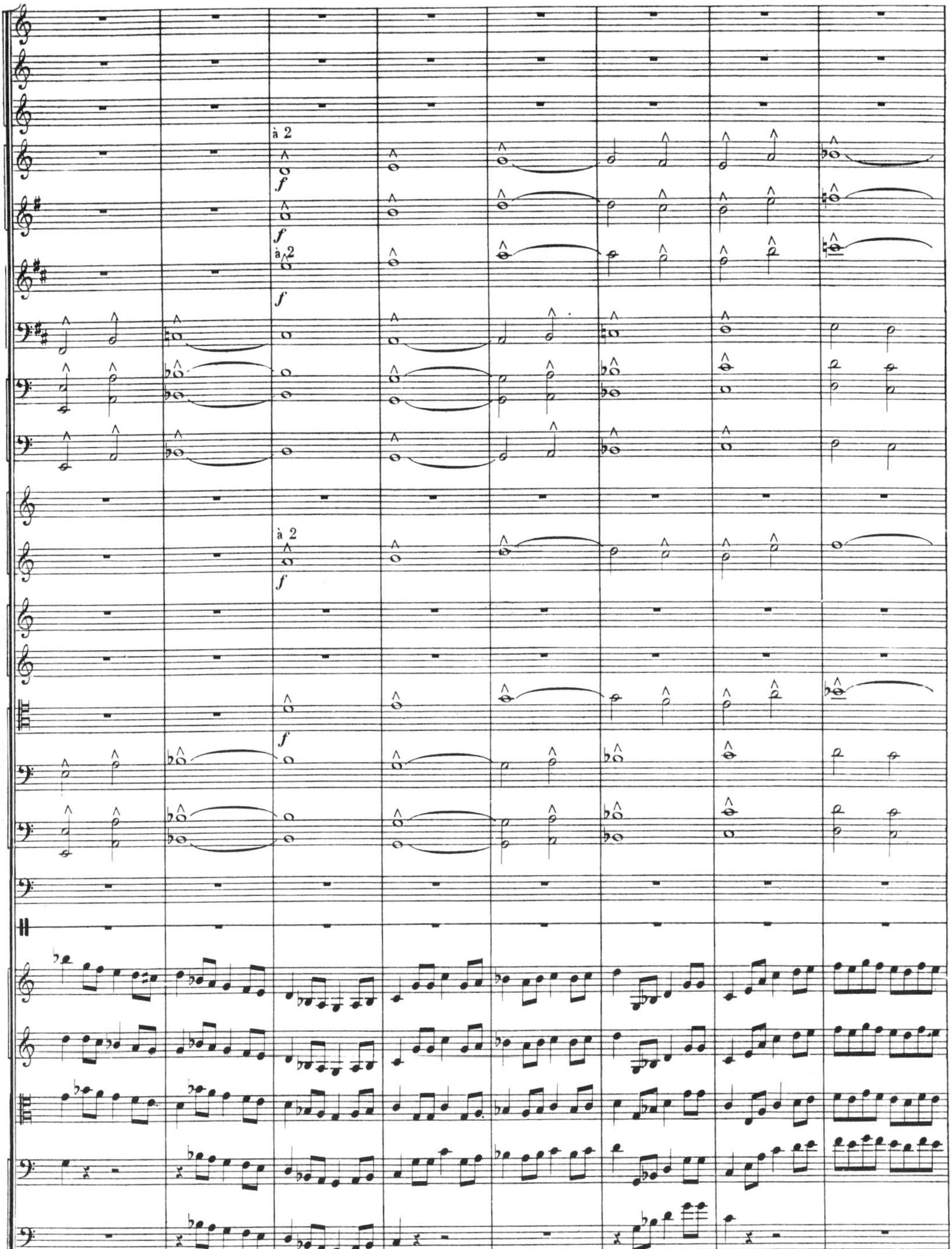

à 2
f
f
à 2
f
à 2
f
f

EE Sans presser

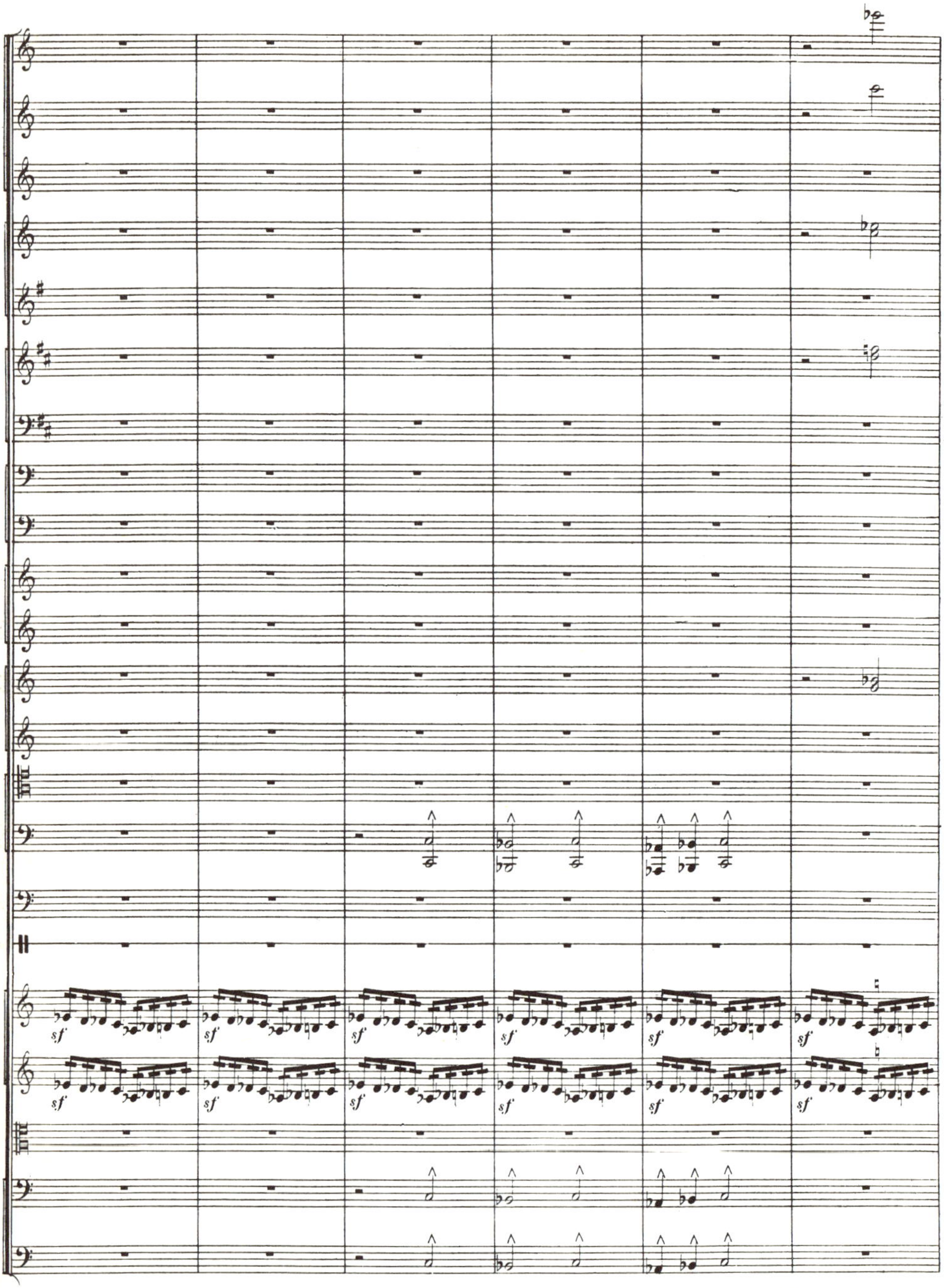
sf
sf
sf
sf
sf
sf
sf
sf
sf
sf
sf
sf

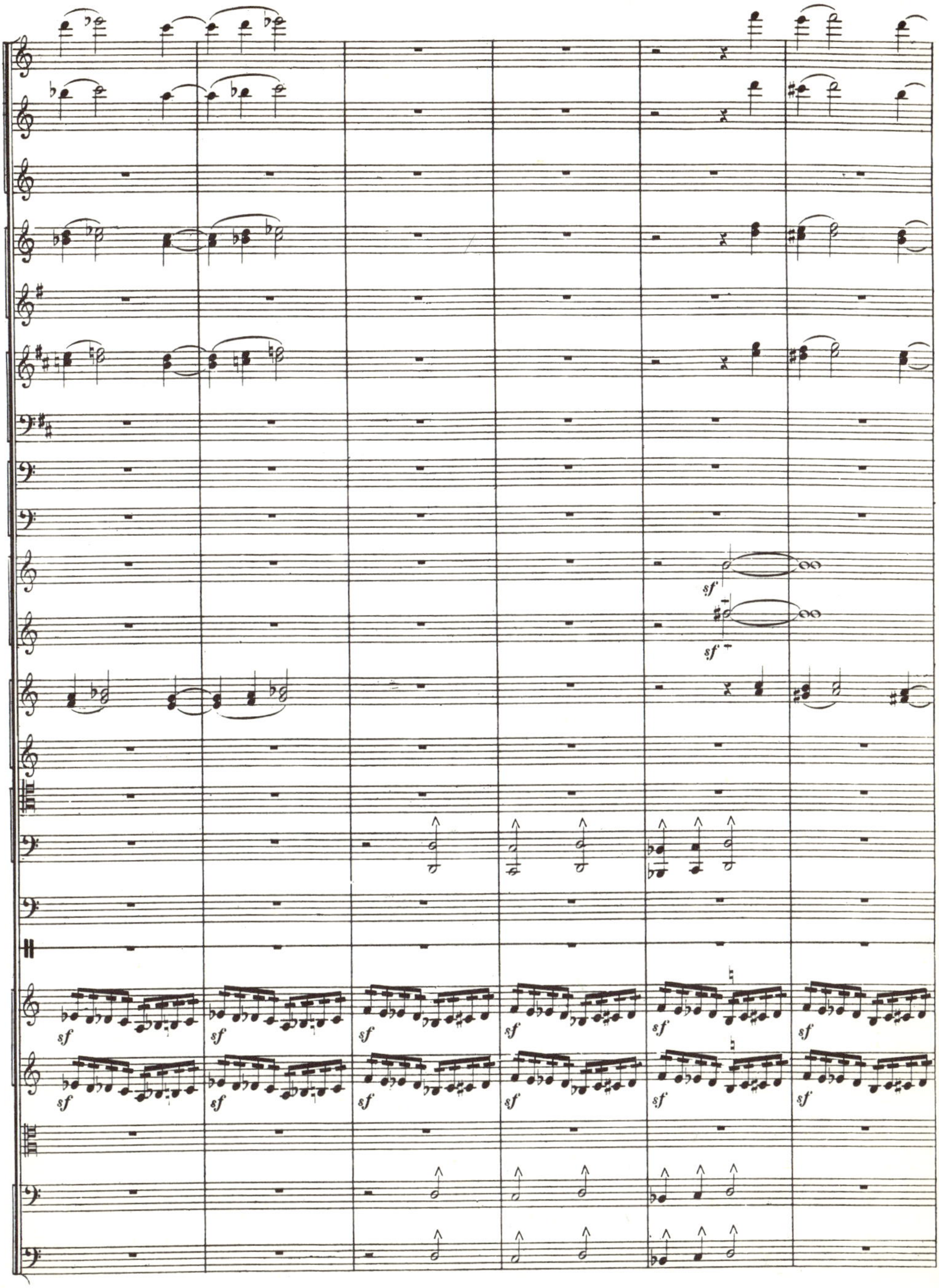
sf

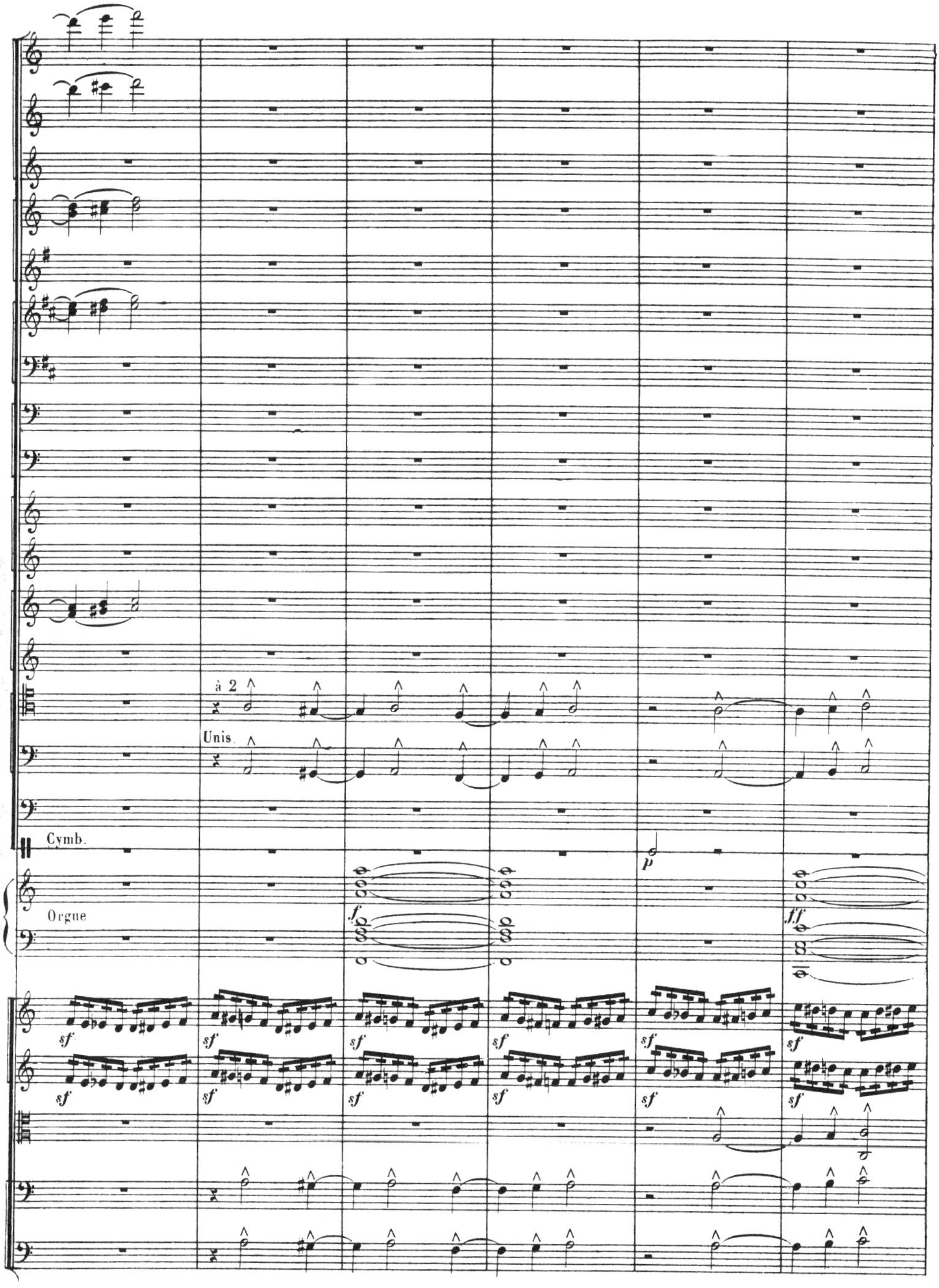
à 2
Unis.
Cymb.
Orgue

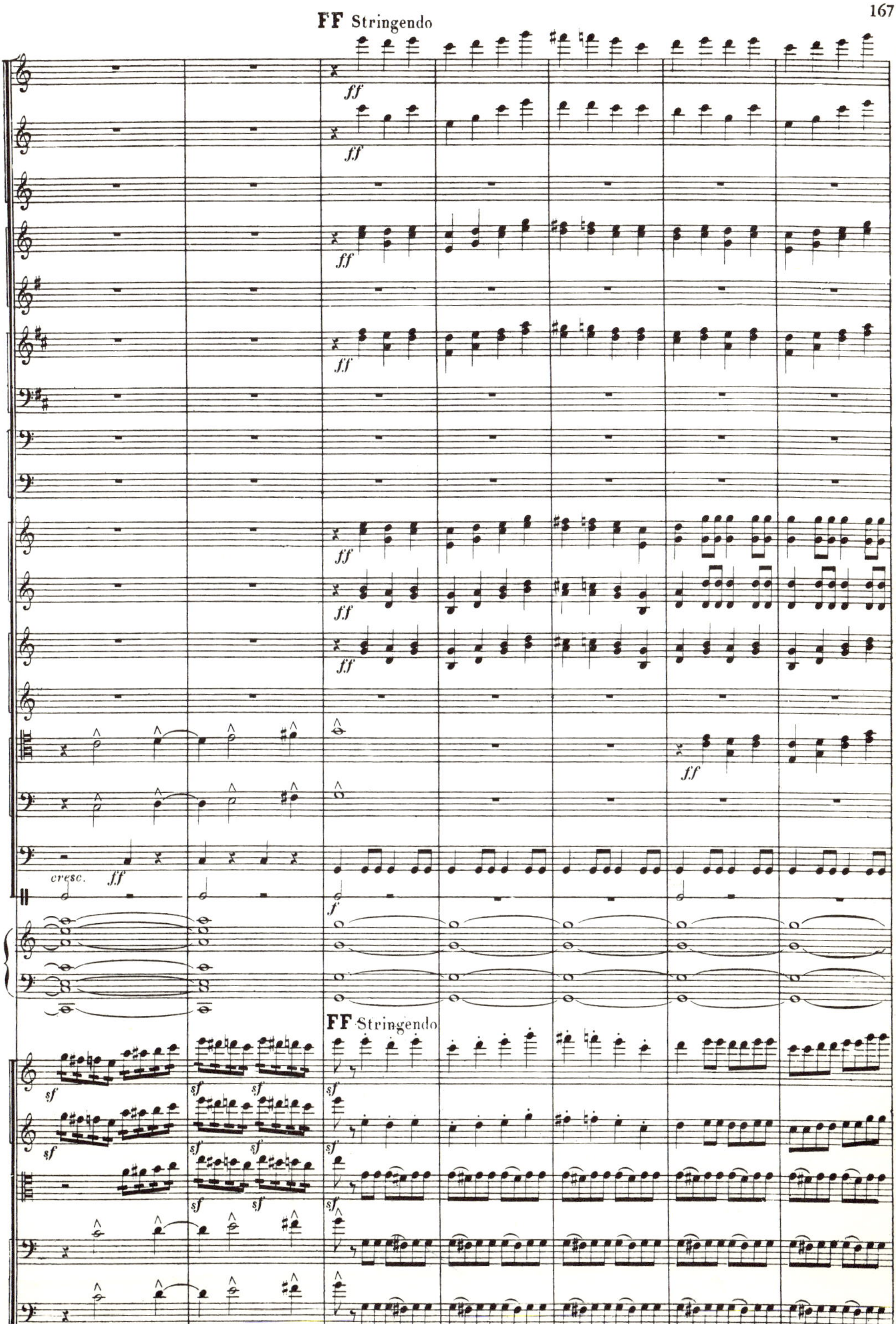
FF Stringendo
ff
cresc.
f
sf
FF Stringendo

Più Allo. 138=♩
(une mesure comme trois du mouvt précédent)

Cymb. et Gsse Csse

Ped.

Più Allo. 138=♩
(une mesure comme trois du mouvt précédent)

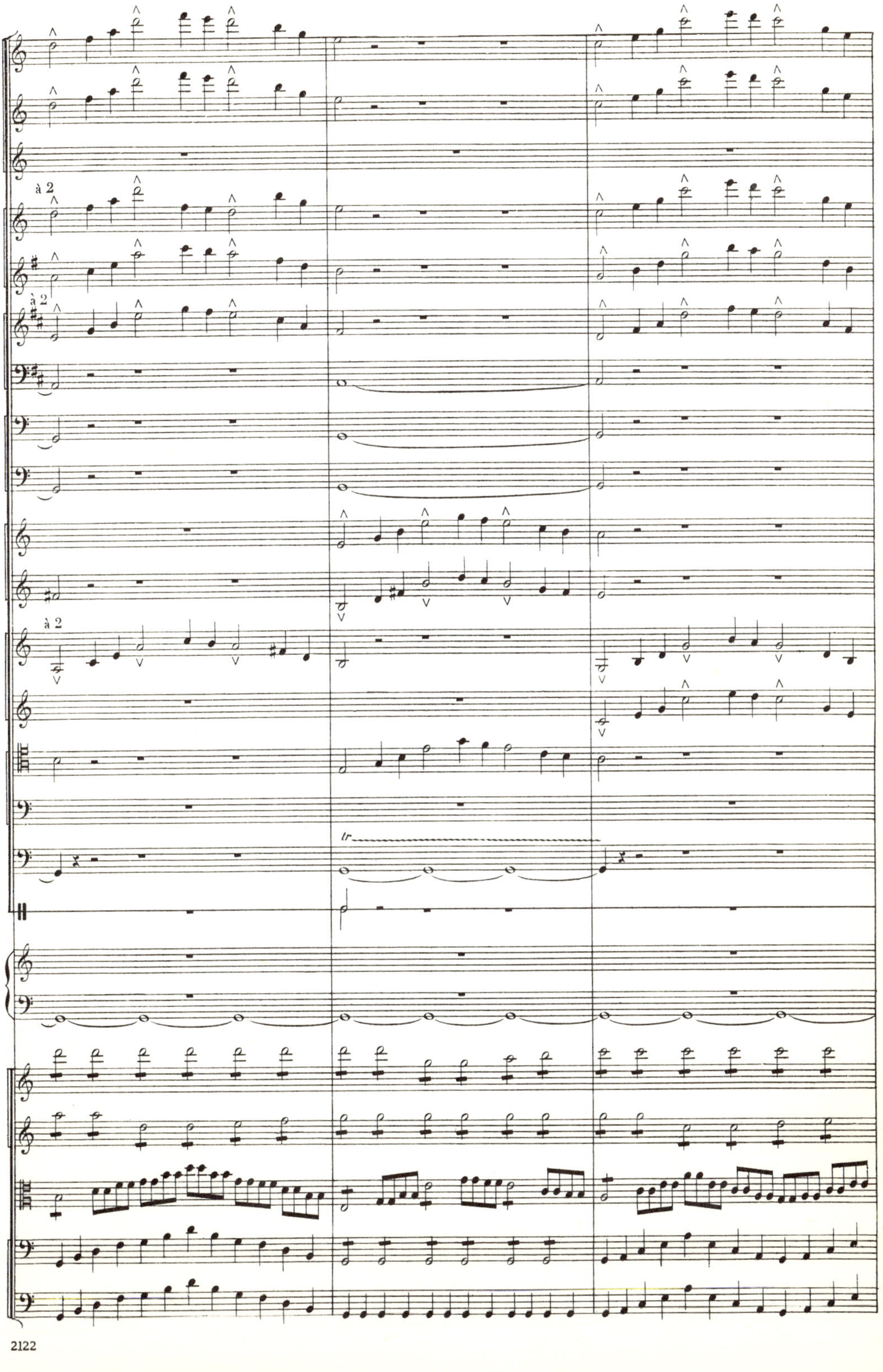
à 2
à 2
à 2
tr

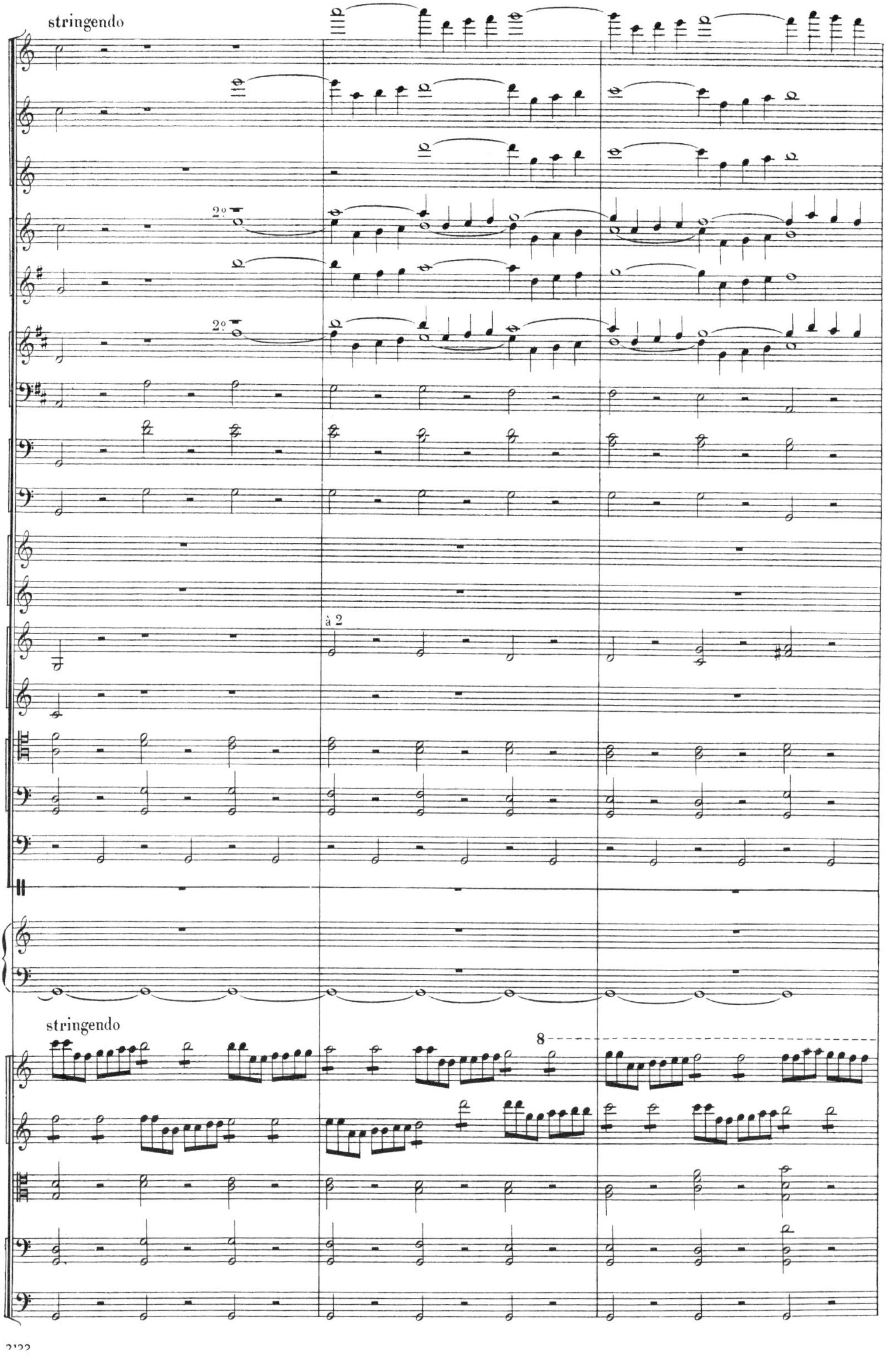
stringendo
2º
2º
à 2
stringendo
8

Molto All°. 88=o
GG Pesante
à 2
1°
2°
3e Tromb.
Molto All°. 88=o
Div.
Unis
GG Pesante
Col C.B.
ff
sf

100 = 𝅗𝅥 même valeur de mesure
sf
ff
à 2
tr
100 = 𝅗𝅥 même valeur de mesure
Col C.B.

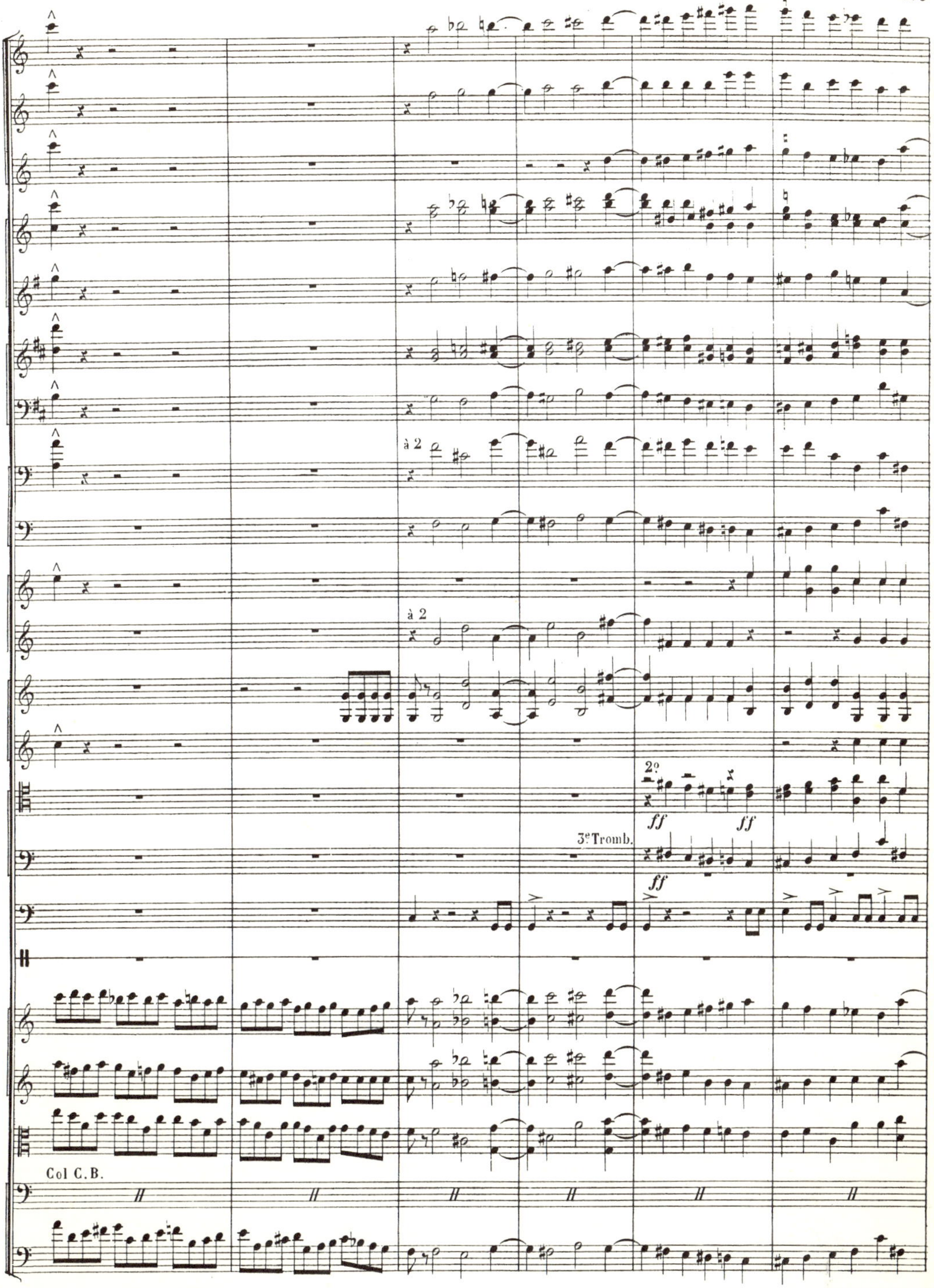
à 2
à 2
2º
ff
ff
3º Tromb.
ff
Col C.B.

100 = 𝅗𝅥 Sans presser
à 2
Cymb.
Orgue
ff
100 = 𝅗𝅥 Sans presser
sf
sf
Div.
Col C.B.

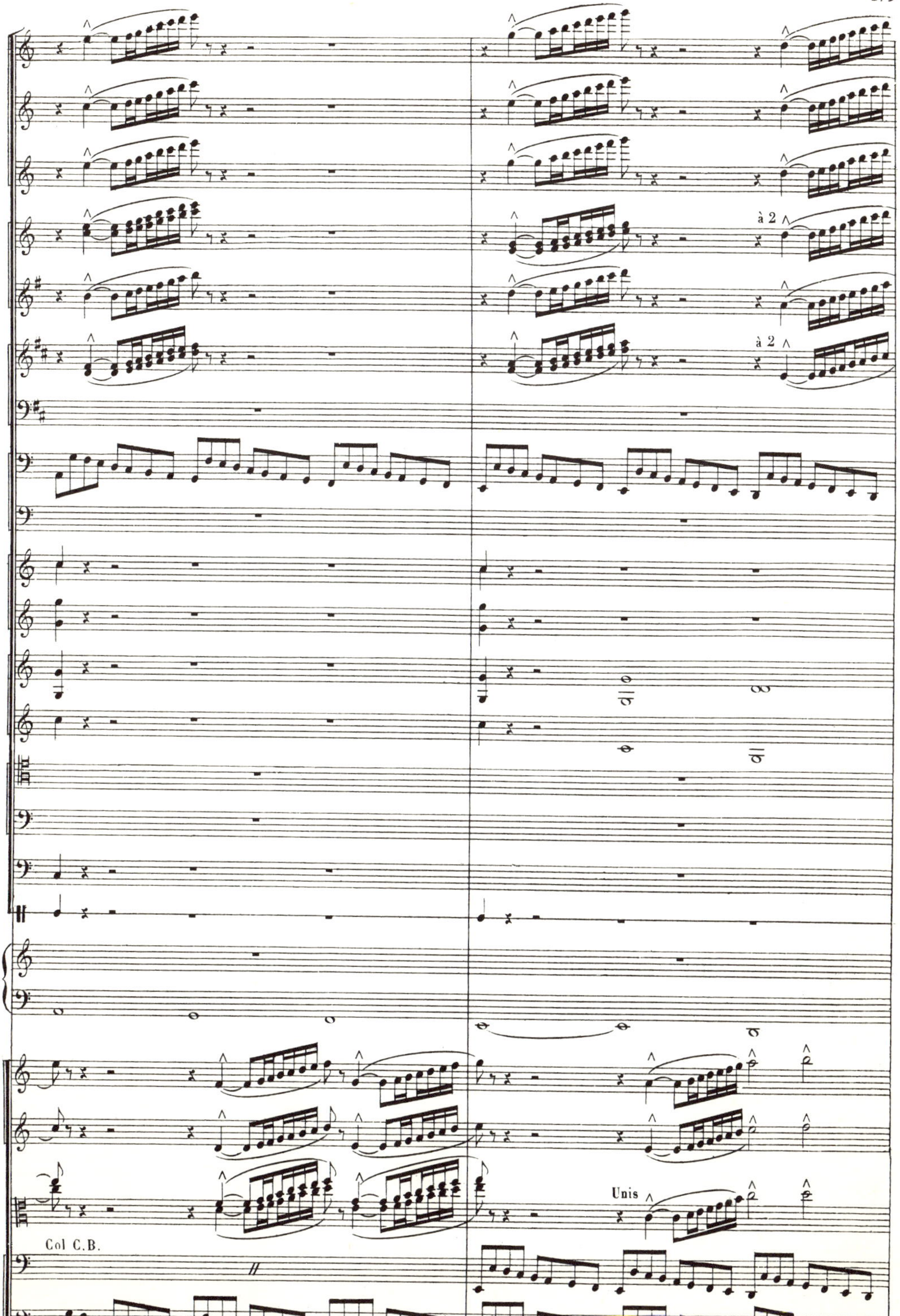
à 2
à 2
Unis
Col C.B.

Cymb et G^{sse}C^{sse}

FIN

MINIATURE SCORES

BACH, Johann Sebastian
Concerto in F min. for Piano & Orchestra   1.25

BARTOK, Bela
Op. 7. Quartet No. 1   2.00

BEETHOVEN, Ludwig van
Op. 16. Quintet in E flat for Piano, Oboe,
   Clarinet, Bassoon and Horn   1.50
Rondino in E flat for 2 Oboes, 2 Clarinets,
   2 Horns and 2 Bassoons   1.25
Op. 71. Sextet in E flat maj. for 2 Clarinets,
   2 Horns and 2 Bassoons   1.50

BORODIN, Alexander
String Quartet No. 2 in D major   1.50

BRAHMS, Johannes
Op. 45. German Requiem   3.75

DEBUSSY, Claude
String Quartet in G minor, Op. 10   2.00

DOHNANYI, Erno von
Op. 10. Serenade for Violin, Viola and
   Cello   1.75

DVOŘÁK, Antonin
Op. 44. Serenade for WW., Cello & Bass   2.00
Op. 74. Terzetto for 2 Violins and Viola   1.25
Op. 96. Quartet No. 6 in F *(American)*   1.25

FAURE, Gabriel
Op.19. Ballade for Piano and Orchestra   2.50
Op. 48. Requiem   3.75
Pelléas et Mélisande. Suite   3.75

FRANCK, César
String Quartet in D major   1.50

HAYDN, Franz Joseph
Symphony No. 45 (18) *(Farewell)*   1.50
Octet in F major for Woodwinds   2.00

d'INDY, Vincent
Op.24. Suite in Olden Style. For Trumpet,
   2 Flutes & String Quartet (with Bass ad lib.) 2.50

IPPOLITOV-IVANOV, Michael
Op. 10. Caucasian Sketches   2.50

JANÁČEK, Leoš
Mladi *(Youth)*. Suite for Flute, Oboe,
   Clarinet, Bass Clarinet, Bassoon and Horn   2.00
Suite for 2 Violins, Viola, Cello and Bass   2.50

JARNEFELT, Armas
Praeludium   1.00

LYADOV, Anatole
Op. 58. Eight Russian Folk Songs   1.75
Op. 62. The Enchanted Lake   1.50

MAHLER, Gustav
Symphony No. 4 in G major   4.00
Kindertotenlieder *(Songs on the Death of
   Children)* For Voice and Orchestra   3.00
Lieder eines fahrenden Gesellen *(Songs
   of a Wayfarer)* For Voice and Orchestra   3.00

MOZART, Wolfgang Amadeus
Magic Flute. Complete Opera *(German)*   9.00
Exsultate, jubilate, Motet (K.165). *(Latin
   text with English translation)*   1.50
Piano Concerto in D, No. 28 (K. 382)
   (Concert Rondo)   1.25
Concerto for 2 Pianos in E flat (K. 365)   1.75
Quintet in E flat maj. (K. 452) for Piano,
   Oboe, Clarinet, Bassoon and Horn   1.50
Divertimento in E flat maj. (K. 563) for
   Violin, Viola and Cello   1.00
The Village Musicians *(A Musical Joke)*
   For String Quartet and 2 Horns. K. 522   1.25

MUSSORGSKY, Modeste
Night on the bare Mountain   2.00
Introduction to the Opera "Khovanshtina"   1.25

PIERNE, Gabriel
Preludio & Fughetta, Op. 40, No. 1. For
   2 Flutes, Oboe, Clarinet, Horn & 2
   Bassoons   2.00

PROKOFIEFF, Sergei
Op. 19. Violin Concerto No. 1 in D   3.00
Op. 34. Ouverture on Hebrew Themes for
   Clarinet, String Quartet and Piano   1.50
Op. 39. Quintet for Oboe, Clarinet, Violin,
   Viola and Bass   2.50
Op. 92. String Quartet No. 2 in F major   2.50

RAVEL, Maurice
String Quartet in F   2.00
Introduction & Allegro. For Harp with
   Flute, Clarinet, and String Quartet   2.00

SCHOENBERG, Arnold
Op. 4. Verklärte Nacht *(Transfigured
   Night)*   2.50

SHOSTAKOVICH, Dmitri
Op. 49. String Quartet No. 1   1.50

STRAUSS, Johann
Overture "Die Fledermaus" *(The Bat)*   1.75

STRAUSS, Richard
Op. 7. Serenade for 13 Instruments   1.25

STRAVINSKY, Igor
L'Histoire du Soldat *(A Soldier's Tale)*   3.00

TCHAIKOVSKY, Peter I.
Op. 32. Francesca da Rimini. Fantasy   2.50

VERDI, Giuseppe
Requiem. For Soli, Chorus and Orchestra
   (Latin text with English translation)   4.00

INTERNATIONAL MUSIC COMPANY
New York City

92-72   *Complete catalog sent free on request*